First of th Notices sent out Nov 1885

Adelphi Academy
Brooklyn N.Y. Nov. 19° 85
Dear Sir   At the meeting of persons
interested in Physical training to be held at
the Academy in this City Nov. 27th
The following Gentlemen, among others, will
be present.
Dr Edward Hitchcock, Amherst. Dr Dio Lewis N.Y
Prof. A.C.Burnham Brooklyn. Dr D.A. Sargent Harvard
Dr J.W.Seaver Yale. Dr Edward Hitchcock Jr. Cornell.
Dr. Chas. McIntire Jr. & J.W. Updegrove Lafayette.
A.J. Turner Princeton. Dr W.A. Ford Haverford & Swarthmore
A.C. Putnam Vassar. Dr C.C. Ladd Bryn Mawr H.J. Koehler
West Point. W.C.Joslin A.M. Staten Island. H.S. Anderson
Garden City School. Geo. Goldie N.Y.A.C. J.D.Andrews YMCA
Prof. W L. Dowd N.Y. H.C.Barrett YMCA Phila. R.J. Roberts
Y.M.C.A. Boston. A.H.Howard University of Boston.
On this occasion papers will be read relative to
these subjects:- Methods of teaching. Systems of
Measurements, Necessity of organization. After which
informal discussions will follow. Morning Session
10 oclock, afternoon session 1 oclock.
Wm Blaikie of the N.Y. Bar & Author of "How to get Strong"
will speak on this occasion.
To reach the Adelphi Academy, Cross Fulton Ferry
or Bridge, take the Elevated Road & get off at
DeKalb ave. & go one block to the left.
The Principals of a number of Institutions have
Notified us that they will be present besides
prominent Physicians in New York & Brooklyn
Leading News papers will be represented.
This notice was written by   Yours truly
Henry S. Anderson   W. G. Anderson
Nov. 16- 1885   Instructor Physical Training

Facsimile of the call for the first meeting of those who formed the American Association for the Advancement of Physical Education that later became the American Physical Education Association, and is now called the American Association for Health, Physical Education, and Recreation, a department of the National Education Association.

Frontispiece.

THE ADMINISTRATION

W. B. SAUNDERS COMPANY

OF HEALTH EDUCATION AND
——PHYSICAL EDUCATION

JESSE FEIRING WILLIAMS, M.D., Sc.D.

Emeritus Professor of Physical Education,
Teachers College, Columbia University

CLIFFORD LEE BROWNELL, Ph.D.

Emeritus Professor and Chairman of the Department
of Health Education, Physical Education, and
Recreation, Teachers College, Columbia University

ELMON LOUIS VERNIER, Ed.D.

Director of Physical Education,
Public Schools, Baltimore, Maryland

Philadelphia and London   *SIXTH EDITION*

Reprinted November, 1964 and April, 1966

The Administration of Health Education and Physical Education

PREFACE TO THE SIXTH EDITION

Great social, economic, and political issues face each generation. In the final analysis, these issues are best met by helping youth to develop and maintain their full powers, to acquire total fitness, to accept moral and social responsibilities, to learn modern ways of healthful living; in short, to realize as fully as possible their native capacities in a changing culture.

Each generation must place ultimate reliance upon human resources, developed strength and skills, protections against accident and disease, and provisions for wholesome leisure. Health education and physical education are deeply concerned with the needs of children and youth for optimum development, the needs of men and women for satisfying experience, and the needs of all for appropriate attitudes and scientific knowledge. This new edition of *The Administration of Health Education and Physical Education* is dedicated to these basic principles.

It is the business of administration to get things done. The good administrator keeps the gears of human effort well oiled by clear policies, exact procedures, and reasonable standards. This book should be a great help in stating policies, defining procedures, and developing standards. The text is planned for those who work in schools and colleges; it stresses problems of the former and presents both information relative to the intricate administration of the large city school system and materials which enable the beginning teacher in a rural community to plan his work more effectively. Its chief function is to be a text for men and women students of health education and physical education. Years of research were devoted to the collection and arrangement of administrative problems. These are discussed in their functional setting. Extended discussion of child and adolescent psychology has been omitted purposely, since information of this sort rightfully belongs in other texts. In presenting the administrative problems, however, the authors have been mindful of the need for including sufficient background material to give direction to the argument, and to recognize conflicting points of view in educational theory.

This *Sixth Edition* provides four main parts or divisions with the various chapters placed in a functional position rather than a logical one; such an arrangement should be approved by teachers engaged in the professional preparation of students, and also by the students themselves.

The four parts of the text are: *Leadership, The Program, Facilities,* and *State and Community.* Under the several parts are chapter discussions of the administrative problems that arise in the leadership of a program, in the conduct of the program, in providing and maintaining facilities, and in establishing desirable state and community relationships.

The revision has been thorough. Changes have been made where needed and not for the sake of novelty; there is much in the text that is old and for those who have used the book is friendly and familiar.

A significant feature of the text deserves emphasis. At the beginning of each chapter the authors present a suitable rationale of the topic under discussion to serve as a foundation upon which to describe the administrative functions concerned therewith. This procedure helps the reader to appreciate and understand the interrelationships that must obtain in sound administration between basic theory and actual practice.

The authors are indebted to many graduate students and to colleagues both at Teachers College and in the field for criticisms, suggestions, and other aid. What we owe to friends and colleagues in these and many other respects is very large. Special appreciation goes to three men who have made substantial contributions to this edition. Listed in alphabetical order they are: Mr. Charles T. Avedesian, Director of Physical Education, Athletics, and Safety, New Britain Public Schools, New Britain, Connecticut; Dr. Bernard W. Dolat, Consultant, Boys Physical Education, Athletics, and School Recreation, Connecticut State Education Department; and Dr. George H. Grover, Director, Division of Health, Physical Education, and Recreation, New York State Education Department.

Errors and omissions are our sole responsibility. Since we hope that this book may give unexampled service to the profession, we request that mistakes, if any, be called to our attention. With us, the pride of authorship is no greater than the desire to be accurate and useful.

JESSE FEIRING WILLIAMS
Carmel, California

CLIFFORD LEE BROWNELL
Avon, Connecticut

ELMON LOUIS VERNIER
Baltimore, Maryland

CONTENTS

PART III. FACILITIES

PART IV.   COMMUNITY AND STATE

PART I

LEADERSHIP

These five chapters of Part I comprise the important areas of action in the leadership of health education and physical education. Discussion of the foundations of health education and physical education attempts to set forth the basic philosophy proposed for these areas of education and presents this at the beginning of the text as a guide to the student as he explores other administrative functions. Other chapters of this part center in those policies and procedures by means of which the administrator accomplishes his functions.

CHAPTER 1

FOUNDATIONS OF HEALTH EDUCATION AND PHYSICAL EDUCATION

A DEFINITION OF EDUCATION

There are many philosophies of education. Hence the administrator or teacher must decide which particular one he proposes to follow. The philosophy he holds shapes the program he proclaims. The leader in health education and physical education can organize and administer the program from any one of several viewpoints. He may regard education as a discipline in routine behavior, or as the transmission of a standard social inheritance that achieves uniformity in the product, as the development of individuals through creative experiences.

The latter view serves best in a democratic society, and the authors agree with John Dewey who defined education as follows: "Education is that reconstruction of experience which adds to the meaning of experience, and which increases ability to direct the course of subsequent experience."* This definition conceives the process of education as something more than merely learning facts out of a book, or of reproducing assigned tasks without thought, or of acquiring a skill that begins with a technic and ends with its repetition. On the contrary, experience adds to past experiences and takes on meaning in the light of them, so that the individual is more alert to factors in the next experience, or more informed about the conditions that surround certain kinds of experiences, or more devoted to the outcomes that certain experiences may develop.

* John Dewey: *Democracy and Education.* The Macmillan Company, New York, 1929, pp. 89–90.

THE INFLUENCE OF AN EDUCATIONAL PHILOSOPHY

It is inevitable that one's definition of education is an expression of the educational philosophy that one holds; and this philosophy affects *goals* sought, *program* promoted, and *relations* established with people.

There can be no doubt that an educator has a philosophy whenever he sets goals to be achieved. As he has goals so he has a philosophy. Thus, philosophy enters into all educative experiences, and by so doing it gives a certain tone to the method of instruction, the administrative regulations, and the teacher's objectives. But the philosophy may be quite inadequate; the goal not worth the effort, "the game not worth the candle."

Philosophy deals with ultimates and considers remote ends. It cannot afford to ignore the appealing present, but the distant goal must also be visualized. It is a philosophic sense of values that urges youth not to reproduce the stupidities, the shortages, and the liabilities of an older generation. Better living is needed in the world; this is the concern of philosophy.

The philosophy of democracy declares its purpose in terms of the maximum development of all, equal opportunity for all, and special privileges to none; but no social philosopher can justify this position when the net result is to do as one pleases. The young are to be educated but society never can be satisfied with less than the best from each individual. Moreover, this best is to be judged by society and not by the individual. There need be no claim that community values are superior to individual ones; what is best for the individual also is best for the community. There is no community welfare except the welfare of individuals who make up the community. This is obvious when all factors are considered. It is a mere truism that school spirit is the spirit of individuals who compose the institution.

The individual will be free, of course, to develop his maximum powers; this is the hope of the future. A better world is not a miracle to be brought about by some legislative act, but accomplished through better living by the people in the world. The hope, therefore, that the young can be educated to a better living than their parents is the reasonable aim of a social philosophy, and in a democracy it rests upon the development of the best in individuals. In all education there should be the clear call for superior performance; on the contrary, the low level of achievement by pupils in manners, in speech, in ideals, in character, in postural skills, in physique, in mastery of tools is to be interpreted not as the performance of poor material but rather as the mark of routine, uninspired teaching.

Devotion in teachers is not enough. One may be devoted to dullness. Obviously education must work with the material it has both in teacher and pupil. Pupil material is to be improved only by a long and laborious process of social betterment; teaching personnel by better standards of selection, better professional preparation, and a continuous inservice program of professional improvement.

One's educational philosophy also affects programs. When education is regarded as a continual reconstruction of experience that leads to increasingly richer experiences, there can be no acceptance of a program of mere drill. A considerable part of health education and physical education may be of the routine type. The historical relationship with military drill in one, and the influence of scientific method in the other, have left a deposit in method and concept that all but obscures freer ways of acting. Routine drill in certain functions always will have its place. Foul shooting in basketball, learning anatomical structure and physiological function, technic in dance, safety measures in the pool, and numerous other illustrations readily become apparent. Some routines are essential, but the dead uniformity of set routines that never lead on and never relate back are to be deplored. Routine action may increase skill but it tends to end there. It fails by the rigidity of the routine to lead on to other skills, interests, and attitudes. Thus, when the environmental situation changes, the routine skill leaves the individual quite unprepared. The coach who attempts to reduce all team play to routine action obtains machine-like play that works marvelously at times but fails ignominiously at critical moments. In baseball, outfielders learn to return certain balls to second base, but this procedure is not a set rule because of changing game situations that develop.

And finally, one's educational philosophy greatly influences relations with other persons. When education seeks ever richer experiences for people, there is no place in human relations for behaviors that are mean, provocative of fear and distrust, domineering, and cruel. On the contrary, when growth and development of the best in persons is a goal, there must be respect for personality, mutual confidence and trust, tolerance of racial, religious, and sex differences, and readiness to consider fully opposing opinions.

A DEFINITION OF HEALTH

Much confusion exists about the meaning of "health"; it is regarded by some persons as the mere absence of disease. This confusion is evident in the popular use of the term "health insurance," when clearly what is meant is "sickness insurance"—obviously not the same thing. Some persons attempt to express the nation's health in terms of mortality statistics. The error is evident: mortality statistics measure the death rate and reveal nothing about the vigor, vitality, endurance, poise, and living habits of a people.

The weakness of a definition of health as mere freedom from disease lies in the failure to take into account the individual and social forces that promote superior levels of living and optimum states of being. The prevention of disease is important but disease may be absent and the health of the individual may still remain at low level. The health objective for every person is to develop and maintain vigor and vitality, to acquire interests and habits in ways of living that are wholesome, and to meet the demands upon the individual with efficiency, energy, and satisfaction.

The very character of the individual organism shows that change is possible, and that improvement in personal powers is within the reach of all; it also indicates that the conditions of life that denote health arise as by-products of continued ways of living. This character of the human organism leads to the following definition of health: *health is that quality of life that enables the individual to live most and to serve best.*

This definition may be made more explicit by analysis of the phrase, "to live most and to serve best." To live most means to live most now. It demands good living today as the best guarantee of good living tomorrow. Immediately and without reservation this view renounces the idea that one can live a poor, thin, and narrow life now, and then sometime in the future live deeply and fully.

Moreover, "living most" means living at one's best. Superficial and careless thinking might suggest anything but this, and interpretations given accordingly correspond with antisocial, selfish, and vicious manifestations. It is a commonplace that philosophers find happiness in contemplation, and this explains why the various philosophies recommend it. The person is ultimately the definition of the term, and hence the interpretation of "living most" is to be discovered in events of significant lives. Health education might well be concerned with helping boys and girls understand what living most means to them.

The companion phrase, "to serve best," appears on first examination to have direct or indirect ethical meanings. Its deeper meaning, however, is hygienic rather than ethical. Man is so constituted neurologically that he functions in his organic capacities best when he engages in objective forms of activity.* Let him turn his thoughts exclusively upon himself in contemplation of his own functions and he tends to disorganize their automatic character. His energies, his capacities for work, his achievements rise as he loses himself in objective causes that lie outside himself, that are greater than he is. Examples of this fundamental fact are numerous. The youth "lost" in playing baseball illustrates the intensity of function of the whole psychomotor mechanism. The adult devoted to a political cause—and not his own candidacy—grows in power and capacity as he gives more and more of himself to the cause.

This definition refutes the narrowness in health programs that seek the avoidance of disease as the sole aim. It challenges as unworthy and positively injurious the efforts to teach the dry husks of anatomy and physiology in the vain hope that children may learn how to live by learning how secretions occur and nerve impulses react. It demands a

* This principle applies with equal force to physical education and constitutes one of the important reasons why health education and physical education are brought together into one administrative program.

devoted leadership of youth in the finest living of which they are capable —living in which superior physical accomplishments are matched by emotional and mental developments.

DEVELOPMENT OF THE TERM "HEALTH EDUCATION"

For more than a generation there have been sporadic and desultory efforts to protect the health of children. State legislation that requires teaching the effects of alcohol and tobacco, the medical-inspection movement, school lunches, safety campaigns, and regulations for vaccination against smallpox are well known efforts in this direction. After World War I, the nutrition of children attracted the attention of both lay and professional groups, and the health conditions of American youth called to military service during World War II and since have stressed the importance of correcting defects, physical vigor, mental and emotional poise, social hygiene, and adequate nutrition.

The many competing agencies and the uncoordinated efforts for promoting children's health presented serious administrative problems. Administrators soon appreciated that the numerous agencies dealing with school health should be brought together, and these groups accepted the term "health education" as covering the various services and forces affecting child health.

During this period some cities changed the name of the department of physical education to the department of health education, but this was against general trends in the field. At present health education and physical education are closely associated, administratively, and generally in teaching situations they enjoy cooperative interrelationships.

IMPLICATIONS OF THIS DEFINITION OF HEALTH FOR ADMINISTRATORS

Definitions serve the cause of clear thinking. They give starting points, perspective, and a kind of compass. If the preceding definition is accepted, then obviously there are certain implications for all educators concerned with the school environment and curriculum in health education.

First, this definition focuses attention upon the unity of the child. Educational literature and particularly psychological papers emphasize organismic integration. The age-old dualism of a separate mind and body has been discarded in the scientific discussion of human nature.

Second, this view of health suggests that the school cannot be engaged successfully in building up a *quantity* of health in childhood that may be drawn upon in later life. Since health is not a quantity but essentially a *quality* that comes from the kind of living that goes on, the educator must be concerned with the habits, skills, and attitudes that children form. This is the crux of the problem in all education. Living finely today is the best guarantee of fine living tomorrow; thus the administrator must review the curriculum, teaching methods, school environment, and staff to promote the best possible living at the moment for each child in school. To do less is to be remiss in one's professional obligations.

There are habits, skills, and attitudes that express directly the health of persons in a positive and dynamic sense. Since to be free from disease is an essential minimum for health, this must be assured whenever possible, but it is the business of administration to plan for the development of abilities that characterize the healthy person.

Third, this definition emphasizes the close association between theory and practice. Knowledge alone never suffices in matters of health. Learning how to live gains hygienic significance only as one lives according to his best knowledge. It is tragic if boys and girls today acquire the notion that health is something to know, rather than something to practice.

As the implications of this definition of health are examined, the importance of health, wholesome interests, and hygienic attitudes among teachers assume large proportions. Consider the anomaly of an English teacher who has trouble with simple grammar or a teacher of science who believes in astrology, fortune telling, witchcraft, and lucky numbers. Obviously, the teacher of health must be one who is reasonably successful in living wholesomely, who is a fair model for children to imitate, and who has knowledge, a method and procedure that reflect modern ideas in this important field. Hypocrisy is never rated as a virtue regardless of its frequent occurrence in life, but what could be more hypocritical than a teacher engaged in teaching children how to live when he is making a mess of the job in his own life? Clearly this whole problem calls for great care in the selection of teachers. And, moreover, this implication of example demands that attention be given to the education of teachers. Candidates for admission should possess not only superior intellectual capacity, not only organic soundness with its freedom from disease and disabling defect, but also emotional stability, enthusiasm and zest for life, and a personality and philosophy of living which children may profitably imitate. These are primary and indispensable steps in promoting the health of children.

A DEFINITION OF PHYSICAL EDUCATION

Definitions change with the ideas that express people's notions of values, of importance, of measures, and of life. Ideas of the time and place shape and fashion all parts of education. Thus, physical education has responded to dominant ideas. Perhaps the most influential ideas in shaping modern physical education in the United States are the concept of organismic unity, the doctrine of interdependence between organism and environment, and the clear recognition of social and emotional as well as physiological outcomes of physical activities. As a result of these orientations, physical education ceases to be merely a gymnastic technic, a series of steps, or a coordination; it becomes a rich and varied practice that has its focus not in the muscles but in the living of the individual. Although the physical is not neglected in this view, the chief outcome is not *always* perspiration; in some instances it may be the attitudes developed.

From this point of view, then, *physical education is the sum of man's physical activities, selected as to kind, and conducted as to outcomes.* Since physical education is a means of education *through* physical activities rather than an education *of* the physical, the phrases *selected as to kind* and *conducted as to outcomes* assume considerable importance.

Selected as to kind implies that activities differ, that there are kinds, and that a selection is indicated. Activities are of varying worth. Which ones shall be chosen? Obviously some are better than others. A choice is required but, when one chooses, a standard is necessary. What standards should one apply in selecting physical activities? The old ones of muscular strength and endurance are not to be discarded, but they greatly need supplementation with skills and attitudes that contribute to wholesome leisure and minister to the development of personality in desirable ways. Any physical educators who select activities on the basis of mere muscular development are doomed to disappointment and despair when the larger problems of social and individual adjustment in modern civilization are faced with sincerity.

It is the simplest matter of common sense to observe that individuals carry into their free hours of leisure those activities in which they have found joy. Obviously, the school of tomorrow must enlarge its plant and facilities for leisure-time education. A situation in which a football field is used for football alone and a gymnasium exclusively for calisthenics will be known for what it actually is—a tragedy and a despair. Physical education as a way of living requires that all persons regard school days as days of opportunity for the education of youth in preferences; for developing attitudes and skills that bring joy as well as financial competence; for experiences that continually lead on to ever richer experiences.

Conducted as to outcomes is equally significant. One is not to neglect the traditional outcomes in physiological results, in growth and developmental accruals, or in neuromuscular skills; but a proper emphasis in modern education is upon interests and attitudes as well. It is precisely this emphasis that modern physical education is disposed to make. Education in physical activities may mean a real interest in wholesome recreation, that an attitude favoring play, dramatization, and art may touch lives that otherwise would be merely dull and dignified.

The authors believe sincerely that physical education can enable boys and girls to secure an education that enriches and deepens life.

Implications of the Definition for Administration. The definition of physical education suggests three implications that need elaboration: physical education is (1) an indispensable education, (2) an education *through* the physical rather than *of* the physical, and (3) an integrator of school life.

Physical Education an Indispensable Education. Physical education is indispensable in modern culture. First, aside from the influence of heredity and nutritive conditions, physical education is the sole source for the development of vitality. Organic power is dependent in large part upon the activities of youth, and neglect of physical education in childhood produces abnormal adult types.

Second, physical education is the sole organized means for the development of neuromuscular skills so essential for the proper functioning of the individual as a moving, motor mechanism. There are, also, vast contributions from these skills to the complete orientation of the individual as a thinking, feeling, and acting organism.

Third, physical education is indispensable as the most important agency to develop attitudes toward play and to combat the sedentary life and its associated evils. No subject in schools and no agency outside schools is so well prepared to promote the idea that play is a part of the good life. There is no need to argue the necessity for such teaching. Society gives numerous signs that play and recreation are essential. To keep alive the play motive requires education of people in skills and attitudes that provide satisfactions in the activities of recreation. Dubs do not enjoy activities in which they falter. Some excellence is necessary.

Fourth, physical education is indispensable for setting standards of sportsmanship. Games offer the laboratory where vital attitudes are formed and the teaching of these, so essential for sport, is equally demanded in all walks of life.

Physical Education an Education through the Physical. No one can examine earnestly the implications of physical education without facing these two questions: Is physical education an education *of* the physical? Is physical education an education *through* the physical? It is clear that an education *of* the physical has some concomitant learnings in addition, and also that an education *through* the physical produces some distinct physical gains. Nevertheless, there are in these questions two ways of looking at physical education.

Education *of* the physical is a familiar view. Its supporters are those who regard strong muscles and firm ligaments as the main outcomes. Curiously enough this restricted view is not heeded alone by physical educators; it is embraced by those who talk about educational values, objectives, and procedures. In effect, such a view is a physical culture and has the same validity that all narrow disciplines have in the world. The cult of muscle is merely another view of the narrowness that fosters the cult of mind or the cult of spirit.

The desire to focus human effort on well defined objectives may lead to partial views. In educational endeavor, whether secular or religious, the partial view frequently obtains. The history of man is replete with records of special disciplines. Vestiges of the supersensual discipline that ruled Europe from the fourth to the fourteenth century remain in the Western world today. Speech, customs, beliefs, attitudes— all share in this heritage that found the only true reality in spirit. The cult of mind never has declared its principles so boldly, although its practice in schools and colleges for generations needs no descriptive statement.

Physical education as an education *through* the physical seeks no single justification for its service to man. Pressure groups of various kinds may reveal physical deterioration among youth, but no modern physical educator, sensitive to the complex and varied needs of man, will rush to the conclusion that strength and endurance are the sole purposes of an adequate program. Neither "body" nor "mind" alone supplies an answer to the vexing problems of modern life. Science has taught too well. Physical education views man as a unity. Not yet knowing the possibilities of the physical, it follows Aristotle in declaring that society never shall know until the physical finds its true function as an instrument for the whole of which it is an indissoluble part. Materialism consists not in frank recognition of the physical, but in assigning to it a spurious supremacy. "There can be no materialism in utmost emphasis upon physical education," writes MacCunn, "so long as 'Body for the sake of soul' is, as it was with Plato, the presiding principle of educational action."

This recasting of the scene is no superficial move but a tendency of deeper growth. It holds that physical education needs to aim higher than health, than victorious teams, than strong muscles, than profuse perspiration. It views physical education primarily as a way of living, and seeks to conduct its activities so as to set a standard that surpasses the average and the commonplace. There is in such a view something of the loftier virtues of courage, endurance, and strength, the natural attributes of play, imagination, joyousness, and pride, and through it all the spirit of splendid living—honest, worthy, competent.

Physical Education as an Integrator of School Life. Physical education activities sometimes are judged harshly by academic colleagues because of the power of physical activity to enkindle high enthusiasm among students. Students care greatly about games, sports, and dancing because these activities touch fundamental drives and express strong racial impulses. Some academic programs in schools are tolerated by students only because other parts of the curriculum give meaning to experience. The assemblies, the band, the newspaper, the clubs, and other student interests are real. Only by the greatest effort is Gaul divided into three parts and the binomial theorem is trivial compared to the real complexities of the zone defense in basketball or the T-formation in football.

The fact is, of course, that physical education helps tremendously to integrate school life. It is a powerful socializing agent and provokes participation in many ways. Although it does aid in this direction, it often fails through lack of inspired leadership to attain its best in this respect.

The teacher of physical education must understand that education gains in its effectiveness as individuals share or participate in experiences. There are two lines of effort for him to exploit. One is to broaden the experiences for as many as he can in the varied activities of the program. To overuse the "star" athlete is not only to injure him but also to deprive others of opportunities. The other effort is to see in the whole school the opportunities which should be explored by all, even the athletes. When a teacher of physical education can say to a boy, "You are spending too much time on games; pay more attention to the academic subjects," he aids in socialization. Although academic teachers may not reciprocate in recommending physical education, the counsel remains the same. Education is a professional responsibility, not ward politics.

THE SCOPE OF HEALTH EDUCATION

Health education may be divided into three sections (Fig. 1):
1. Healthful school living
2. Health services.
3. Health instruction.

Each section has specific functions, but all of them serve the general purpose of educating the child in health.

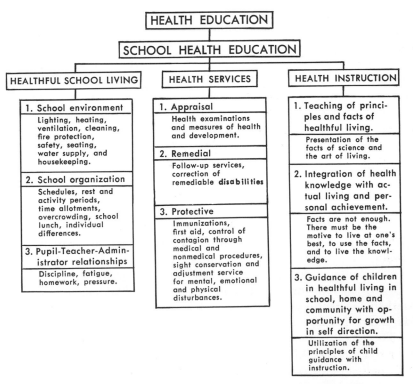

Figure 1. Diagram of the three divisions of health education.

Healthful school living covers the hygienic and sanitary aspects of school plants and also includes attention of those procedures of school organization and pupil-teacher-administrator relationships that affect the mental, emotional, and social health of pupils. Health services include examinations for disease and disability, protective measures of first aid, vaccinations and inoculations, and the follow-up procedures for children with remedial disabilities. Health instruction deals, of course, with the materials by which children are helped to acquire health habits, learn health skills, master health knowledge, and develop health attitudes. All these experiences are educative and by this token all experiences related to healthful school living, health services, and health instruction are in their nature and effect those of health education.

THE SCOPE OF PHYSICAL EDUCATION

Physical education covers the whole range of acknowledged physical activities. The field of interest may be indicated by the classification into which its activities fall. Commonly there are five sections:
1. Organized class instruction program for all students
2. Intramural athletics
3. Interschool athletics
4. Individual programs*
5. School club or activities program.
The scope of the field may be indicated also in terms of the activities, as follows: 1. play and game activities; 2. rhythmic activities; 3. self-testing activities; 4. recreational activities; 5. individual activities.

THE TREND TOWARD LARGER ADMINISTRATIVE UNITS

The scope of health education and physical education as a joint program reflects the general trend toward larger administrative units. It is a sound policy for administration to conform to educational needs, but it is also true that educational efforts should be fashioned into workable administrative units. There is a tendency in administration to group allied interests into logical units not only for better teaching but also for better administration. The social science movement illustrates this trend; history, geography, and civics often are organized and administered as a social science unit. There are other examples in biology and general mathematics.

Health education and physical education are grouped together into one administrative unit for several important reasons. First, this brings

* The individual program is designed to meet individual needs. It includes the modified and adaptive activities for those having deviations from normal physical health. Logically this program belongs under health services but the corrective gymnastic portion of the program belongs historically to physical education. Like other therapeutic procedures, the use of exercise in correction of defects requires special preparation of its practitioners. This program represents an excellent example of the close relationship between health education and physical education.

together two closely related fields. The relationship is more than fortuitous. Physical education personnel have promoted health programs for
over fifty years. Their interests are definitely directed toward health promotion and health conservation among children. Second, these two fields
have the unique opportunity of teaching all children in the school, and,
administratively, this favors a combined relationship. Third, administrators prefer to work with as few directors as possible. Problems of
budgets, programs, and personnel channeled through one source rather
than two or more are handled more effectively. Finally, this combined
plan of administration is cheaper, it reduces the overhead; this doubtless
is one reason why most state departments of education favor this plan.

**Hindrances to Administrative Unity in Health Education and Physical
Education.** Several factors explain the lack of unified programs in the
field. First, the various parts of health education developed singly, and
retain in many instances the organizing personnel who object to unifica-
tion. Health services often were and are assigned to the municipal health
department which, except in unusual circumstances, refuses to give up
this program to the school. Second, school administrators often fail to
understand the problems involved and hence neglect this part of the
program. Third, many physical education teachers, especially men, evince
little interest in health education, and are not prepared adequately either
to teach or administer it. The assignment of responsibilities in this way
may be a disservice to everyone concerned. Finally, in some instances
reorganization is difficult or impossible because it seems necessary to
retain the directing personnel of physical education, or medical inspection, and these individuals, unless recently prepared, are not qualified to
organize and administer a unified department. Attention is called to a
recent practice in some communities to place the health services under
pupil personnel services, and to combine health instruction with science
instruction.

COOPERATION BETWEEN SCHOOL HEALTH EDUCATION AND PUBLIC HEALTH EDUCATION

The varied aspects of health education naturally lead to relationships
between the department of education and the department of health. With
respect to the negative aspects of health that include control and prevention of disease and correction of remediable disability, the department of
health has knowledge, personnel, and facilities that are immensely valuable for such purposes; while the department of education with its knowledge of children and its opportunity to help them in the development of
habits, skills, and attitudes can contribute greatly to positive aspects of
health. These contributions of the two departments are unique and distinctive and this statement does not imply that their roles are exclusive,
nor that their functions operate in watertight compartments. Moreover,
for many years these two departments of government have shown limited

cooperative endeavor, partly because of failure to define their functions in the health area. More recently, significant advances have been made in a joint effort to improve the health of school children. An indication of this is the establishment of joint health committees composed of representatives from both the department of education and the department of health.

In any cooperative enterprise, it is important to define the areas where joint effort is possible and desirable and the areas where responsibility is single and undivided. General cooperative agreements with areas undefined and duties in doubt are of little value. The school has the clear responsibility for health instruction in the classroom and for healthful school living; the health department is legally responsible for the control and prevention of communicable disease. It is at this point where cooperation can begin because children live in the community as well as in the school and the school is a part of the community. The department of education is properly interested in the social, economic, cultural, and hygienic aspects of community life. The department of health is properly interested in the sanitary aspects of the school, the health beliefs of teachers, and the health materials presented to children as well as the control of communicable diseases among them.

It is easy to state the basis of cooperation between two agencies with a common interest, but it is not easy to achieve mutual understanding and generous assistance. There is always the problem of budgets, public credit for work accomplished, and the human equation. People cooperate according to their ability to forget themselves and remember a cause. Confusion in terminology often prevents ready cooperation. Public health departments at all levels of government are responsible for and engage in functions to control and prevent disease; in a positive and dynamic sense they are not "health departments" at all but disease-prevention departments. If the forces and agencies that produce disease could suddenly and permanently be destroyed, there would be no need for such health departments, but there would be then as there is now a need for institutions and education that can influence children and youth to develop their full powers in vitality, energy, and living at their best. Cooperation can go forward readily when the unique and distinctive functions of departments are kept clear.

It is not wise to plan permanent and cooperative arrangements that depend upon fortuitous conditions of the present. State departments of education have been slow to provide funds for school health education, although many states have developed central staffs in this area. State departments of health, on the other hand, have been generously supplied with federal funds and in many states a health educator has been added to the staff and assigned to work in school health education with the state department of education. When one department of state, plentifully supplied with funds, offers to help, then cooperation is easy. The test of cooperation comes when funds are cut off. It would be far better for state departments of education to plan for the development of school health education, to budget for this program, and to cooperate with the state department of health according to the plan that operates in California, Connecticut, and several other states. The California plan is described in a joint statement by the State Superintendent of Public Instruction and the State Commissioner of Public Health:

> In California the Joint Committee on School Health, composed of representatives of the staffs of the State Department of Education and the State Department of Public Health, has made significant progress toward the establishment of cooperative planning at the state level. All publications dealing with health in the schools are considered by the committee and are released under the auspices of both departments. Functions of the two departments concerning nutrition and school lunch programs, special programs for handicapped children, school health records, the curriculum in health, in-service and pre-service training of school and health department personnel, and many other areas have been correlated through the medium of the joint committee. The work of the committee serves as an outstanding example of joint planning and cooperation for the best interests of the children of the State.

THE AMERICAN ASSOCIATION FOR HEALTH, PHYSICAL EDUCATION, AND RECREATION

The foundations of a field are often indicated by the character of the professional societies supporting a movement. The national organization promoting the development of health education, physical education, and recreation is the American Association for Health, Physical Education, and Recreation, a department of the National Education Association. The Association is one of the oldest national societies. It was founded in 1885 as the American Association for the Advancement of Physical Education, and its sponsors were a group of physicians, educators, and specialists in bodily development. A facsimile of the call for the first meeting, contributed by the late Dr. W. G. Anderson, appears in the frontispiece.

Organization. The present Association is divided into six districts (Fig. 2): Eastern, Southern, Mid-West, Central, Northwest, and Southwest. Each district has its own constitution and by-laws which determine the structure and function of the organization. The district and national conventions are held annually. The Association has six main divisions in addition to the general division: health education; physical education; recreation; men's athletics; girls' and women's sports; and safety education.

There are active sections, councils, and affiliated organizations of the Association which are concerned with special interests. Through their officers and committees, efforts are devoted to professional studies and projects as well as the planning and operation of convention programs.

The official publication of the Association is the *Journal of Health–Physical Education–Recreation*. It is published monthly from September to June inclusive. Another publication of the Association is the *Research Quarterly.*

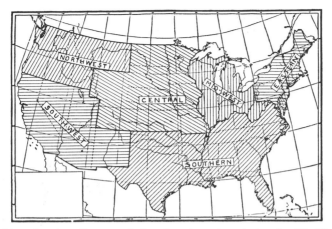

Figure 2.   Map showing districts of the American Association for Health, Physical Education, and Recreation.

Professional Platforms.   The divisions of the Association have formulated platforms which represent current basic beliefs of the professions in these areas. Copies of these statements may be secured from the Association's office, 1201 16th Street, N.W., Washington 6, D.C.

PROBLEMS FOR DISCUSSION

Discuss the following problems on the basis of a sound educational philosophy:
1. A principal serving on a secondary school curriculum committee seeks to eliminate health instruction classes. He contends that the teaching of the subject is sufficiently covered through science, physical education, and home arts. Furthermore, he declares health teaching in his school is unnecessary because the high average of the daily attendance record indicates a "healthy student body, free from diseases."
2. A person recently appointed to the principalship of a new high school stresses the need for a strong physical education staff. He is particularly concerned with procuring coaches who produce winning teams because this contributes so much to the integration of school life.
3. A school board member declares that the physical education program in the local schools places too much emphasis on games, sports, and dancing. He maintains that the program should emphasize vigorous big-muscle activities. Therefore, he requests that a specific muscular fitness test be administered to all pupils three times each year and that a system-wide program of calisthenics be conducted daily for every class. Discuss this request in regard to the modern concept of education and outline your recommendations.
4. A board of education is appalled at the cost of physical education facilities for a new high school. The president agrees that the football stands and field should be included as well as a standard basketball court, with spectator accommodations. He contends, however, that the girls' gymnasium, auxiliary gymnasiums, multiple use outdoor courts, and the swimming pool should be eliminated and bases his decision on the belief that sufficient exercise can be administered through the medium of calisthenics, and swimming opportunities are available at nearby lakes.

5. Instructors and students may implement the above with problems gained from their own experience and observation.

REFERENCES

Cox, P. W. L. and Mercer, B. L.: *Education in Democracy.* McGraw-Hill Book Company, Inc., New York, 1962.

Educational Policies Commission: *The Unique Function of Education in American Democracy* (1937), *Education and Economic Well-Being in American Democracy* (1940), *Health and Physical Fitness for all American Children and Youth* (1945), *Education for All American Youth,* rev. ed. (1952), *School Athletics—Problems and Policies* (1953), *The Central Purpose of American Education* (1961): National Education Association, Washington.

Hanna, P. R.: *Education.* McGraw-Hill Book Company, Inc., New York, 1961.

Joint Committee on Health Problems in Education of the National Education Association and the American Medical Association: *Health Education.* ed. 5. Washington and Chicago, The Associations, 1961.

National Conference on Interpretation of Physical Education: *Conference Report.* The Athletic Institute, Inc., Chicago, 1961.

Nixon, E. W. and Cousins, F. W.: *Introduction to Physical Education.* ed. 6. W. B. Saunders Company, Philadelphia, 1964.

Oberteuffer, D.: *School Health Education.* ed. 3. Harper & Row, Publishers, New York, 1962.

Williams, J. F.: *The Principles of Physical Education.* ed. 8. W. B. Saunders Company, Philadelphia, 1964.

CHAPTER 2

ADMINISTRATION

ADMINISTRATION AND ORGANIZED PLANNING

Every person concerned with health education and physical education needs to understand the principles of administration. The chairman or head of the department must use technical information as the basis for organized planning, analyze problems according to their functional relationships to other affairs of the school and community, and plan a program which begins with the situation as it exists and moves forward toward the realization of broader and more comprehensive goals. All members of the staff, including teachers and supervisors, have administrative functions to perform in the daily conduct of their work which contribute to the successful accomplishment of avowed educational outcomes. Thus mutual understanding and support of established administrative practices is the professional responsibility of each staff member.

A DEFINITION OF ADMINISTRATION

Administration means *providing the constructive leadership that plans and maintains the program, and that enables the program to function effectively in accomplishing the established and worthwhile goals.*
There are many tests of a good administrator. He may be compared to an efficient engineer who lubricates his machine so that it runs smoothly and without friction, or to a competent manager who handles his funds in relation to essential functions to be served, or to an experienced runner who sets his pace in relation to the length of the race. But of course, the administrator is more than these because he is concerned with the purposes for which the machine is run, the sources from which funds are derived, and when, where, and how to have a race.

ADMINISTRATIVE TOOLS

The student of any educational field may be confused at first by the terms that denote the tools with which education operates. These terms identify important educational *tools;* with some of them the administrator is concerned, particularly philosophy, principles, standards and criteria, policies and procedures, and evaluations. These tools are really very simple; there is no need to be confused about them.

Philosophy. Every administrator starts his work with some sort of philosophy which he has acquired through the experiences of living. It may be characterized by prejudice and misinformation, or it may be fair minded and well grounded. But when he becomes responsible for the direction of a program, it is incumbent upon him to examine the items of his philosophy and, as he studies the field, to formulate more clearly the values that he believes in and the purposes that shape his decisions and actions.

What values are uppermost? What basic beliefs regarding persons does he hold? If he finds that for him the highest value in athletics is the winning of games, then other considerations take second place. If staff personnel serve only to accomplish the objectives set by the administrator, then the development, ideas, needs, and purposes of subordinates are secondary.

With respect to children and the nature of a good society, one may formulate a philosophy by setting forth in detail the goals for any youth at a given age or grade level. In doing so, one might seek answers for such questions as the following: What does a youth look like who is physically educated or health educated? What does he know how to do? What ideas, attitudes, skills, habits, and appreciations has he formed? What might he become in all these abilities as the result of experiences in health education or in physical education that lead on to ever richer experiences? Or one might approach the problem in a more general way and attempt to set down the items that comprise one's philosophy of health education or of physical education. Items like the following might appear in the list: I believe that health is much more than mere freedom from disease. I believe in the unity of the organism. I believe in the possibilities of growth and development of each person to a maximum. I believe in the sacredness of the personality, in the dignity of the individual, and in the democratic process.

Principles. Principles grow out of experience or the opinions of experts that reflect experience, and are based upon the facts of science. They come in time to be distillations of both experience and science. Continually refined in the retort of actual practice, principles take on the majesty and force of laws. Ultimately they help to shape and fashion a philosophy whether or not the philosopher considers in detail the principles before or after he formulates his creed. The philosophy that gives a satisfactory synthesis to the various detailed phenomena of life must account for the pertinent facts that underlie it. Hence the philosopher dare not ignore the facts that support or deny the interpretation he attempts to make.

The teacher or administrator confronted with the problem of planning a program of health education and/or physical education may pursue one of several methods. First, he may say that he will do what was done by his predecessor and thereby avoid the danger of innovation. This has certain advantages, of course, but obviously serious disadvantages. Perhaps the predecessor's program was faulty, unworthy, obsolete. One fearful of innovation is apt to rationalize by finding reasons of merit in existing procedures.

Second, he may be content to yield to pressures of the local school administration or out-of-school forces whose primary interest lies in strong interschool athletics or other activities. The true administrator in this field strives for a broad and comprehensive program of health education and physical education.

Third, he may say that he will follow the program given in another city, or formulated at professional school, or even the one pursued in his last position. This may be good or bad for the situation he now faces. He needs basic principles on which he can rest his decision and by which he can judge what he does.

There are five major principles to keep in mind: (1) the importance of an aim; (2) objectives; (3) study of individual needs, interests, and previous experiences; (4) availability of facilities; and (5) the worth of different activities.

The Importance of an Aim. The teacher or administrator must have an aim. It charts his direction; it points the way. This aim should be general in character and beyond realization so that it can serve continually as a goal. As Browning's lines suggest,

> Ah, but a man's reach should exceed his grasp,
> Or what's a Heaven for?

This ideal character of an aim is not visionary but the practical way of indicating purpose. Thus, if one says that physical education should aim to provide skilled leadership and adequate facilities which afford an opportunity for the individual or group to act in situations that are physically wholesome, mentally stimulating and satisfying, and socially sound, he has indicated a purpose, a direction, and yet the aim never will be realized; there will always be better opportunities that can be provided.

Philosophy plays a large part in the statement of an aim. It is apparent that the aim given above does not attempt to make anyone do anything. It does not seek to drill someone into this achievement or to dragoon someone into that. It aims "to provide an opportunity."

Considering the philosophy involved, one observes first that teachers cannot *make* children learn anything; they can *help* children to learn by providing opportunities that facilitate the learning process. Second, one notes that health is not hygienic knowledge or even physical exercise alone, but if health is a condition of good living then the opportunities should be of a kind to promote healthful living. Therefore, the opportunity will be "physically wholesome." Third, physical education, being an education of the whole individual, is concerned with the promotion of opportunities that help to educate the whole individual. A person's mental reaction, emotions, and social conduct are important; they cannot be ignored.

Or one may declare that the aim of health education is to establish and maintain the most favorable physical and social environment for the individual, to appraise his weaknesses and to correct those conditions that are remediable, to assess his strengths and to stimulate to higher levels the virtues he now possesses, and to teach him the essential facts of his own human nature along with a philosophy of how to live in the midst of complex social forces that play upon him.

The value of such a high aim cannot be overestimated.

Objectives. Objectives are the particular and precise means employed to realize an aim. For example, one may aim to contribute to the welfare of man; this is merest fantasy until one visualizes the steps along the way, the everyday achievements in relation to the aim.

Objectives, then, are steps, advances, and realities *in relation* to the aim. They are judged worthwhile as they measure up to the standard of the aim. The teacher or administrator who, when setting up particular objectives for children, takes his bearings in the educational venture from his aim is following sound procedure. On the contrary, if objectives are merely capricious or fortuitous, then he lacks a fundamental approach to the problems in his field.

Study of Individuals. An educational process that seeks to offer individuals an opportunity must exhibit evidence that it is based upon knowledge of the material with which it works. Some important factors are known. The individual, for example, always responds in relation to the total situation; the individual in a situation is the unit, and hence heredity and environment both act upon him.

Where an aim is declared and objectives isolated, the teacher will study children. Both aim and objectives must be examined in the light of human nature. In effect, the teacher or administrator says, "With children of these characteristics this is my aim and these are the outcomes I propose to seek." The characteristics refer to the individual's needs, interests, and previous experiences, his stage of development, his strengths as well as his weaknesses; they portray the total person.

Availability of Facilities. Facilities condition what one can accomplish. Teaching personnel, equipment, plants, and fields limit or make possible the realization of objectives. However, an aim should never be stated in terms of limitations of facilities. Certain objectives may reflect facilities but even with these there should be objectives that lie beyond present possibilities. The reason for this is apparent. If educational theory is built upon the limitations of facilities, the whole program falls to the ground the moment facilities improve. There are notable illustrations of this principle. Several public school systems in large cities developed their physical education theory upon the limitations of artificial school situations. For years, after plants had been improved and facilities had been enriched, the program of activities retained the traditions of an earlier day.

In effect, limited facilities are nothing more than challenges to a progressive administrator. They are obstacles in his way to the realization of his hopes for children. To chart his course entirely by them would be false to his aim, unworthy of his best self, and treason to childhood.

The Worth of Different Activities. In any day there are just so many hours; in any school there are a precise number of gymnasiums, pools, or fields; in any class session there are time and opportunity. Many activities may be taught, and the uncritical teacher, supervisor, or administrator is confronted with the very old question, "*What knowledge is of most worth?*"

Where two or more choices exist, the relative worth of one over the other will determine preference. One may teach the number of bones in the body or how to develop strength in them, the digestive juices of the intestine or how to control emotions so that digestion is unimpaired by worry, fear, and anger. Everything cannot be taught; a choice must be made. One may teach sixth-grade children innumerable forms of the shuttle relay, or the fundamentals of basketball, or a dozen other activities. Which shall be taught? What of all that may be taught is most valuable for children? Relative worth should determine the activities selected and the procedures followed.

Standards. Another administrative tool is the standard against which something is evaluated. When one wishes to know how long an object is, it can be measured by a ruler; this instrument is a practical tool for measuring length. Standards are needed, also, for judging the worth of activities. Since some activities are more important than others, that is, have relative values, a statement of standards for judging is needed. Standards of the kind proposed below have been developed over a period of more than a quarter-century.* They have been rated and tested by numerous leaders in the field. Obviously, they are standards for judging physical education.

The practice must provide physiological results, scientifically determined, indicative of wholesome, functional activity of organic systems, and sufficient for the needs of the growing organism. This standard seeks to avoid those practices which claim physiological outcomes but which on scientific experimentation are shown to be faulty. An example is breathing exercises. Obviously, no administrator can determine scien-

---

* These standards were first presented to the profession in an address by the senior author before the national convention of the American Physical Education Association, April, 1923.

tifically the results of all the activities he promotes, but he can be expected to be informed regarding available scientific data by which he may judge the value of the activities in the program.

The practice must have meaning and significance for the individual and should provide a carry-over interest. This standard upholds the established facts regarding the nature of psychomotor activities; it emphasizes the view that man is a psychophysical unit; and it makes a clear demand upon the administrator to take into account the attitudes, emotions, and ideas of individuals in all programs of physical education. Obviously, the full operation of this standard eliminates the notion that physical education merely is a technic for exercising muscles.

The practice must provide opportunity for the individual to satisfy those socially desirable urges and impulses of nature through engagement in motor activities appropriate to age, sex, condition, and stage of development. Man has inherited desires for certain reactions and activities that have given him satisfaction for generations. These racial impulses are embedded in the organization of neurons in the spinal cord and the basal ganglia of the brain. Desirable traits of character that man possesses are not added mysterious elements to his nature but a flowering of his intrinsic possibilities. Accomplishment in fine motor performance, impulses toward generous play and sportsmanship, and the thrills and satisfactions that come from the use of basic neuron patterns are essential in education.

The practice must offer opportunity for the individual, under wise leadership, to meet educative situations as one of a social group. This standard is illustrated in modern programs of education. Rugged individualism gives way to cooperative activity which seeks to foster appreciations of individual responsibility to others. Since physical education promotes group activities in all sorts of instructional and recreational situations, stresses between individuals always appear and hence there emerges some kind of standards. The teacher, alert to the relationships involved in these situations, will be eager to establish those standards that are socially useful and acceptable.

Another term commonly heard in education is *criterion.* Its use is associated with the meaning of standard. When a standard is used for evaluating anything, then the standard is the criterion of the evaluation. Criteria may be exact measures, such as scales and tapes for measuring weight and height, or they may be quite general, such as the ones described above.

Policies and Procedures. As one develops a philosophy of health education and of physical education, basic beliefs emerge in the aim and objectives. But these must be put into operation, and so policies and procedures are formulated to implement one's philosophy.

Administrative *policies* reveal one's purposes to pursue the goals, the ideals, the hopes that one has for the field. One might, for example, select a generally accepted *policy:* "A program of physical education that meets the inherent and individual needs of each child." Many administrators would approve another *policy:* "Credit toward promotion and graduation for health education and physical education awarded on a basis comparable to academic subjects." Some persons do not believe in credit for health education and physical education and would, therefore, exclude the second example. *Policies* are used in administration for the same purpose that aims are employed in constructing the course of study.

A person may be guided and influenced by study but his basic beliefs and *policies* are his own, carved from the foundation of his biological and social inheritance and fashioned after the pattern of his education.

Administrative *procedures* are interpretations of policies in terms of time and place. Administrative *procedures* adapt policies to meet local conditions; the wise thing to do for the present; plans which lead toward the fulfillment of policies. *Procedures* in administration are like objectives in curriculum building.

A person might, for example, willingly accept the policy of providing a program of physical education to meet the needs of each child, but putting this policy into practice involves *procedures* affecting the entire school system. Is the school organization of traditional type or does it follow the principle of individual needs? Were the teachers of physical education prepared in colleges or universities which emphasized sports skills, or were they prepared in schools emphasizing a broad and varied physical education program? Are students assigned to physical education classes on the basis of reasonably homogeneous groups and in small numbers, or do the wide range of interests and abilities and huge class size restrict consideration for individual needs? Numerous factors relating to the local situation must be taken into account in listing the *procedures* to be followed which lead to the accomplishment of an administrative policy.

Surveys.   The *survey* is used to obtain information relative to existing local conditions and to provide the basis for intelligent future planning. The *survey* represents one of the technics of the larger program called *evaluation.*

First, all pertinent data are collected; these may be designated as the *findings* of the surveyor. Second, proposals are made for improving conditions found; these are the *recommendations* of the surveyor. The *findings* tell what the conditions are, and the *recommendations* disclose what the investigator believes should be done to improve the situation.

Surveys may be classified into two types; the *general survey* and the *special survey.* The *general survey* includes all parts of the program such as facilities, personnel, finance, curriculum materials, health examinations, instruction, and others. The *special survey* is confined to one aspect of the program. At the beginning, the *general survey* is superior to the *special survey* because the former gives a broader picture of the entire program with interrelationships and implications shown in perspective.

Later the *special survey* may be used to advantage for detailed study of one or more administrative activities.

Some years ago *survey* technics consisted of collecting pertinent information about affairs in the local situation, and comparing these data with established standards. Recommendations were based on such comparisons. For example, the findings might show that each school nurse supervised 4000 children. Since a generally accepted standard is 1500 to 2000 school children per nurse, it would be recommended that the number of nurses be increased.

A more recent development in survey technic directs greater attention to the functional operation of the program than to statistical comparison. Instead of comparing obtained data with established standards, the attempt is made to determine how well the school is accomplishing its avowed purposes. Followers of this plan believe that it is more significant for administrators to establish policies and procedures on a local functional basis, and to evaluate success in terms of the degree to which these goals are attained, than merely to compare conditions in the local situation with standards based principally on the law of averages. If the avowed purposes of the program are adequate in meeting the needs of children, the plan appears highly commendable. In either case the technics of collecting information are essentially the same.

Surveying is a continuous process. Change is inevitable, and change in one school activity brings modification in others. The *continuous evaluation* in one form or another is an administrative tool which functions best in relation to the use of other tools available, namely, philosophy, principles, standards and criteria, policies and procedures. In the proper use of all these tools the administrator can arrive intelligently at a *one-three-five-year program*.

ONE-THREE-FIVE-YEAR PROGRAM

One should not assume that all administrators formulate a philosophy, acquire principles, develop standards and criteria, establish policies and procedures, and conduct surveys without reference of these important tools to the staff of the department. Those who do so lose a fine opportunity for professional growth of all concerned. The entire staff, working together with the various tools available, will find it necessary to improve some of their tools as they proceed.

At the outset the controlling philosophy must be formulated, the guiding principles stated, and the standards specified. Then administrative policies and procedures must be declared to implement the philosophy, principles, standards, and the findings of the survey.

The next step is to arrange administrative procedures into three groups: the *first-year* group; the *third-year* group; and the *fifth-year* group. In the *first-year* group are those procedures which may be completed during the first year. Those requiring more time are assigned to the *third-* or *fifth-year* program, respectively.* Allocation of projects or activities to one year or another provides a definite plan for the administrator. In the event of unforeseen developments certain items may be transferred from one year to another, either up or down the scale.

The question is sometimes asked, "How am I to know which year's program best fits this particular item?" There are no hard and fast rules governing the assignment of procedures, since the types of school organization vary in different communities. Generally speaking, items in the *first-year program* include those over which the department of health education and physical education has control. Suppose, for example, the policy is established, "To provide inservice education of personnel in the department." In a college or university one might assume that the procedures would be: staff meetings, visitation, attendance at conventions and summer sessions, and others. Nearly all of these procedures could be effected by the department and hence belong to the *first-year program.* In public schools the department would have less responsibility for the inservice education of its members, since this responsibility often rests with the principal and superintendent. However, the director assumes responsibility for planning details pertinent to the department program. A *first-year program* for a public school department might include the following projects: to extend the intramural athletic program for girls; to secure the cooperation of students in the sanitary care of locker rooms; or to cooperate with the school physician in securing correction of remediable conditions.

The *third-year program* includes those items involving school interrelationships, i.e., affairs beyond the administrative province of the department but confined to the school organization. The following policy is an example: "To regulate the supervision of elementary classroom teachers by appointment from the central office and upon request by the building principal rather than by the rotation-inspection method." The procedures might be listed as: approval of change by the school superinetndent and board of education; approval by supervisors; approval by building principals; approval by classroom teachers; reorganization of curriculum materials; starting with one school where the plan has greatest chance to function smoothly. Administration of functions involving school interrelationship takes time; such items belong in the *third-year program.*

The *fifth-year program* contains those items concerned with community interrelationships. The following policy is an example: "To make physical education facilities and equipment available for out-of-school recreational groups when not in use by school children." Here the procedures involve a wide range of people and interests. In establishing the procedures a number of questions must be answered. Does the board of education have legal right to loan these facilities for general com-

* Instead of the "one-three-five-year" program, some administrators prefer to use such terms as "immediate," "delayed," and "remote."

munity purposes? Perhaps certain groups will be allowed to use the school premises while others will not; what basis will be used to accept or reject requests? Shall outside groups be expected to provide adequate supervision of activities? Who will pay for or replace broken equipment? Administrative matters involving community interrelationships usually require a formulation of policy by the office of the school superintendent and approval by the board of education; but since many forms of community use of the school plant involve physical education facilities, the department is often responsible for some administrative details.

The *one-three-five-year program* is an indispensable administrative aid. It gives direction to the program. It requires serious preliminary thought followed by careful planning and organization. It is to be used as a guide. It is not to be followed slavishly, but continuously evaluated and reorganized in accordance with changes in the school or community. The successful administrator understands his community. He recognizes changes in the community and knows the reasons for these changes before they are apparent to the general public. He adapts the *one-three-five-year program* to meet these changing conditions, sometimes postponing a first-year project because of unusual developments, sometimes coming forward with a fifth-year plan for the same reason. The *one-three-five-year program* means looking ahead, planning for the future; it means meeting the needs of today.

AUTOCRATIC AND DEMOCRATIC ADMINISTRATION

Administrators are not all alike in the way they handle the tools of administration. They differ in many respects. Some are efficient in office routine. Others excel in formulating policies, delegating to associates the execution of details. Some prefer to direct personally the affairs of the department. Others place the responsibility on staff members. If the administrator is an autocratic disciplinarian, he dictates the policies and procedures, asserts that he, as the administrator, knows best what should be done, claims the responsibility is his, and contends that since he is to be held responsible by higher authority he will determine the course of action. If he is imbued with the principles of democracy, the administrator shares responsibilities and conducts his department with greater freedom.

Examples of autocratic and democratic administration may be expressed as follows: Years ago Jowett's advice to administrators was, *"Never retract, never explain. Get it done. Let 'em howl."* A superintendent in one of the largest cities has adopted the policy, *Administration should be organized in such a way that all persons affected by the decision shall share the responsibility in making the decision.*

Many school superintendents, principals, or directors of health education and physical education conduct their professional affairs according to one pattern or the other. Formerly, the dictator type of administrator was most frequently encountered. In more recent years the trend has been in the opposite direction.

Doubtless most administrators accept a middle ground somewhere between the two extremes. One administrator may arrive at a decision, call a meeting of those persons affected by the decision, and try to get them to accept his point of view. Through his salesmanship or fear of consequences the subordinates accept the decision without question. At best this closely resembles the autocratic type of administration. Another administrator delays making a decision until the various interest groups have been given the opportunity to voice their opinions. After carefully weighing the evidence on all sides the administrator makes his decision, which then becomes the departmental policy. Decisions arrived at by this latter method more closely approximate the democratic type of administration.

But the student of administration should give some thought to the kind of cooperative action that comes naturally with the experience of shared decisions. It is generally true that when the pertinent problems of the department are known, considered, and attacked by staff members, greater wisdom is brought to bear, staff productivity is increased, and larger sympathy prevails. It is true, of course, that a crowd is not wiser than the wisest man in it and for purposes of the voyage the crew does not know more than the captain; but it is also true that the staff of a department is not a mob and that their full cooperation is needed to bring the program into port. No administrator, unless imbued with sublime confidence in his own superior wisdom, would forego the opportunity to promote the growth of junior staff members, to arouse high morale in the staff, and to secure loyalty and enthusiasm from them.

The administrator should experiment with many actual problems and choose the kind of administrative practice which seems most satisfactory to him. Unquestionably the plan employed by his superior officer, the superintendent or principal, will guide him in making his decisions, since the conduct of affairs in health education and physical education should follow the general plan of administration established for the school system as a whole or by the principal as the chief executive officer of the building.

PROBLEMS FOR DISCUSSION

1. The democratic concept of administration recognizes that all staff members have administrative functions to preform in the daily conduct of their work. Discuss this concept in relation to: (a) the teacher of physical education in a large city high school; (b) a teacher in a centralized rural school; and (c) an elementary school supervisor.
2. Some school superintendents regard the director or supervisor of health and physical education as a "consultant" or a "resource person." Discuss this point of view in the light of the definition of administration given in this chapter.

3. A department head who desires to broaden the health education and physical education program recognizes the need for additional facilities, personnel, and time allotment. Describe ways in which he might make wise use of several administrative tools in presenting his problems to the board of education.
4. Select three administrative problems and explain how they might be solved. In your explanation propose both autocratic and democratic types of administration. Give reasons for and against each type of administration. In your opinion which type of administration probably will insure better schools? Why?
5. Instructors and students may implement the above with problems gained from their own experience and observation.

REFERENCES

American Association for Health, Physical Education, and Recreation: *Current Administrative Problems.* Washington, 1960.
American Association of School Administrators: *Professional Administrators for America's Schools.* Twenty-Eighth Yearbook, The Association, Washington, 1960.
Grieder, C., Pierce, T. M. and Rosenstangle, W. E.: *Public School Administration,* ed. 2. The Ronald Press, New York, 1961.
Hagman, H. L.: *The Administration of American Public Schools.* McGraw-Hill Book Company, Inc., New York, 1956.
Hunt, H. C. and Pierce, P. R.: *The Practice of School Administration.* Houghton-Mifflin Book Company, Boston, 1958.
Latchaw, M. and Brown, C.: *The Evaluation Process in Health Education, Physical Education, and Recreation.* Prentice-Hall, Inc., Englewood Cliffs, 1962.
Morphet, E. L., Reller, T. L. and Johns, R. L.: *Educational Administration—Concepts, Practices and Issues.* Prentice Hall, Inc., Englewood Cliffs, 1959.
Reller, T. L. and Morphet, E. L.: *Comparative Educational Administration.* Prentice Hall, Inc., Englewood Cliffs, 1962.
Walton, J.: *Administration and Policy Making.* Johns Hopkins University Press, Baltimore, 1959.
Williams, J. F.: *The Principles of Physical Education.* ed. 8. W. B. Saunders Company, Philadelphia, 1964.

CHAPTER 3

PERSONNEL AND FUNCTIONS OF THE STAFF

PERSONNEL SPECIALIZATION

Attempts to improve the educational offering result naturally in the specialization of personnel. Occasionally specialization goes too far and persons charged with school responsibilities lose sight of the needs of the whole child as they concentrate upon the functions of their own field. This is not a necessary outcome of specialization but the way such persons are professionally prepared for their work.

Education demands a high degree of specialization in order to expose youth to a variety of developmental experiences that strengthen life in home and community. As services improve in methodology and broaden in scope they tend to require greater competence in specific areas.

Abundant evidence illustrates the weaknesses of narrow specialization. Teachers vie with each other for school time in which to promote their individual subjects. School administrators frequently emphasize child-accounting and schedule-making with less regard to programs aimed to enhance normal growth and development.

In health education and physical education the conflict continues. The athletic coach may expect regularly scheduled classes and intramural programs to give way to interscholastic competition. Some teachers of adapted physical education would assign a majority of students to individual forms of activity. The school physician often disregards opportunities to teach values of healthful living in the health examination.

This kind of professional narrowness convicts the specialist. The teacher of physical education who remains unconcerned about the prog-

31

ress of students in the social sciences deserves equal censure with the teacher of history who regards physical education merely as exercise.

Specialization is meritorious in any expanding science or growing enterprise. Failure results when the function of specialization becomes lost in the intricacies of a single purpose and forgetful of the individual with his various needs. School people who understand the phenomena of growth and development seldom persist in the dichotomy of mind and body.

The community has the right to expect of its teachers a broad background of preparation; of its supervisors, successful experience in addition to preparation. Teachers, supervisors, and administrators must have personalities that enable them to get along with people and to inspire confidence and respect. They must understand the philosophical, psychological, sociological, and political bases of general education. They must possess a philosophy of health education and physical education which clearly indicates the function of these programs in the complete education of youth. They must have ideals but be patient and practical in achieving them. They must be able to plan intelligently, take the program where they find it, consider the needs and resources of the community, and establish policies and procedures that give direction to the program for years to come.

THE DIRECTOR OF HEALTH EDUCATION AND PHYSICAL EDUCATION

In a public school organization, the term *director* usually refers to a member of the superintendent's staff who is charged with administrative and supervisory responsibilities of a specific area of the program. Sometimes the terms *supervisor, coordinator,* or *consultant* are used for the same purpose. In health education and physical education any one of the terms may apply to the person who has charge of this program in a city or county school system. It is not uncommon to refer to the head physical education teacher of a centralized school or a department head in a high school as *director* or *coordinator*. However, this term generally applies to the person charged with the responsibilities of health education and/or physical education, possibly including recreation and safety, in an organizational structure involving several schools. Duties of the *director* in a large city, small city, or a single centralized school are similar in principle but may differ in scope.

Scope of Responsibilities. Responsibilities of the director or coordinator are various and sundry but generally they may be grouped under the following headings:

Administrative.
1. Works with staff, building principals, and other administrative-supervisory personnel in developing and implementing departmental policies.

2. Works with staff in program development and implementation.
3. Selects and implements procurement of supplies and equipment.
4. Prepares departmental budgets and directs the expenditure of funds.
5. Works cooperatively with agencies responsible for community health and recreation programs.
6. Coordinates relationships between department program and plan of education for entire school system.
7. Recommends the selection and assignment of teachers.
8. Serves as chief consultant to the superintendent and general staff concerning matters pertinent to the particular field and total school program.
9. Advises on planning and use of facilities concerned with the program.
10. Develops and applies a broad public relations program.

Supervisory. Stimulates best development of staff members through practice of sound techniques of educational supervision, such as:
1. Acquaints newly appointed teachers with policies, procedures, and details pertinent to the program.
2. Conducts an inservice education program.
3. Provides opportunities for all staff members to participate actively in staff and committee meetings.
4. Makes arrangements for staff to attend professional conferences.
5. Establishes effective channels of communication through bulletins, conferences, visitations, and other media.
6. Establishes good rapport between his office and the staff.

Qualifications. The person qualified to direct a program of health education and physical education possesses high standards of character and personality. The very nature of his duties require him to be a good leader. He exhibits approved qualities of total fitness. He displays enthusiasm for his work and has the courage of his convictions.

The Directors' Association of New York State summarizes a director's qualifications as follows:

Thus the director may be described as a healthy and intelligent individual, capable of fostering sound human relationships and earnestly believing in his task. And he has the capacity to turn that conviction to the benefit of the pupil, whoever remains the greatest concern.*

Preparation. Logical preparation for the director of health education and physical education includes an undergraduate major in his field plus at least two years of graduate study. During the latter period he pursues advanced courses in educational administration, philosophy, psychology, sociology, guidance, and public speaking. In the major field of graduate study the advanced courses include principles, methods,

---

* Joint Study, Directors' Association, New York State Association for Health, Physical Education, and Recreation, and the Division of Health, Physical Education, and Recreation, New York State Education Department. *The Person for the Position of Director.*

supervision, administration, evaluation, research, and public relations, as well as subject matter to supplement deficiencies in undergraduate preparation.

Practical experience in community recreation, teaching on both the elementary and secondary levels, and coaching athletics are desirable. Demonstrated administrative and executive ability as well as good leadership are essential.

In New York State specific standards have been adopted for certificating the director of health, physical education, and recreation.

Status. From the preceding discussion it is apparent that the director holds a responsible position. His status depends on certain factors, such as: (1) size of the school system; (2) organizational structure of the school system; and (3) point of view of higher authority. In smaller communities, where a part of his time is devoted to teaching and supervision, the director may be classified as a supervisor. Occasionally in cities of from 50,000 to 100,000 the man or woman in charge of this program receives the title of director, and assumes a position on a parity with secondary school principles. In cities with a population exceeding 100,000 his title of assistant superintendent may be more appropriate. This is particularly desirable if the director is responsible for health education, physical education, and recreation. The current practice is to classify such a person as *director* (Fig. 3) with a salary equal to or slightly above that of a building principal.

The terms "line" and "staff" officer create some confusion relative to the position held by the director. A "line" officer is directly responsible to the person above him until the superintendent of schools is reached; thus, the teacher is directly responsible to his principal, who in turn is answerable to the elementary or secondary assistant superintendent, and finally to the superintendent. A "staff" officer works anywhere along the line. Thus, the director may be responsible to a deputy superintendent, although he works in conjunction with the assistant superintendent in charge of elementary or secondary schools, with elementary or secondary school principals, or even with the teachers themselves. The supervisor of nurses or the supervisor of physical education belongs to the department of health education and physical education. They are staff officers immediately responsible to the director. In a limited sense, the director of health education and physical education is a "line" officer, but the majority of his work involes "staff" relationships.

The Director's Advisory Council. Many directors of health education and physical education in large school systems appreciate the cooperative assistance rendered by an advisory body of staff representatives known as an *advisory council*. Council members are elected by their associates in the department and serve under the chairmanship of the director. The purpose of such a council is to study departmental problems, to present

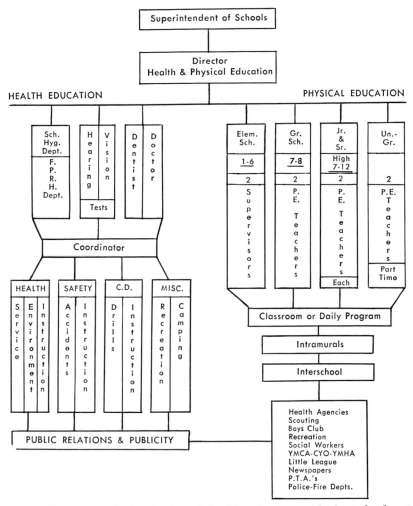

Figure 3. Departmental organization of health education and physical education. (Courtesy of Fall River, Massachusetts, Public Schools.)

the findings at staff meetings, and to recommend appropriate action as the need arises.

THE FUNCTION OF SUPERVISION

The primary function of supervision relates to the improvement of instruction through the inservice education of teachers. Administrative factors of supervision include appropriate organization of the following:

1. Determination of the professional competencies and needs of individual teachers
2. Teacher visitations and intervisitations
3. Conferences and meetings
4. Demonstration teaching
5. Directed readings
6. Study groups
7. Working conferences
8. Refresher courses
9. Summer session study
10. Individual and group research
11. Membership in professional associations
12. Writing for publication
13. Participation in policy making
14. Curriculum revision
15. Public relations
16. Assistance with selected community activities
17. Continuous evaluation of the program and methods of instruction.

The role of supervision has passed through numerous stages, from inspectorial to consultative. Tradition often determines whether the person responsible for this activity serves as an inspector with a checklist who "rules with an iron hand," or as a consultant who cooperates with teachers and principals in making schools better places in which to live and learn. Likewise, terminology has changed. Many school systems retain the title of "supervisor," while others prefer the terms "consultant" or "resource person." This text continues in the use of "supervisor" for reasons of clarification, and because the national organization in this field, a department of the National Education Association, is called the Association for Supervision and Curriculum Development.

The Supervisor and Building Principals. The principal as the chief executive officer is responsible for all activities and services of the school. The success of supervision depends largely upon the cooperation of building principals. Most of the difficulties which arise grow out of misunderstandings between the principal and supervisor regarding their mutual responsibilities. Supervisors are employed because the work of a given department is so complex that both principals and teachers need assistance. On the other hand, the principal is charged with the responsibility of unifying the instruction in his school. Unless supervision is regarded as a cooperative enterprise between the supervisor and principal, personal and professional difficulties may arise, such as led one school executive to remark, "Apparently it is the specialist's job to take the child apart and the principal's job to put him back together again."

The qualified supervisor gives professional aid to principal and teachers, being constantly aware of the objectives and plans of organization established for the school as a whole. The principal, on the other hand, expects reliable suggestions from the supervisor to improve the quality of instruction.

Occasionally honest differences of opinion occur between these two school officials. Perhaps the principal fails to heed the advice of the supervisor, or the principal regards the suggestions as detrimental to the routine organization of the school. Usually a frank discussion of the problem brings a clear understanding of the mutual relationships to be assumed. Should this conference fail to solve the difficulty, recourse to higher authority is imperative. A policy is needed to meet this type of situation.

Supervision of Physical Education Teachers. Adequate supervision of teachers represents sound administrative policy. Even teachers with broad educational preparation and years of experience profit by the interchange of ideas, coordination of effort, and professional stimulation provided by efficient supervision.

Supervision is a cooperative enterprise. Older ideas of inspection and authority must give way to the realization that teachers and supervisors have equal rank and equal responsibility in improving the quality of instruction. When proper relationships are established, teachers regard the supervisor as a counselor or friend concerned with the mutual task of enriching the educational opportunities of students. These relationships are discussed in the section that follows.

Supervision of Classroom Teachers. In some elementary schools teachers of physical education are employed. In others this responsibility is delegated to the classroom teacher. As a general policy specialization in physical education depends on the degree of departmentalization practiced in other instructional areas. Classroom teachers nearly always assume the major responsibility for health instruction in elementary schools.

The supervisor of health education and physical education in elementary schools must be thoroughly familiar with the contributions of these programs to the growth and development of youth within the specific age range, and recognize the organization peculiar to each school. In brief, the function of supervision in elementary schools is to: (1) cooperate with building principals in the development of a program consistent with the avowed purposes of the school; (2) assist teachers with the improvement of instruction through observation, demonstrations, conferences, and other types of inservice education; and (3) effect departmental policies and procedures designed to raise standards of accomplishment within the school system as a whole.

Among the more significant qualities necessary for effective supervisory leadership, the following items deserve consideration:

1. *A sympathetic, constructive, and cooperative attitude*—at all times the supervisor must be able to put himself in the place of the teacher, to feel as he does, to aspire with him, to be disappointed with him, and with him to pledge anew purposeful goals of achievement.
2. *A genuine interest in and friendliness toward people*—not to be confused with unwarranted privileges; friendliness constitutes an essential attribute to success.
3. *Respect for individual personalities*—teachers differ in abilities, preparation, and experience; these differences must be recognized in the acceptance of ideas, development of attitudes, and the quality of instruction.

4. *Building slowly upon a sound foundation*—enduring progress takes time; formulation of appropriate policies for supervision and adoption of procedures leading to the constructive inservice education of teachers requires patience, a healthful personality, and deep-seated wisdom.
5. *Credit for successful accomplishment*—to those who actually do the work, credit is due; the machinery for cooperative planning is the responsibility of the supervisor; actually putting these plans into practice depends on principals and teachers, and to them should go the major rewards for program success.

Types of Supervision. Some supervisors visit classrooms periodically to teach a lesson which is practiced or drilled until the supervisor returns a week or a month later. This is supervision in name only and should not be confused with cooperative technics wherein teachers are guided in the improvement of instruction.

In another type of questionable supervision the supervisor follows a definite schedule and visits each teacher in rotation, irrespective of individual teacher needs and abilities. Obviously, certain teachers require more assistance than others; hence provision should be made to give assistance where it is most needed and in accordance with adopted plans for improving the entire program.

The type of supervision gaining favor is known as the *two-way approach*. This provides opportunity for the principal of the school to invite the supervisor to his building to assist with specific problems or with general plans for program improvement. Likewise, this type of supervision enables the supervisor to consult with principals and teachers when he believes such visitation is desirable, even though requests from the schools have not been received by the central office.

Transportation of Supervisors. Transportation of supervisors should be provided at public expense. To expect the supervisor to furnish his own conveyance may lead to inefficiency due to personal interests in economy; schools in remote districts may receive less attention than those located nearer the central office. In a few cities automobiles are owned and operated by the board of education; in others the supervisor uses his personal automobile, receiving a nominal mileage fee for professional duty, or a stipulated amount per month for traveling expense. Occasionally transportation is calculated and added to the original salary of the supervisor. While local policies differ in this matter, some provision should be made for defraying the expense necessitated by traveling from one school to another.

Reports and Conferences. In well organized departments each supervisor confers frequently with the director indicating the work accomplished and outlining future plans. Although these conferences may be informal, the supervisor plans his discussion and carries it out in a business-like manner. The director also holds periodic conferences with the entire supervisory staff.

Preparation of Supervisors. Numerous state certification codes, and indeed the majority of local boards of education, require the supervisor to have obtained the baccalaureate degree with a major in his chosen field. Graduate work or its equivalent is not uncommon for those who would obtain this post. Although rich experience and high competence may constitute a substitute for advanced scholastic attainments, some graduate study is highly desirable.

TEACHERS OF HEALTH EDUCATION AND PHYSICAL EDUCATION

Education depends largely upon society providing situations in which the child is expected to act, to weigh relative values, to formulate judgments, and is stimulated to act in a manner approved by the group as a whole. To facilitate the learning process public schools are maintained. Basic principles governing the conduct of these schools are developed in accordance with biological and social inheritances.

Insofar as the child is concerned, biological urges are more fundamental than those prompted by social stimulation. In the development of civilization, however, numerous primitive ways of reacting, caused by natural biological hungers, have been redirected to serve the needs of society.

Health education provides unusual opportunities for reconciling nature and nurture. On the one hand, the teacher in this field is concerned with the development of organs and systems, and with factors responsible for biological preservation of the individual. On the other hand, instruction in health relates to an interpretation of man's environment and the institutions he has created for wholesome living in the home and community.

The teacher of physical education enjoys a unique position because he is directly concerned with many of the child's innate desires—to run, jump, throw, climb, and dance—and at the same time he is concerned with directing those desires into channels representing approved social conduct.

It is this understanding of the importance of health education and physical education that has caused teacher-education institutions to emphasize these fields as a means of educating children. Likewise school superintendents and building principals recognize the need for employing health educators and physical educators who are thoroughly grounded in principles of teaching as well as in public health and neuromuscular skills.

Preparation of Physical Education Teachers. The success of any enterprise involving human relationships depends largely upon wise direction. Health education and physical education require competent professional leadership. While an understanding of public health and skill in a wide range of neuromuscular activities are important, an understanding of the purpose of education and the contribution which these specific fields make to complete living is likewise essential. Other things being equal, professional preparation is reflected in improved student progress.

In all human relationships quality takes precedence over quantity. But quality is so difficult to measure, so fleeting to describe, that customary practice often relies upon quantitative standards in the hope that qualitative outcomes will result.

The preparation of teachers in health education and physical education should approximate standards required for teachers of academic subjects. Thus, if physical education teachers are employed for the elementary school, their qualifications will be equal to those prescribed for classroom teachers. This trend in secondary schools definitely indicates four years of preparation leading to the baccalaureate degree, and in some states the education requirement has been raised to five years. The teacher who devotes all his time to health education and/or physical education should have majored in this field. The minor is merely a substitute for the major and is appropriate only for those who must teach several different subjects.

PREPARATION OF CLASSROOM TEACHERS IN ELEMENTARY SCHOOLS

The number of physical education teachers in elementary schools is comparatively small because of the general belief that education in the first six grades is best served when the classroom teacher coordinates the various school activities which surround the child. While this principle is educationally sound, health education and physical education frequently suffer because the classroom teacher lacks adequate technical preparation in these fields. Under the careful guidance of an efficient supervisor, consultant, or resource person, together with adequate professional preparation, the classroom teacher may obtain satisfactory results, although most persons competent in the field consider such "results" as the exception rather than the rule.

Realization of the need for specific preparation has caused several state departments of education to require from four to six semester hours of study in health education and physical education for all persons working for an elementary credential. This procedure insures some degree of technical competence and an understanding of methods which may be employed to articulate health education and physical education with other subjects. For elementary teachers now employed and who have not been exposed to such courses, inservice preparation is essential. This may be obtained through supervision, extension courses, carefully planned teachers' meetings, discussion and practice groups, directed readings, working conferences, field visits, and work experience.

TEACHER CERTIFICATION

Most state departments of education establish regulations governing the certification of personnel in health education and physical education. Usually certification is based upon professional preparation in an approved teacher-education institution. Except for elementary classroom teachers, permission to teach, supervise, or direct programs of health education and physical education is granted to those persons who have fulfilled requirements for the major or minor in undergraduate or graduate schools appearing on the state's approved list, although some states permit those who hold a general secondary credential to teach in these specialized fields. Revised certification codes may demand specialization still further in that qualifying certificates, based upon preparation and experience, are issued separately for teachers, supervisors, and directors. Indications of this procedure appear in a number of the more progressive local districts which have established higher certification standards than those required by the state.

INSERVICE EDUCATION FOR TEACHERS AND SUPERVISORS

The director is responsible for the professional growth of his staff. The more common methods of inservice education are supervisory visits, teacher conferences, intervisitation, professional study workshops, and demonstration meetings. Supervisory visits should be made in relation to the needs of the situation, intervisitation of classes may afford stimulating observation, and demonstration meetings offer an excellent opportunity for observation of good work and subsequent discussion of objectives, methods, and procedures.

One of the best methods of improving the staff is through attendance at summer schools. Although four summer sessions are not as valuable as one year of academic study, the summer school does provide an opportunity for obtaining new ideas and meeting associates who are engaged in similar kinds of work. The professionally minded teacher or supervisor plans to attend a summer school every three or four years.

Another method of inservice education involves the reading of new books and professional magazines. Most professional material of importance appears in printed form about every eight to ten years, hence the teacher or supervisor who conscientiously reads the literature in the field will be conversant with changes in the profession.

Extension courses represent a popular means of inservice education. Not only does the student obtain new material, but such courses often are used for academic credit at colleges or universities. Such courses may be arranged with nearby colleges or universities.

Special conferences or workshops present excellent opportunities for study of specific or general problems. Teachers and supervisors from neighboring communities may hold meetings to exchange ideas and experiences relating to procedures of mutual interest. Often a series of conferences produces the best results. Success depends upon how well the conference or workshop meets the needs of the participants; all preliminary planning, the discussion leaders, and the follow-up efforts after the meetings should be directed to this end.

State, district, and national conventions are conducted primarily for the purpose of improving teachers in service. The professional spirit engendered by these meetings is a prime factor in perpetuating the professional interest of teachers. The American Association for Health, Physical Education, and Recreation at its national, district, and state conventions offers lectures, discussions, and workshops rich in material for those who desire to improve the effectiveness of their work. Most district and state conventions follow similar procedures.

Growth in attendance at meetings of the National Education Association among persons in health education and physical education is a favorable indication of professional growth. Closer articulation with general education, which recognizes the interrelationships of different fields, leads to improved educational results.

DEPARTMENTAL MEETINGS

Of first importance is the responsibility of staff members to general teachers' meetings called by appropriate authority. Personnel in health education and physical education sometimes hold themselves strangely aloof from such meetings, thus perpetuating the unfortunate belief that health instruction and physical activity are "special" subjects apart from education in general. Departmental staff members not only should attend these meetings, but they should take an active part in the discussions which follow.

In some communities regular departmental meetings are held monthly, in others such meetings are held only as the need arises. Probably the second plan is better, although an efficient staff will find many professional problems in need of further study. Matters pertaining to course of study revision, the use of equipment, and the general effectiveness of the department challenge the interest of teachers and supervisors. Frequently the director divides the staff into groups for special study. Departmental meetings where everyone participates are preferable to those planned and conducted entirely by the director who "lays down the law" which his subordinates accept and put into practice.

In a department devoted to democratic procedure, the director sets the tone of the department by refraining from arbitrary decisions and by stimulating group participation in the solution of common problems. Complete agreement in the group is not always possible and there will be at times sharp divergence of views. This kind of conflict should be welcomed. The head or director has the responsibility to decide on problems that require decisive action. At these times it should be clear that the issue is not closed, that the decision is temporary and not final, and that later the problem will be considered again. It is this spirit of interest in and concern for the opinions of associates that reflects the democratic character of administration. And by a kind of reciprocity, it has an effect upon the teaching and administrative behavior of the staff so that they too begin to manifest democratic attitudes in their relations with others. In this way a department or an entire institution may exemplify a spirit of good will, confidence, helpfulness, and mutual trust among students and teachers.

This matter of fostering democratic attitudes is not trivial. The great revolutionary forces loose in the world today conflict most sharply on the issue of human rights; the contest between East and West is in reality between respect for human dignity and disregard of every human right. Indeed the issue is so clear that the United Nations has agreed upon a Universal Declaration of Human Rights.

TEACHER LOAD

The general belief persists that teachers of physical education maintain a heavier load of instructional activity than academic teachers. When the number of hours devoted to extra-class activities are included, doubtless the teacher load in physical education is excessive. If proper educational results are obtained, the teaching load of physical educators should approximate that of academic teachers.

Two leading cities possibly illustrate a trend in teacher load. In one city with a junior high school enrollment of 4000, 20 teachers of health education and physical education are employed. Here each student receives four 60-minute periods of health education and physical education per week—three of physical education and one of health education. The senior high school and vocational school enrollment totals 3500 with 17 health education and physical education teachers. In these schools the time allotment approximates one period per day; some schools schedule a double period of physical education or health instruction every other day. Each teacher assumes responsibility for 25 teaching periods per week of physical education or health instruction. In addition, all of these teachers remain on duty three after-school periods per week, except coaches of interscholastic sports who work every afternoon during the season. After-school or Saturday assignments include outing clubs, riding clubs, winter sports, and similar events.

In another leading city each elementary school teacher of physical education is assigned a daily teaching load of seven 30-minute periods, with extra remuneration for after-school activities not to exceed two hours each afternoon. Senior high school instructors assume responsibility for 22 class hours per week, plus 8 hours of after-school activities distributed over four days. The program is organized by subjects, is taught in daily rotation, and consists of: (1) gymnastics; (2) aquatics; (3) individual health training; and (4) safety education.

The above reports indicate commendable progress but much remains to be done.

SALARY SCHEDULES

Matters pertaining to the adoption of salary schedules frequently confront the director. Should salary schedules be used? If so, upon what bases should they be formulated? The department of health education and physical education must follow the general policy adopted by the school system in such matters.

It is not uncommon to find salary schedules in this field differing from those used for other specialists with equivalent rank. Sometimes teachers of physical education are paid more than teachers of academic subjects in the same school, and occasionally persons in this field receive less than their associates in academic education. While granting that provisions must be made for varying teacher loads, it is recommended that salary schedules in health education and physical education be comparable to those affecting other teachers of equivalent rank. Unequal salary schedules tend to break down morale and arouse professional jealousies.

Most schedules provide for increasing the wages of teachers annually or biannually from an established minimum until the maximum is reached within a comparatively short time, perhaps eight to ten years. Another plan does away with a maximum altogether and provides indefinite salary increases for meritorious service. This plan rewards the person who accepts education as a life profession. An increasing number of public school districts are experimenting with or have adopted a merit system for teacher salaries. In this system teachers receive salary increments based upon determined criteria of excellence. When the plan involves democratic procedures in determining "excellence," and when reasonably objective standards are employed, the plan has considerable justification. It should be pointed out, however, that most state teachers' associations have voted heavily against the merit system when the matter appears on the official agenda.

SELECTION OF STAFF MEMBERS

Methods used in selecting staff members differ in various school systems. The employment of teachers and supervisors in health education and physical education should follow policies approved by the board of education for all school personnel. The director has a definite responsibility in *recommending* to the proper administrative officer individuals who will maintain the effectiveness of his organization.

Members of the staff should be of a grade in education and general culture that compares favorably with other members of school personnel. Where the administrative head has the responsibility for *selection,* this duty should be discharged with thoroughness and care. The exact relation of skill to successful teaching is unknown, but it appears that in physical education the teacher should be able to demonstrate the skills, abilities, and accomplishments set for pupils.

In selecting a candidate one should judge other qualities in addition to skill. Personal appearance and use of spoken English are important; absence of offensive mannerisms is often vital, and knowledge of the field is essential. Personality is such a vague quality that it defies definition and one resorts to a person as defining the term. Thus, comparisons are made between the candidate and the person the examiner would like him to be. This technic is vague and usually results in the classification of a person as forceful, nervous, enthusiastic, assertive, or colorless. Yet personality often marks the difference between brilliance and mediocrity, if not between success and failure.

The director should be fair and frank with the candidate. He should avoid misunderstanding by not promising more than he can deliver. If the situation allows the director to *recommend*, he should avoid making a promise beyond his power to act. His recommendations in the past may have been accepted, but one failure may be inconvenient and even unpleasant.

Written data concerning the applicant's preparation and experience should be placed on file together with letters relating thereto.

Other qualities being equal, the director should select the younger person, the one with better preparation, the one more attractive in appearance, the one with better personality, or the one who dresses neatly and in good taste. In any event the director should search for the staff member on the basis of his qualifications, rather than attempt to fit the person to the position at hand.

Whatever list of personal, professional, and social qualities the director may select to guide him in the recommendation of staff members, it would appear that the following traits deserve consideration: (1) professional preparation; (2) demonstrated competence in necessary skills; (3) personality; (4) enthusiasm; (5) interest in the student; (6) integrity in personal and social relationships; and (7) belief in the importance of the position for which he is a candidate.

Many large city school systems require applicants to pass an examination for a place on the eligible list. Usually there is a comprehensive written test on the general field of education. In addition, there may be a written or practical test in the candidate's special field as well as an interview with a board of examiners. Candidates are assigned to positions according to their ratings on the eligible list.

Although such a procedure may be valuable in screening large numbers and in preventing the influence of political pressure, it leaves much to be desired in the selection of best persons for the positions concerned.

Some boards of education adopt policies that define the working conditions of employed personnel, and make available a printed statement of these policies to facilitate mutual understanding among the instructional and administrative staffs.

FACULTY RECREATION

A responsibility of the departmental staff deals with faculty recreation. Provision for wholesome faculty recreation is a relatively new venture in educational administration. Teachers should be urged to avail themselves of the opportunity offered to play tennis, swim, dance, or use the athletic fields. In fact, the alert department provides instruction for faculty members who wish to become more proficient in such activities.

A special time should be set aside for teacher participation, leagues or groups formed, and individual or team scores recorded. Where school facilities are inadequate to meet adult interests, community bowling alleys, skating rinks, and golf courses may be used. There is no better way to arouse an abiding interest in, and support for, the program of health education and physical education than to encourage faculty recreation.

PROBLEMS FOR DISCUSSION

1. A director of health education and physical education in a city school system served five years each under two superintendents. The first five years he was regarded as a staff officer and charged with the responsibilities of administration and supervision of his particular area of education. He was given authority commensurate with his responsibilities. The second superintendent regarded him as a consultant without authority to act. Discuss the effects such a change might have on the health education and physical education personnel in the conduct of their respective assignments.
2. Assume that you are the director of physical education in a school district where the responsibility for physical education in the twenty elementary schools is vested in the classroom teachers. The only resource help available is that which you can give occasionally. The superintendent asks you to submit a plan which will upgrade physical education instruction in these schools as well as provide for more effective supervisory services. What are your recommendations?
3. The school has a "football conscious" board of education, and the townspeople demand a winning football team. The high school has an excellent football coach who produces good teams. Therefore, he is regarded as a good teacher by school officials and citizens. In addition to his football assignment, the coach is responsible for teaching physical education classes, which he neglects. How would you, as director, handle this problem?
4. Instructors and students may implement the above with problems gained from their own experience and observation.

REFERENCES

Burton, W. H. and Brueckner, L. J.: *Supervision.* ed. 3. Appleton-Century-Crofts, New York, 1955.

Castetter, W. B.: *Administering the School Personnel Program.* The Macmillan Company, New York, 1962.

Caswell, H. L. and Foshay, A. W.: *Education in the Elementary School.* ed. 3. American Book Company, New York, 1957.

Elsbree, W. S. and McNally, H. M.: *Elementary School Administration and Supervision.* ed. 2. American Book Company, New York, 1958.

Elsbree, W. S. and Reutter, E. E., Jr.: *Staff Personnel in the Public Schools.* Prentice-Hall, Inc., Englewood Cliffs, 1955.

Griffiths, D. E.: *Human Relations and School Administration.* Appleton-Century-Crofts, New York, 1956.

Irwin, L. W. and Humphrey, J. H.: *Principles and Techniques of Supervision in Physical Education.* Wm. C. Brown Company, Dubuque, 1960.

Reeder, W. G.: *The Fundamentals of Public School Administration.* ed. 4. The Macmillan Company, New York, 1958.

Wiles, K., Brown, C. and Cassidy, R.: *Supervision in Physical Education.* Prentice-Hall, Inc., Englewood Cliffs, 1956.

CHAPTER 4

BUDGET AND FINANCE

WHAT ARE BUDGET AND FINANCE?

The foundation of an efficient administrative organization includes plans for budgeting and financing the project or, phrased somewhat colloquially, the funds to build the organization and to insure its continued operation. If a scale could be devised to rate administrators in health education and physical education on the basis of their interest in matters pertaining to finance, certain principles would become apparent at once. At one extreme would appear those who concern themselves primarily with improved methods of departmental organization, without regard to the cost involved. At the other extreme are some who devote a disproportionate share of their time and energy to monetary problems. On the one hand, matters of finance belong to someone else—the principal, business manager, or superintendent; this is especially true in small communities. On the other hand, affairs of budget and finance are such tangible factors as to command the major interest of the director; this condition often prevails in a large department where the pressure of detail overshadows the primary function of the school—to educate children. Doubtless a middle ground is essential for effective administration with a program developed to meet local requirements, and a budget planned with meticulous care to consider both community and child needs.

In the final analysis *finance* is concerned with: (1) obtaining money, and (2) spending it. In a narrow sense the *budget* is a statement of estimated receipts and expenditures; in a broader sense it anticipates the needs of the department prior to the time of expenditure and insures the necessary economies.

HOW MONEY IS OBTAINED FOR PUBLIC EDUCATION

Except for gifts made to support worthwhile activities for which public funds have not been apportioned, the method of obtaining revenue for the operation and maintenance of public schools is through taxation. The manner in which local taxes are levied and bond issues circulated (merely a form of deferred taxation) is definitely fixed by legal enactment. In addition to sums obtained from local taxation, state aid is often available. State aid is determined basically by the ability of the municipality to pay its own educational bills, in keeping with certain minimum standards required by the commonwealth. State school money is secured through imposed taxes similar to those employed in local areas. Thus, public education receives its chief support from the taxation of property within a given area, and methods of securing school money are governed by law.*

Mounting school costs, as well as increased budgets for other municipal and state affairs, result in a constant search for new and improved means of financing education.

GROWTH IN EDUCATIONAL EXPENDITURES

Difficulties encountered by city officials in balancing municipal budgets are partially responsible for the careful scrutiny given to the rising cost of public education. Actually public school costs have increased markedly during the past half-century and current estimates for the years ahead place the cost of public education at astronomical figures when compared with those of a century ago.

Like every public venture, school expenditures are based upon what the people can afford and what they are willing to spend. An awakened public consciousness results in better schools with numerous added educational advantages, of which health education and physical education are worthy examples.

Retrenchment and austerity budgets should be planned, not upon the basis of subjects or programs of most recent origin, but upon the needs of children in their biological and social development, and the contribution which any subject or program makes to the happiness and service of mankind. Unwise boards of education and uninformed townspeople sometimes ignore this principle and blindly insist upon lowered school budgets without due regard to the educational factors involved.

BASES FOR DETERMINING SCHOOL COSTS

In general, school costs depend upon three factors: (1) needs of

---

* The term "property" is defined differently in various states. Thus in some states property refers to real estate while in others property includes numerous types of wealth.

the community; (2) resources of the community; and (3) willingness of the people to support public education.

Implications contained in the above factors place a grave responsibility on the administrator. On the one hand he surveys the community to determine its needs and plans an educational program in accordance therewith. But changes in school organization usually require additional funds; hence the administrator, in his planning, reconciles community needs, financial resources, and willingness of the people to support improvements in education. Some administrators become confused in this triangular maze (in which pressure groups operate continuously) and settle down to a dull regime of *status quo*—a condition soon recognized in the schools and community. Other administrators ignore the true implications of one or more of the three factors and push blindly forward—a situation in which the public may lose confidence in the schools and the administrator.

Sound administrative practice might suggest the following procedures: (1) analyze the needs and resources of the community upon the basis of all the scientific evidence available; (2) use these data to construct a valid and progressive working plan; (3) execute the plan insofar as possible; (4) evaluate the plan as it develops; (5) modify the plan as the need arises, according to changing conditions; and (6) conduct a continuous and reliable program of public relations throughout the entire process.

THE COST OF HEALTH EDUCATION AND PHYSICAL EDUCATION

Wide variation in methods used to determine school costs in different communities obstructs the possibility of obtaining accurate comparative data relating to health education and physical education. Thus one school system may determine expenditures upon the basis of *aggregate attendance,* another by *average daily attendance,* and a third by *instruction-hour units.* Again, the budget for health education and physical education sometimes includes the salaries of teachers, whereas in other districts all teachers' salaries in the various schools are listed under an item called *instruction costs* or *personnel services.* When unequivalent basic methods are used to determine costs, accurate comparison is impossible.

The matter is complicated further by the tendency in some districts to combine costs for health services and the supervision of plants with health education and physical education. In other cities these items are recorded separately. More uniform methods of accounting are needed in compiling data before reliable comparisons can be made.

Probably the actual cost of health education and physical education exceeds most educational and service programs associated with the school. Facilities, equipment, and services are especially expensive in these fields, although a "per-use" cost may be low. Doubtless the actual *instruction* cost approximates other areas of education, and may be lower because of large classes in physical education and extensive use of facilities during after-school hours. Construction and maintenance expenditures soar because of the need for gymnasiums, health rooms, special equipment, and other accessories.

In reality, estimation of cost should depend upon the relative contribution to education of a given program, rather than upon its expenditures in relation to other subjects.

THE BUDGET FOR HEALTH EDUCATION AND PHYSICAL EDUCATION

Two general plans for preparing budgets in public schools are: (1) budgeting by schools; and (2) having the budget prepared by the central office and later reviewed by school principals. Occasionally, such departments as health education and physical education prepare separate budgets covering the items of expenditure for that department in the entire school system.

Budgeting by Schools. The trend in modern administration is toward budgeting by schools. In this method the principal submits to the superintendent a list of items, and the proposed expenditure for each, needed for the fiscal year. The principal should be assisted by the head of the department of health education and physical education in preparing that section of the individual school budget concerned with his special field. Funds necessary for maintaining the central administrative office of health education and physical education are obtained from the general administrative budget for the school system as a whole. Thus the budget for a given school system is composed of two types of items: (1) budgets for the different schools, and (2) budgets for the various administrative divisions in the central office.

Budget Prepared by the Central Office. This method differs from the first in that budgets for the different schools are tentatively arranged in the office of the superintendent and later reviewed by school principals. Also, a procedure is followed whereby budget needs from individual schools are received by the superintendent or director and used as a guide for final budget preparation. The chief values are: (1) experts in the central office are better equipped to deal with matters of finance than school principals whose preparation often is limited in budgetary practice; and (2) experts can amalgamate facilities and research in determining school needs, hence the avoidance of needless duplication. Opponents of the plan agree that these experts doubtless understand finance and research but fail to recognize the educational needs of individual schools.

Separate Budget for Health Education and Physical Education. Occasionally the director plans the budget for all expenditures in health education and physical education throughout the various schools. Those opposed to this practice believe that separate departmental budgets tend to perpetuate narrow and selfish attitudes quite apart from the general problems of the school system which demand integrated and cooperative effort. However, the director who works cooperatively with building principals on budget needs is the person best qualified to make recommendations concerning allotments for his particular area.

All Budgets and Reports to Follow Same General Plan. The larger the school system the more the superintendent delegates responsibility. and the more he depends upon school and departmental reports for information relating to needs of various subdivisions. It is essential, therefore, that financial statements made by school and department heads be consistent in form, content, and principle with those proposed for the school system as a whole. While it is true that some activities—such as interschool athletics—involve special financial problems, school and departmental budgets, inventories, and reports in general should present data which approximate the form adopted by the school system.

THE INTERSCHOOL ATHLETIC BUDGET

The peculiar nature of interschool competition, with attendant advertising and admission charges, presents important problems of budget and finance. Emphasis on interschool athletics and athletics for all has produced a critically minded public increasingly sensitive to the financial implications involved. Launched originally as extracurricular programs, in which only students were supposed to be interested, these activities have become a vital part of the school with inevitable educational and public consequences.

Interschool athletics should be financially supported by board of education funds in the same manner that other areas of the school curriculum are supported.* Administrators should strive to do away with an admission charge for interschool athletics, and encourage the general public to attend these events as guests of the school. Where this policy is in effect there is a noticeable decrease in the undesirable features associated with these contests. At the same time, there is an improvement of educational values inherent in them.

Where it is necessary to charge admission for interschool contests, the custody of money received from paid attendance at games, and from student athletic association, presents another problem. From a legal

---

* It is assumed here that interschool athletics represent a worthwhile educational activity. The law is not always clear in permitting boards of education to expend money for the support of interschool athletics. For example, an attorney general of a Midwestern state holds to the view that boards of education are without power to expend public school funds under their control to support or promote the competitive playing of games between picked teams composed of pupils from the public schools of two municipalities. He further states that interschool athletics are not a proper public school activity within the scope of physical education as the term is used in the statutes, and, therefore, boards of education have no legal power to expend money for coaches, uniforms, and equipment. The matter should be decided in each state, by test cases in court or by legislative action, and with administrative procedures based upon sound educational and legal policies.

point of view property rights to funds obtained from more or less detached school agencies presumably reside in those bodies. Fortunately the question of property rights to interschool athletic money seldom reaches the courts, although such a procedure might help to awaken school superintendent and boards of education to the need for exercising responsibility in safeguarding and controlling these accounts. Many school administrators favor placing all interschool athletic money, including gate receipts, guarantees, and donations, under the supervision of the secretary-treasurer or business manager of the board of education. As long as gate receipts must be continued, this policy is recommended. The next best plan is to designate a faculty member, preferably someone in the commercial department, as custodian of interschool athletic funds as well as of sums obtained from other school functions for which fees are charged. All school officials responsible for handling money should be protected from possible criticism, and the funds in their charge guarded against improper manipulation. The individual is protected by having his accounts audited, and the funds insured against loss by bonding the custodian. Laws regulate the amount of surety bonds necessary, commensurate with the amount of money involved.

General school funds may be used for dramatics, band, glee club, orchestra, and cafeteria, as well as for intramural and interschool athletics. Separate budgets are then planned for each activity supported by the general fund. Money is taken from this fund only upon pay-orders signed by the organization sponsor. Interschool athletic pay-orders are signed by the departmental director or school principal, or by someone delegated by the principal to perform this function.

In keeping with the policy previously suggested that budgets should be planned by schools, every high school should have an interschool athletic budget representing estimated receipts and expenditures for each event. If correctly organized the athletic council may prepare this budget which is approved by the proper administrative authority. The person in charge of a given activity, such as football or track, then knows exactly the amount of money he has to spend and conducts his sport accordingly.

It is difficult to suggest a satisfactory method of determining the budget for each interschool athletic activity, owing to the range in amount of equipment needed, the varying cost of this equipment, the popularity of the sport, and its educational value. These items never are comparable. Football is more expensive than track, and basketball costs more than tennis, but expense is not the sole criterion. Intramural athletics frequently provide greater educational value than interschool competition, but the latter affords outcomes that the former can never produce.

Under the system of admission fees, the sport which contributes the largest number of dollars to the athletic fund too often receives the lion's share of the budget. This is unfortunate because it assumes that money pouring into the athletic coffer is synonymous with the educational value of the activity. It would be just as logical to assume that the person paying the largest tax for the support of education should receive the greatest benefit from schools.

While the plan of budgeting by schools has been proposed as the most satisfactory method, a variation of this procedure may be advisable in cities with several high schools, and where gate receipts are used for the maintenance of interschool athletics and other activities. This variation is especially applicable where athletic receipts in one or two schools far exceed the money obtained in others. Under these conditions it may be desirable to apportion the funds so that all institutions profit in an equitable manner. In a Midwestern city, for example, there were two large high schools each enjoying sufficient support from the municipality to maintain their athletic programs in a most luxurious manner. The board of education decided to build a third high school, and finally a fourth was added. Athletic funds at the older institutions continued to pour in whereas the newer schools were unable to provide even the most meager equipment for their teams. In several cities the policy has been adopted that money obtained from paid admissions belongs to the general physical education budget for the use of all students of the municipality.

There is no complete agreement among administrators about this matter. Those executives who hold to the belief that budgets should be arranged by schools find little merit in the above plan. Many school principals and departmental heads believe that revenue obtained at a given school should be used wholly to benefit that particular institution. Such persons oppose a policy that seeks to transfer funds from one school to another, irrespective of the source of these funds. On the other hand, administrators who favor the plan have a strong argument in stating that the amalgamation of separate schools into a unified city school system was based upon the principle of equalized educational opportunity for all children residing in the municipality. The superintendent and board of education largely fulfill the implications of this principle in apportioning public funds according to the needs of individual schools. Although the board of education cannot control a fickle public, which might prefer to support the interschool athletic team of one school instead of another, it can control the distribution of funds accumulated by reapportioning them to the various schools so that each profits in an equitable manner in promoting worthwhile educational enterprises. Further application of this policy is seen in the use of athletic funds to assist in the support of intramural athletics and other activities of the school, as well as for interschool competition.

THE PURCHASE OF SUPPLIES AND EQUIPMENT

Efficiency in the purchase of supplies and equipment involves a careful study of community and school needs, existing prices, the quality of workmanship, and satisfactory materials. Formerly the director controlled the purchasing for his department, and this plan still persists in numerous cities in spite of the fact that such antiquated practices have been abolished in other administrative matters. Indeed, years after teachers ceased to act as venders of pencils and paper, one may find the physical educator peddling suits, gymnasium sneakers, towels, and soap. Teachers of physical education should be taken out of the merchandising business.

The purchase of all school materials through one central office, presided over by a person known as the business manager or purchasing agent, is both economical and effective. It is his duty to keep on hand adequate records relating to standardized materials, requisition blanks, and a card index of supply houses. Purchasing is greatly facilitated if adequate records are kept. He checks the receipt of materials with respect to quantity and quality, distributes them to their proper destination, and insures prompt payment on contracts made. The business manager or purchasing agent is guided in the selection of goods by the departmental director who recommends the amount and quality of equipment needed, but the actual buying of all school supplies is best confined to a single office.

Most purchasing agents or business managers urge the director to standardize the equipment of his department, whenever possible, as a matter of economic policy. Standardization of equipment permits the business manager to request bids from competing manufacturers or distributors, thus reducing the actual cost of most items. Further, such standardization enables the purchasing agent to buy expendable equipment in quantity at a markedly lower price.

The problem of bid-buying often confronts the director. Some manufacturers and distributors of equipment and facilities prefer to avoid the practice by local school districts of submitting bids to several concerns in the purchase of materials used in physical education. Further, a director or teacher may prefer one trade name to another. But the fact remains that most boards of education have adopted the policy requiring the submission of bids to competing vendors when the cost of materials exceeds a stipulated amount.

PROBLEMS FOR DISCUSSION

1. The superintendent regards the principal as the officer in charge of his school with the right to spend the school's budget allotments as he desires. At the same time, he holds the director responsible for individual school allotments and requests his signature on all requisitions submitted by principals for health education and physical education supplies and equipment. Discuss this policy in the light of sound business management.
2. In a city school system, some schools have active parent-teacher organizations which conduct successful fund-raising campaigns and turn money over to

principals for the purchase of supplies and equipment. Other schools are less fortunate in this respect. In such instances, should all schools receive their budget allotments of tax funds on a standard per pupil enrollment basis?

3. The physical education department head of a particular school, commenting on centralized purchasing, said: "A centralized purchasing plan for all schools may save some money and relieve the individual school of its responsibility for procuring materials. However, the merchandise received is often of inferior grade and it is very difficult to make adjustments. When each school did its own purchasing I had close connections with a sporting goods dealer who would procure what I wanted and deliveries were prompt. Furthermore, I could make exchanges without all this red tape and paper work."

As director of health education and physical education in a system consisting of several schools, how would you react to this statement?

4. The proper usage of gate receipts from school athletic contests offers a vexing problem. Many schools, in order to increase gate receipts, resort to undesirable methods and destroy the educational value of interscholastic activities. Some persons believe that gate receipts should be abolished and guests admitted free. Other persons believe that all gate receipts should be consolidated into one fund, divided among the various schools according to need. What plan do you recommend?

5. Instructors and students may implement the above with problems gained from their own experience and observation.

REFERENCES

American Association for Health, Physical Education, and Recreation: *Current Administrative Problems.* Washington, 1960.

Educational Policies Commission. *School Athletics: Problems and Policies.* National Education Association, Washington, 1954.

Forsythe, C. E.: *The Administration of High School Athletics.* ed. 4. Prentice-Hall, Inc., Englewood Cliffs, 1962.

Grieder, C., Pierce, T. M. and Rosenstangle, W. E.: *Public School Administration.* ed. 2. The Ronald Press, New York, 1961.

Hunt, H. C. and Pierce, P. R.: *The Practice of School Administration.* Houghton-Mifflin Book Company, Boston, 1958.

Morphet, E. L., Reller, T. L. and Johns, R. L.: *Educational Administration—Concepts, Practices and Issues.* Prentice-Hall, Inc., Englewood Cliffs, 1959.

CHAPTER 5

OFFICE MANAGEMENT

THE IMPORTANCE OF OFFICE MANAGEMENT

Office management is essential for handling a multitude of details connected with the program in a manner which increases its effectiveness. Managerial arrangements in the office of the director depend largely on the kind and extent of activities for which the department is responsible. Office routine for the director in a large school system varies only in degree from that in a small department with limited clerical service. In either situation there is need for a central location where the director and his staff may conduct, with dignity, the numerous details pertinent to their assignments.

SOURCES OF INFORMATION

The director needs certain types of information readily accessible at all times. Some of this information is for his own use, other data will be helpful to members of the staff, teachers of other subjects, and students. Where books, periodicals, or bulletins are removed from the office a plan must be devised for checking them to prevent loss.

Among the numerous sources of information are:

1. *Laws and Regulations:* school laws, regulations, and court decisions, with sections dealing with health education and physical education marked appropriately; state and local public health laws, ordinances, and sanitary code; local board of education regulations.
2. *Reports:* annual reports and bulletins of the state department of education; reports and bulletins of the United States Office of Education; annual reports and bulletins of the local board of education; reports dealing with local, state, and national standards.

3. *Curriculum Materials:* state courses of study; local courses of study; selected list of *curriculum materials* from other cities.
4. *Books:* an adequate professional library with provisions for lending these books; a list of suitable books in the local public library.
5. *Magazines:* several professional magazines including the *Journal of Health–Physical Education–Recreation* and the *Research Quarterly.*
6. *Map:* a map showing location of all schools.
7. *Clipping Service:* perhaps the board of education subscribes for this service and departmental news will be provided; otherwise obtain clippings dealing with health education, safety, and physical education, including athletics.
8. *Miscellaneous:* school directory; telephone directories; train, air line, and bus schedules; world almanac; dictionary (regular and medical); current list of public officials; selected mailing list; scrap book of records and publicity.

EQUIPMENT AND SUPPLIES

Furniture and equipment for the office include: full-length lockers, flat-top desk and chairs; table; rugs; bookcases and magazine racks; appropriate files—vertical, horizontal, and card; telephone; buzzer; desk light; letter trays; waste basket; usual clerical accessories.

CONFERENCE ROOM

One or more conference rooms are essential depending on the size of the office staff. There should be one room of sufficient size to accommodate a large conference table and several chairs.

OFFICE ROUTINE

Systematizing details to a routine of organization represents the goal of every well qualified administrator. Behind this system are the policies and procedures adopted to make the organization work smoothly and efficiently. In their functional application it is often impossible for the uninitiated person to separate the acts themselves from the spirit or ideals which prompt them, but the experienced person looks for the motive behind the act as well as for precision in the performance of it. Thus, as in other affairs of administration, policies and procedures go hand in hand. No one would condone an administrator, even though he were meticulously careful about details of office routine, if he curtly replied to a parent that "he was too busy to confer with a citizens' committee regarding playground conditions in their neighborhood." The director and his staff always should be accessible. On the other hand, few persons succeed in positions of executive responsibility who fail to establish effective ways of handling office details, notwithstanding the fact that they may greet each visitor with sincere cordiality. There is a fine distinction between organization of details and the spirit of service which motivates them; both are essential. This balance of policies and procedures is implemented through the routines which follow.

Office Hours.   In large school systems definite office hours are necessary. In all schools a sufficient amount of time should be set aside for conferences, committee assignments, correspondence, new projects, and matters of like nature. By carefully scheduling appointments and other duties time is saved and the efficiency of the department increased.

Greeting and Caring for Visitors.   The office is not a lounging room. If the department really functions, however, an increasing stream of persons will seek information and guidance in matters pertaining to the welfare of children in an individual school. Students come to the office with problems; staff members and teachers from other departments are always welcome for discussions of a professional nature; and the general public learns that the department appreciates the privilege of serving citizens of the community. All of these activities are conducted in a cordial, accommodating, helpful, and efficient manner which fosters an attitude of respect and loyalty toward the department and the work it does.

Answering Correspondence.   Prompt answers to letters requiring a reply mark the efficient administrator. Desk trays marked *incoming* and *outgoing,* with mail placed in the appropriate receptacle, serve as a reminder that letters are to be answered with dispatch. Letters should be phrased carefully with a simplicity of style that is professional yet cordial. Keep a carbon copy of each business letter and be sure that it is filed in the proper folder. Address lists and telephone numbers of persons with whom communication is routine help to increase departmental efficiency.

Using the Telephone.   The office telephone is installed for professional purposes. Incoming calls should be answered promptly and courteously. When messages are received by the secretary they should be relayed promptly to the person desired by means of a buzzer or other appropriate signal. If the person being called is available, he answers promptly. If he is not readily accessible, the secretary should request the name and telephone number of the party calling and advise that the party called will return the call. The secretary's request to hold the line should be avoided if there is apt to be more than a momentary delay. On outgoing messages be ready to talk as soon as the call has been put through.

When speaking over the telephone some persons affect a personality quite different from their usual manner of speech. Assume a conversational tone of voice and speak clearly and distinctly into the mouthpiece; talk to your listener as you would if he were sitting in your office.

When the administrator is away from his office and calls are taken by a secretary, it is well to provide forms for recording these messages.

Figure 4. Report of telephone calls.

Figure 4 shows a form which may be used for this purpose (size 3 by 5 inches).

Preparing an Activity Calendar. As a means of systematizing details, the activity calendar is proposed. At the beginning of the school year several sheets may be ruled for each month (Fig. 5). The calendar provides for insertion of dates at the left of the page; next comes the item receiving attention on that date; at the right of the page appears the name of the person or official responsible for the particular item.

Developing a Filing and Finding System. The science of indexing and

	OCTOBER	
5	Teachers' meeting at Franklin school.	Miss Roberts.
7	Football rules interpretation meeting at Dover.	Mr. Stone.
11	Conference of school physicians and nurses.	Dr. Childs.
16	Letter reminding officials of Watertown game.	Mr. Abbot.
17	Committee meeting to adopt girls' uniforms.	Miss Lea.
20	Speak at Townsend P. T. A.	Mr. Abbot.
22	Meeting of all departmental directors.	Mr. Abbot.
23	Field hockey game with Salem Central.	Miss Ryan.
24	State convention at Harrisburg.	Staff.

Figure 5. Monthly activity calendar.

filing deals with the arrangement of correspondence and records according to a predetermined plan which preserves them and makes them readily available. That no two filing systems are alike is due to a misunderstanding of the basic principle creating the system. When a filing system is already set up, it must first be decided if the system is satisfactory.

In general, the filing plan provides for two types of material, *informational* and *correspondence.* Since there are actually only two methods or arrangements for indexing and filing, *alphabetical* and *numerical,* it should be fairly easy to determine which method is better suited to cover any individual and specific problem. Although there are deviations from the basic system, these may be considered as shades of the two methods, just as in art all colors are shades of the three primary colors.

For instance, in filing by subject (alphabetically) it is only natural that "B" should follow "A," and so on; in filing by subject (numerically) several forms could be adopted, such as serial numeric (consecutive), decimal numeric, terminal-digit numeric, duplex numeric, or numeric coding.

In the *numerical* system, a code is set up and the code number attached to the folder or divider in either the vertical or horizontal file. Vertical filing means placing papers on edge in the folder, usually indexed by guides. In this system the folder, instead of the drawer or shelf, is the unit. Vertical filing saves both time and space. Correspondence, sheets containing information, and cards are filed in this way. For maps, blueprints, or catalogues too large or not the right shape for vertical filing, the flat or horizontal filing system is used. The numerical system is somewhat complex, preventing its widespread use except in large departments where expert file clerks are employed.

The *alphabetical* systems refers primarily to names, such as the names of individuals, schools both within and outside the city, and organizations such as the state department of education, the American Association for Health, Physical Education, and Recreation, or the American Medical Association.

As implied by its title, filing according to *subject* means placing together those materials associated with a specific topic, such as staff reports, communicable diseases, catalogues, applications of teachers, or publicity. In this system one of the first tasks is to analyze and classify a complete list of subjects. Many subjects are not easily classified, although experimentation with several plans usually results in the adoption of a satisfactory technic. The principal difficulty seems to be in not having adequate controls set up wherein definite instruction is given as to the "where and why" of the document, the length of time it should be retained, and when it should be transferred or destroyed. Such information should precede anything within the file. The majority of departments employ a modified form of filing which combines certain aspects of both the alphabetical system and the use of subjects.

Irrespective of the system used, *cross references* are necessary, since letters, reports, or bulletins should be filed in only one place, whereas the contents may involve several subordinate subjects. The most common uses for *cross references* are: (1) two or more subjects treated in the same document; or (2) changes in the name of a firm or organization.

The creation of a *cross reference* helps to break down the it-will-be-remembered attitude, which usually leads to trouble for the finders. Delays and long searches break down confidence that the system is correct or that the department is efficient.

SECRETARIAL ASSISTANCE

A good secretary is an important member of the director's office staff. She is in a strategic position to greet either in person or by telephone most persons with whom the director is concerned professionally. An intelligent secretary with a neat appearance, a cheerful personality, and a courteous manner is essential. Adequate and competent office help is the most economical service the school system can furnish the staff. Most of the office details described above can be done by a good secretary. Large departments with administrative responsibilities of wide scope need a corps of secretaries properly supervised. In such instances it is desirable to delegate the supervisory responsibilities to a qualified *chief secretary.*

PROBLEMS FOR DISCUSSION

1. A newly appointed director inherits from his predecessor a chief secretary who is much older than the administrator and definitely set in her ways of office routine. She is a civil service appointee and an active worker in her political party. She has her favorites among the office personnel and the department teaching staff. Six years remain before she is eligible for retirement. She does not hesitate to express her viewpoint that "our new director's ideas are too progressive and his aggressiveness will never work in our schools." What should be done?
2. A recently appointed director keeps his office door closed. He maintains that he is better able to concentrate under this arrangement. Furthermore, he believes that it is an expression of fairness to insure privacy for those with whom he holds conferences. Other administrators and supervisors keep their doors open at all times. They follow the direction of a former superintendent who argued that public school personnel always should be accessible. How should the problem be resolved?
3. Assume that you are a director of health education and physical education for a centralized school of 1,500 pupils, kindergarten through grade twelve. Due to your teaching and supervisory responsibilities a limited amount of time is available for "desk work." The budget provides no funds for secretarial help. How would you resolve this problem?
4. Instructors and students may implement the above with problems gained from their own experience and observation.

REFERENCES

Herrmann, I. A.: *Office Methods, Systems, and Practices.* The Ronald Press, New York, 1950.

National Association of Educational Secretaries: *File It Right.* National Education Association, Washington, 1959.

Neuner, J. W.: *Office Management: Principles and Practices.* ed. 4. Southwestern Publishing Company, Cincinnati, 1959.

Odell, M. R. and Strong, E. P.: *Records Management and Filing Operations.* McGraw-Hill Book Company, Inc., New York, 1947.

Strong, E. P.: *Increasing Office Productivity.* McGraw-Hill Book Company, Inc., New York, 1962.

PART II

THE PROGRAM

These nine chapters center the administrative problems that arise out of the program. There is first the problem of curriculum materials and then planning the organization of the program. After these considerations, the student will consider the administrative procedures that arise in special parts of the program.

CHAPTER 6

THE PREPARATION OF
CURRICULUM MATERIALS

THE CURRICULUM

General agreement favors the view that the *curriculum* represents
the experiences of the child at home, in the school, and in his community.* It stands more precisely for his planned experiences, and ranges
from drill in spelling to various activities of the physical education period.
Nothing that happens in the planned experiences can be truly outside
the curriculum. The greeting between teacher and children, assemblies,
passing in corridors, visits to the zoo, recreation periods—all contribute
to the education of the child. Formerly there existed a number of school
activities outside the curriculum proper such as the assembly, school
paper, glee clubs, and others that were known as *extracurricular* activities. There is a clear tendency to regard these as important aspects of the
curriculum.

Curriculum materials for a subject or field represent the series of
planned activities for children at various levels. There are curriculum
materials in health education for the sixth grade, curriculum materials
in physical education for the eleventh grade, and others.

The curriculum should be constructed with reference to a philosophy of education so that all materials in specific fields present a harmonious interrelationship. If the philosophy, expressed in the policy of the
school, holds that children should discover for themselves the interests
to which they attend, that child initiative and creative response are sufficient criteria of what children are to do, then the whole curriculum and

* Instead of the term "curriculum," some schools prefer "course of study," "curriculum
guide," or other titles. The authors employ the term "curriculum" for brevity.

hence the various materials reflect this philosophic outlook. If on the other hand, the theory prevails that adult wisdom, experience, and needs are adequate for deciding the steps of a child's education, then this view dominates in the planned experiences for children. Of course, there are intermediate positions between these extremes that recognize the importance of interest and of duty.

APPROACHES TO CURRICULUM MATERIALS

The approach used defines the road taken to a particular set of values considered important. Several approaches are commonly recognized.

First is *the child-experience approach*. This approach emphasizes the importance of an individual's experience and therefore this road is marked by opportunities for many and varied experiences. Materials following this approach are purposeful for children and provide rich opportunity for them to initiate and execute, wholly or in part, the experiences they have.

Second is *the creative-values approach*. Not only experiences are important but *creative* experiences are the sign posts along this road to educational outcomes. Indeed this view has attained a certain prominence, and the educational literature of recent years is characterized by such phrases as creative art, creative poetry, creative dance, creative music, and others. Creative activity provides dynamic learning situations.

A third approach aims to travel through the fog of current affairs by means of highways described by those who are, at times, called *frontier thinkers*. It is said that schools as well as society tend to become set in rigid institutions so that progress can be achieved only by following the lead of those persons who have the vision and courage to think out on the "edge of things." Obviously if the curriculum reflects the proposals of frontier thinkers, there are sharp divergences from present practices, considerable ambiguity about the margins of the frontier, and neglect of certain practices that customarily appear valid but are damned by being traditional.

A fourth approach reflects the stress in educational philosophy to *secure social and moral outcomes that benefit the individual and society*. It seeks to make permanent the prevailing social order. *Status quo* is in this approach the basis of good citizenship. Obviously this view is supported by older persons and by "solid substantial business men."

A fifth approach expresses *the culture-epoch theory*. This theory holds that each individual in his development passes through stages that correspond to the successive steps of man's evolution.

Although any one of the above approaches might be used in constructing curriculum materials in health education and/or physical education, there are three determinants most commonly used:

1. The child-experience determinant emphasizing the interests and activities of children.
2. The social-values determinant stressing traditional content.
3. A combination of the above.

The combination suggested above is frequently found. Most school people affirm that the child-experience determinant alone is impractical; it is time-consuming and fails to provide adequately for the rich social inheritance of mankind. The time available in school is too short to wait for the child to find experiences for all situations considered necessary to complete social life in modern complex society.

The social-values determinant alone is equally faulty. It places too large an emphasis upon the adult-need philosophy, and neglects the values that come from adventuring in experiences pursued for their own sake. In these two views, one readily sees the old conflict between nature and custom, between the being that man is and the life that now is. Because both are imperative, every effort is made to harmonize and bring the demands of both to the service of education.

ORGANIZATION OF MATERIALS

Considerable emphasis is now placed upon the organization of materials into *units of instruction*. The theory of the unit is based upon the fact that many fields of traditional study may be used to give a *whole* view, with a greater appreciation and knowledge of the whole than could be secured by a *piecemeal* attack, regardless of how carefully planned the course might be. Thus a unit in Irish folk dancing includes not only dances but background in social customs, folk lore, and social experiences of the Irish people of the particular period in which the dances originated. A unit in Greek life might well include Greek customs in civil life, their practices in the arts, Greek games, and contests of that period.

The Unit of Unplanned Experience. Free play is an example of this. In the free-play period, children ought to perform some of the skills learned in class instruction. The teacher observes in such periods fundamental drives in children. In similar fashion a unit in health education may develop out of an opportunity given children to discuss what appears worthwhile to them. This type of material may appear significant at times and mislead the young teacher by its apparent profundity.

The Unit of Planned Experience. These units start with an adjudged worthwhile life experience and eventuate into whatever subject matter they will. An athletic contest previously held between two sixth grades is an example. In health education the visit of the school nurse or school physician may serve as the starting point for developing whatever subject matter appears. This may be a profitable experience for children, but its success depends largely upon the skill of the teacher in guiding the discussion. Also, there is the example of the teacher planning in advance subject matter to be mastered and activities that eventually terminate in a desired end.

The Theme or Generalization Unit. This is sometimes called the "Big Idea" unit. It starts with such a theme as, "How man has kept himself well throughout the ages," and is developed by teacher and pupils. It thus combines child interests and adult guidance. The teacher's part is the presentation of such topics related to the unit as: man's use of food; the dangers in water; how man learned to cook; the age of germs; forgotten enemies of our ancestors; and numerous others. The theme serves to direct the child's attention in various activities to one large area of interest and provides correlation quite naturally. Moreover, it gives opportunity to teach subject matter that adults believe valuable for children to know.

The Subject Matter Unit, Involving Correlation. Examples are given above in the discussion of Irish dances. This type of unit is easy to organize for elementary school children. It is difficult in the secondary school, because of its departmental structure. This type of unit features some of the more recent curriculum materials.

In selecting the type of unit it is not sufficient to consider *form* alone. Care should be exercised to include the *kinds* of subject matter along with the activity which enrich child experience by adding to the skills, knowledge, attitudes, and appreciations which the pupil has previously gained. This view corrects the faulty notion sometimes proposed that all health instruction or all physical education can be taught through integration. Certain information about health and most skills of physical education need to be learned through direct teaching. The well organized unit of instruction provides not only for the integrating aspects of the situation but also for direct learnings which are essential if the full educative value of the experience be realized.

PRELIMINARY ORGANIZATION PROCEDURES

When it is determined that the existing curriculum materials need revision it becomes necessary to make arrangements for doing the work required. The revised materials cannot be prepared quickly, thus time enters into the plans. Then it must be determined how to proceed. The curriculum workshop has become increasingly popular and profitable. In an eleven-month schedule, teachers may assemble for a summer workshop, or in the shorter session they may attend a summer school for this purpose either voluntarily or with compensation. In workshops organized by universities, curriculum specialists guide the project; in workshops operated by the local school system, specialists may be employed or the local committees may be fully responsible. The various committees of teachers may be selected by the director and appointed by the principal or superintendent. It is good administration to give teachers an opportunity to volunteer. Appointment of a temporary chairman in the beginning often avoids inefficient delay. There should be regular meetings of committees, and also called meetings as needs arise. Assignments to the various committees should be small at first, well defined, and thoroughly coordinated in the whole plan.

STEPS IN CONSTRUCTING CURRICULUM MATERIALS

The following twelve steps indicate how the committees may proceed:

Step 1. Determination of Philosophy. This may be the task of the whole committee or assigned to a special group. It is important to state the basic beliefs, the principles of health education or physical education which will be followed. Obviously this determination is significant because all that follows must be viewed in light of the philosophy adopted. Moreover, the philosophy of the institution for which the guide is intended must be taken into account as well as the various philosophies operative in the field. Indeed, the philosophy of the local community may dominate, and progressive and socially minded committee members may find their basic beliefs at sharp variance with local citizen groups, or even with some teachers, principals, and superintendents.

The committee should not get "bogged down" in its own philosophical soundings, arguing about fine distinctions in phrases and terms. It is far better to set a time limit on philosophy and agree to come back for refinement later.

Step II. Interpretation of the Philosophy Selected. This step aims to set forth the function of health education or physical education in light of the philosophy stated, and also to indicate their functions with respect to local conditions. It is necessary to survey the social, economic, racial, industrial, and educational influences of the community. In this step, principles should be stated and the philosophy thereby interpreted. The following principle interprets a philosophic point of view: physical education should provide an opportunity for the individual and the group to act in situations that are physically wholesome, mentally stimulating and satisfying, and socially sound.

Step III. Determination of Objectives. There are many objectives, and these contribute to the philosophy and harmonize with basic principles. In determining objectives a person should be guided by several criteria which may be stated as a question.

1. What is the *nature of the individuals* for whom the experiences are planned? Man is conceived as a multiple series of sensory mechanisms responding to a wide variety of impulses that represent: (1) drives or urges; (2) physiological states of the organism; and (3) stimulations from the environment. Thus education cannot deal with a body *per se,*

or a mind *per se,* but with an organism that has physical aspects and mental aspects. These aspects must be recognized in stating objectives, but they are not to be misunderstood as portraying a dualistic point of view. The answer to the question then must include a statement of the child's interests, the growth tendencies, and the strengths and weaknesses of different periods.

2. What does *society* need to have developed in its children, and what does the *community* expect of the health education and physical education programs? This is obviously a criterion of adult needs. It reflects the social-values approach.

3. What do *experts in the field* consider to be important objectives? This is capitulation to authority and, if taken alone, may or may not produce an acceptable list of objectives. Its weakness is the lack of real ownership, the sense of belonging that ought to evolve out of the effort by any group to arrive at a statement for themselves.

4. What do *frontier thinkers* hold as objectives? Those on the fringe or frontier in thinking about values, outcomes, and objectives may see ahead and propose objectives in harmony with present social forces, and thus describe quite accurately the course of education for 10 or 20 years ahead. But the frontier is rough country with innumerable hazards. It is possible that frontier thinkers may be lost themselves; that as guides they will be unsafe. They serve their best function in education as challengers to the stay-at-homes. Pointing out the new route to the Indies and describing the country just over the mountains are needed. But one may not wish to go beyond the divide.

5. What is the *best practice?* For the determination of *best,* criteria are necessary. While the median practice or the best present practice may not be the best that *could* be done, it is infinitely superior to the selection of items without the use of criteria.

Doubtless no single method suggested above will suffice; rather, several methods are preferable, gauged to meet the varying and peculiar needs in school or community. The traditional use of scissors and paste leads to curious mixtures of material—uncritical, aimless, and without unified objectives.

After the objectives have been determined by reference of items to the criteria employed, there remains the important task of *rating* them with respect to the responsibility of the school to provide opportunities through which they may be realized. There should be basic or *general objectives* which reflect best practices in the total educational effort, as well as *specific objectives* pertaining to health education and/or physical education practices. The rating may be done by the use of a scale with the following five categories:

1. Very important
2. Important
3. Of some importance

4. Of little importance
5. Of no practical value.

Step IV. Allocation of Objectives According to Grade Placement. The sequential order in which objectives are placed is significant. For example, certain health habits may have been determined as objectives. Where shall they be sought? Experiences of others may be helpful, knowledge of how and when children learn best is imperative, and the relationship to other objectives should have an influence in the proper decision. The committee may have to decide without a great deal of exact knowledge and merely on the basis of their best judgment. Often an objective is of sufficient educational value to justify including it in more than one grade.

Step V. Determination of Content and Activities. Study has been made of what children are like; their various characteristics are known. Principles have been formulated and the objectives determined and allocated. With such children and such outcomes in mind the committee is confronted with the problem of what to teach to realize the results desired. Three methods may be used: (1) content and activities for health education may be classified; (2) content may be selected and rated with respect to the criteria as indicated for Step III; and (3) content may be selected with respect to the characteristics of children and rated on the basis of the five categories given in Step III, using as a criterion their possible contribution to related objectives. For example, assume that seventh-grade boys are growing fast, showing considerable disproportion between size and strength. Assume further that an objective for this grade is the ability to develop a strong heart and circulatory efficiency. Assume, finally, that available activities are marching, calisthenics, folk dancing, soccer, baseball, swimming, track activities, military drill, various stunts, and self-testing activities. What will be selected? Which is very important; which of little value?

Step VI. Allocation of Content and Activities According to Grade Placement. If the third method of Step V is followed, allocation of content will have been made, but if the first or second is employed this step is still to be done. In the final analysis the committee assigns activities according to its best judgment, realizing that a given activity may be used in more than one grade.

Step VII. Association of Specific Objective wth Specific Content and Activities. Many activities may contribute to one objective, and several objectives may be advanced by a single activity. Nevertheless it is important to associate objectives and content throughout each unit of instruction and the entire guide. Such association tends to prevent needless overlapping of gaps in education.

Step VIII. Preparation of Preliminary Units. With completion of the first seven steps by the various committees, numerous individuals should then attempt the preparation of units. These units should be tried out in school situations. On completion they should be submitted to the general committee. Units submitted may conform to an outline similar to the following:

1. Title
2. Statement of objectives
   a. General
   b. Specific
3. Statement of activities
   a. Initiatory
   b. Developmental
   c. Culminating
4. Suggestions for evaluating the outcomes
5. Equipment necessary for teaching
6. References
   a. For teachers
   For pupils.

Step IX. Experimental Use of Preliminary Units. The general committee selects the best units for wide experimentation. Teachers chosen to try out the units should be urged to criticize them after actual use. It is important to have each unit used by several teachers so that more than a single viewpoint is secured. This experimental period may continue for at least a year.

Step X. Revision of Units. After the experimental period the units are again reviewed by the committee and the suggestions of teachers examined. The units are then revised.

Step XI. Editing of Units. All units should be edited according to one form of organization. A committee or one person may be selected for this purpose. Pages should be numbered, footnotes employed whenever necessary, and all references complete and in standard form.

In general the make-up of the guide may be as follows:

1. Letter of transmittal.
2. The title page—this should tell exactly what the work represents. For example, *Curriculum Materials in Health Education for Grades* 6–8.
3. Acknowledgments—this should contain the names of committee members and sections indicated for which certain groups are responsible.
4. Table of contents with page references.
5. Statement of the situation for which the guide is intended.
6. A brief statement of the philosophy expressed in the guide.
7. Units by grades or years following the form suggested in Step VIII.
8. References.

Whether the report is printed or mimeographed depends upon several factors, chief of which is cost. The committee must decide on the binding and will consider the loose-leaf form and the permanent book. Other problems that arise are those of binding by grades, the grouping of certain grades, and other pertinent questions relating to the best possible use. When these matters are decided, bids from commercial concerns are received, the contract let, and the job is done, except for the important business of proof-reading and preparation of the index. If the publication is sold, a price should be set to cover the cost of printing and mailing.

Step XII. Revision of the Guide. Completion of the guide is the first step in revision. The revision committee should be a *standing committee* constantly studying the curriculum. The guide is never finished. To be a living, dynamic, growing means of education, it changes with the constantly shifting social and educational scene. However, care must be taken to develop the teachers' security in having them work with the guide a few years before uprooting it. There remains the important work of maintaining the proper balance between changes in the development of the program and concepts expressed in the printed or mimeographed materials.

The material contained in this chapter gives specific directions for persons unaccustomed to work of this kind. Administrators and teachers experienced in such matters, or school systems which employ *curriculum directors* or *coordinators,* may prefer to draw upon their own resources in planning a curriculum designed to meet individual and community needs.

PROBLEMS FOR DISCUSSION

1. A new director of health education and physical education discovers that it has previously been a practice to issue curriculum directives from the central office. He desires to change this procedure and attempts to enlist staff aid in cooperative curriculum planning. Outline the preliminary steps that should be taken in initiating this change.
2. A curriculum committee is formed from volunteers among a system-wide staff. It is discovered that most volunteers have had no experience in curriculum construction and joined the committee to learn. Outline the steps the director and his committee should take.
3. A committee is selected to develop a curriculum guide for physical education. Agreement is reached that the initial task is to formulate a statement of philosophy. After considerable work the committee decides to procure copies of guides and courses of study from other cities. The committee elects to take from these materials those parts that best fit the philosophy agreed upon. Discuss the pros and cons of such practice.
4. Instructors and students may implement the above with problems gained from their own experience and observation.

REFERENCES

Alberty, H. B. and Alberty, E. J.: *Reorganizing the High School Curriculum.* ed. 3. The Macmillan Company, New York, 1962.

Burton, W. H.: *The Guidance of Learning Activities.* ed. 3. Appleton-Century-Crofts, New York, 1962.

Irwin, L. W.: *The Curriculum in Health and Physical Education.* Wm. C. Brown Company, Dubuque, 1960.

Kozman, H. C., Cassidy, R. and Jackson, C. O.: *Methods in Physical Education.* ed. 3. W. B. Saunders Company, Philadelphia, 1958.

Nixon, E. W. and Cousins, F. W.: *Introduction to Physical Education.* ed. 6. W. B. Saunders Company, Philadelphia, 1964.

Pritzkau, P. T.: *Dynamics of Curriculum Improvement.* Prentice-Hall, Inc., Englewood Cliffs, 1959.

Schneider, R. E.: *Methods and Materials of Health Education.* ed. 2. W. B. Saunders Company, Philadelphia, 1964.

CHAPTER 7

PROGRAM ORGANIZATION IN HEALTH EDUCATION AND PHYSICAL EDUCATION

THE BASIS OF ORGANIZATION

Successful administration depends upon the soundness of departmental *policies* and *procedures*. Policies indicate the goals to be accomplished, procedures the steps along the way. In adapting procedures the administrator keeps in mind the goals sought and investigates the various possible solutions to problems before deciding upon the best course to follow.

General agreement is not difficult to obtain in the determination of policies. Adaptation of procedures to fulfill the policies often results in a series of conflicts involving personnel interrelationships and limitations of material resources.

TYPES OF PROGRAM IN HEALTH EDUCATION

Programs in health education vary from a perfunctory medical inspection of children by physician and nurse with no organized health instruction at all to thoroughly organized, efficiently conducted, and comprehensive health services, excellent supervision of school plants, and well organized courses in health instruction. In some schools the principal responds to a question concerning the health education program with the statement, "The doctor and nurse take care of the health of the school," meaning *pupil illnesses and first aid*. The programs in health services are more advanced than other portions of health education; the most serious deficiency is in the organization of health instruction.

Organizing for Health Education. Almost every school or school system now has in operation some part of the health education program. As a school moves toward a more complete or more effective program, it considers the formation of a *health council* composed of persons who can give competent guidance to the development of a program. In large city schools a health education administrator may be appointed to organize and direct the program, but the health council remains an important adjunct to his administration.

The council may be large or small, and serve the several schools of the community or be duplicated a number of times to serve in individual schools. In the latter arrangement the individual school health council may be represented by one of its members on a larger health council concerned with general administrative plans for the development of the health program in the school system.

TYPES OF PROGRAM IN PHYSICAL EDUCATION

Programs in physical education may be classified roughly into three types: (1) those emphasizing teacher-imposed activities; (2) those employing informal or play-interest activities; and (3) those attempting to strike a balance between two extremes. Some persons continue the analysis and explain that the program may include formal activities taught by informal methods, or consist of informal activities with formal methods. Within the general type of program adopted, one community prepares curriculum materials containing a preponderance of games and sports, another emphasizes rhythmic events, while others may specialize in adaptive activities, gymnastics, stunts, interscholastic activities, or free play.

Determination of the type and content of program depends upon the expected contribution of physical education to the complete education of youth, and reflects the breadth and depth of understanding of those responsible for planning the curriculum. Thus the *objectives of physical education should conform to the avowed purposes of the school as a whole, with activities regarded merely as the vehicle which carries the objective or objectives toward fulfillment.*

This concept is frequently overlooked. Occasionally one finds a school dedicated to the policy that children should learn through the utilization of life experiences, yet the program of physical education follows the pattern of predetermined and traditional activities and methods. Less often one observes a school where subject matter and the accumulation of knowledge are emphasized in academic subjects, with physical education conducted as free play to relieve the tension of imposed discipline in classrooms. In the latter case, physical activity represents a *service* program rather than an educational enterprise and can scarcely be termed physical education in its best sense. The well organized school gives evidence of a basic philosophy of education into which have been molded the administration, supervision, and instruction of all subject-matter areas.

For convenience, physical education activities may be classified as: (1) fundamental skills—walking, running, throwing, jumping, climbing, and others; (2) games and sports, including aquatics; (3) rhythmic activities; (4) stunts—self-testing activities, tumbling, and gymnastics; (5) individual or adaptive activities; and (6) recreational activities—free play, hiking, camping, and similar events.

Class periods in physical education are designed primarily to *instruct* pupils in the various activities used. Just as classes in mathematics aim to provide skill in the manipulation of numbers and symbols, in the same manner physical education classes aim toward improved performance. Knowledge, attitudes, understanding, and the development of fitness are essential outcomes of a good instructional program. These are acquired best through participation in activities. After-school periods of recreation, intramural athletics, and free play are not to be confused with regularly scheduled physical education classes. All are essential. After-school periods serve as *laboratory experiences* where students recreate the skills learned in scheduled classes.

FITNESS

During the war years both health education and physical education received strong emphasis. The former pursued a sound development with increased attention given to the discovery, prevention, and correction of remediable defects, to nutrition and food supplies, and to health instruction in schools. In physical education some programs gave strong emphasis to strength, following the strenuous physical fitness programs employed by military organizations. This trend was favored by some professional leaders who previously had advocated the need for increased emphasis on bodily development in physical education. Many of these persons believe that strength and endurance represent optimum goals of physical education.

Other professional leaders believe that physical fitness, as an end to be sought, never can satisfy the needs of a democratic people. Members of this group hasten to point out that physical fitness represents a means to an end—the means by which persons may live happier and more useful lives. These leaders emphasize "total" fitness among individuals and groups as being a desired goal in American culture—not "physical" fitness alone. Total fitness embraces emotional, social, and spiritual, as well as physical, welfare.

It is hoped that the American people will continue to regard fitness as a means, not an end. The athlete needs a certain kind of fitness to pursue a given activity with greater skill and safety; he will acquire that fitness. The person desiring to engage in the modern dance needs fitness, which he or she will develop. In like manner the properly educated sedentary worker will investigate the strength and endurance demanded by his mode of living, and maintain the level of fitness best suited to his daily needs. In these and other instances the sole problem is not exercise; health education in all its varied program plays a part.

But, of course, physical education has an important responsibility in this matter. Many students and adults are inefficient in their work and fail to enjoy the fullness of life because of impaired strength and endurance, but fitness comes normally in the desire to excel—as a by-product of the joy of successful accomplishment in wholesome life activities. Physical education should provide opportunity and leadership for the development of these skills. Properly organized classes expose the student to a variety of physical activities, help him to acquire skill in many of them, and promote his enduring interest in healthful physical recreation. Exercise for the sake of physical fitness alone appeals to only a limited number of persons who glorify strength and endurance as end products. For most persons, total fitness should be acquired as needed to perform more effectively the activities that bring satisfaction to the performer.

Another war influence led to increased interest in sports. Thousands of men and women in military service learned to play games, both to maintain fitness and for purposes of recreation. Others became ardent spectators. The growth of sports in postwar years challenged the attention of physical education and recreation personnel, guiding the interests of people toward wholesome participation in and enjoyment of these activities, rather than permitting them to be used for unworthy social and economic purposes.

Public interest in fitness has increased by leaps and bounds in recent years. Sparked by President Eisenhower with his council and lay committee, and continued by President Kennedy with generous support of various kinds, fitness has become prominent in the minds of youth and adults throughout the land. State and local fitness commissions and committees have been established that utilize the resources of numerous official, voluntary, and private organizations; newspapers and magazines contain articles and suggested programs; and speakers of national reputation use their eloquence to extol the virtues of a strong and fit America. Professional associations are especially active here. National, district, state, and local organizations hold fitness conferences, develop and apply objective tests, and prepare instructional materials for use by individuals, schools, and colleges.

Will the future emphasis be directed toward physical fitness or total fitness? The profession, itself, is divided on this issue. Surely the areas of health education, physical education, and recreation hold responsible and coordinate positions in the fulfillment of physical fitness or total fitness. As viewed from the preceding paragraphs, the authors support the view of total fitness for reasons given. School superintendents, boards of education, college presidents, and boards of trustees have specific administrative responsibilities with reference to the problem.

HEALTH EDUCATION AND PHYSICAL EDUCATION REQUIRED

By law in several states, and by state board of education regulation in others, health education and physical education are required of students in public schools. In health matters the requirement usually relates to the control of communicable disease and sanitation of the environment, but often it also includes health instruction. No requirement can make an individual live at his best or apply fully the knowledge gained in health classes. The requirement gives an opportunity that might otherwise not exist. In physical education the requirement seeks to assure normal growth and development. During the years of school life well selected activities stimulate the neuromuscular mechanisms and serve the functional demands of the vital organs. Development of the vital organs and systems results in part from heredity and in part from functional usage encouraged by physical activity. Nothing can replace heredity and, equally so, nothing can substitute for physical activity.

Although the *time requirement* continues in the eleventh and twelfth grades, many school systems provide a list of recreational activities from which qualified students in these grades may elect the activities they desire to pursue. Administration of the elective program takes into account the results of periodic health examinations and evaluation of the degree to which physical education objectives have been realized. Selective choice of activities presupposes freedom from developmental deficiencies justifying application of the required program, and demonstrated proficiency in the objectives prescribed by the curriculum.

EXCUSES

One of the most persistent problems of administration is the determination of a policy, with accompanying procedures, regulating excuses from physical education. Real cases of incapacity, such as diabetes or severe heart conditions, present few difficulties. Complications arise when students, not handicapped in fact, bring notes from parents or family physicians requesting that the requirement be waived.

Since public education is a state function it may be assumed legally that the advice of the school physician takes precedence over parents and family physicians in the matter of excuses. Established procedures whereby requests for exemption from the requirement are finally approved only by the school physician go a long way toward solving the problem. In school systems where medical advisors are not regularly employed, a physician from the local health department may pass on the appropriateness of excuses, or a local practitioner sometimes renders this particular service for a nominal fee paid by the board of education.

The procedure of acquainting parents and family physicians with the purposes and program of physical education deserves serious consideration. Many directors of health education and physical education report a decided reduction in the number of excuses requested when parents and family physicians understand clearly the function and organization of modern programs. Upon the basis of their own experiences, parents often regard physical education as a series of dumbbell drills, uninteresting calisthenics, or just free play. Likewise, physicians may gain the impression from newspaper accounts and other publicity that physical education is largely concerned with athletic participation or exhibitions of various sorts to which the public is invited. It appears fair to conclude that requests for excuses diminish in direct proportion to the manner in which the program is carefully planned, properly conducted, and wisely publicized.*

The technic of acquainting parents and physicians with the purposes and function of physical education varies in different communities. Parent-teacher associations often sponsor programs which present to parents the objectives and activities of the department. Meetings with the local medical society provide opportunities to enlist the support of physicians in the cooperative attitude essential to the success of physical education. In fact, it is advised that the excuse form used by the family physician be prepared by representatives of the school system in consultation with the local medical society.

Valid excuses specify a certain time limitation, usually not longer than a single school term. At the expiration of the time interval the requirement again becomes operative, or the need arises for reviewing the excuse.

In health education some religious groups request excuses from the health examination and the health instruction courses. These irrational requests usually must be granted.

SUBSTITUTION BECAUSE OF PHYSICAL HANDICAP

Satisfactory experiences in physical education improve normal growth and development. There are, however, individuals unable to engage with profit in the required program because of impaired organs, recent operations, serious diseases, injuries, or other physical handicaps. For these students the prescription of activity depends upon the recommendation of a competent physician. No nonmedical person should attempt to decide such questions, which are essentially medical in character. If the school physician recommends temporary discontinuance of all exercise, the student is excused from the requirement; assigned reading and locker room patrol duties represent inadequate substitutes for physi-

* See also Chapter 23: Public Relations.

cal education. If the school physician prescribes restricted activities or exercises, it is the function of the department to follow his recommendations insofar as personnel and facilities permit.

Often, walking is recommended in postoperative cases. Effort to improve the walking function then becomes an important objective of the department. The practice of permitting girls in high heels to stroll aimlessly about the school grounds is of doubtful value as a physical education activity.

Many students with physical disability require an exact prescription of exercise. This implies a diagnosis of the condition by a physician with the selection of a therapy suited to the case. Heart murmurs and posture deficiencies are examples. Those with extreme cases of valvular defect may be excluded from all physical activity, while others with cases of milder degree may be advised to pursue the regular program of physical education with the exception of strenuous competition. Children of junior high school age frequently develop a heart murmur with considerable irregularity of cardiac function. If no organic disease is apparent, the condition is recognized as "adolescent heart" which responds favorably to regular and reasonably vigorous exercise. Poor posture often results from inadequate general muscular development. Some students with faulty body mechanics need special exercises.

Uterine-ovarian disturbances resulting in dysmenorrhea frequently respond to moderate special exercises prescribed for the condition. Advice of the family physician aids in the solution of such problems. The question often arises, should girls be excused from physical education during the menstrual period, or should they be encouraged to continue with regular physical activity? Most girls prefer to continue usual participation at this time, and such activity may prove beneficial rather than harmful. Excessive fatigue, and sports involving emotional and physical strain, should be avoided. The menstrual period interrupts the swimming program, although bathing in water of body temperature or slightly warmer is desirable. Girls who occasionally experience pain during this period may substitute rest for activity, but frequent pain calls for the attention of a physician.

The basic policy relating to substitution of the requirement in physical education because of physical handicap favors approximating the regular program as nearly as possible, consistent with the nature of the specific defect.

SUBSTITUTION FOR OTHER REASONS

Substitution of the requirement in physical education may be proposed for reasons other than physical handicap. Among the more common appear: (1) membership on athletic teams; (2) high score on an achievement or classification test; (3) other school activities; and (4) participation in out-of-school activities.

Many school systems follow the practice of permitting members of athletic teams to substitute such participation for attendance in regular physical education classes. This practice has certain virtues and weaknesses.

Insofar as athletic participation fulfills the objectives established by the department, the plan appears justifiable. When membership on athletic teams restricts the individual to experiences associated with interscholastic sport, without exposing him to a broad range of activities wherein he acquires skills and appreciations of value in later life, the plan fails to accomplish the objectives of a well rounded program. The athlete who graduates from high school with limited skills beyond those contained in major sports cannot be regarded as a physically educated person. In extremely overcrowded schools with limited facilities, excusing members of athletic teams may be justified in order to reduce class size. In any event, the student excused from physical education for athletic participation returns to his regular class immediately following the last contest—the excuse is for the season only.

In some school systems students with superior organic functioning or strength, as revealed by a single test, are excused from the requirement in physical education. This policy is based on a narrow view of program objectives. While health and muscular strength represent worthy objectives of physical education, other desired outcomes are similarly important; these include qualities of leadership, interest in neuromuscular skill, social competence, and wholesome recreational interests.

A student may have no physical defects as revealed by the periodic health examination, or possess strong muscles enabling him to score high on a strength test, and yet fail to meet the standards prescribed in physical education relating to skills, knowledge, attitudes, and appreciations. No single test yet devised will suffice for evaluating properly all of the objectives sought. Thus the policy of excusing students from physical education on the basis of health or strength alone represents an unsound administrative practice.

Similar principles apply with respect to granting excuses from the requirement for other school activities or for out-of-school participation. Physical education makes certain unique contributions to the complete education of youth. Substitution of such activities as assembly periods and playing in the school band, or such out-of-school activities as walking to and from school and playing on community teams, are regarded as inappropriate bases for excusing students from the requirement.

Requests to excuse pupils from physical education classes to participate in other parts of the school program, curricular or extracurricular, reflect disregard for physical education. Usually such requests originate with parents, school administrators, or teachers who lack an understanding of the fundamental values of physical education.

Some students, especially girls, seek excuses because the activity and the shower afterwards disarrange a coiffure or make-up that seems to them more important than physical education. At times there is real justification for student objections, due to dirty locker rooms, lack of towels, lack of mirrors, too little time for showers and dressing, bossy instructors, and similar irritations.

CLASSIFICATION   *Arguments to promote Ability Grouping*

Students are classified in physical education activities to: (1) provide for individual needs; (2) promote fair competition between individuals or groups; (3) facilitate instruction; (4) serve individuals of like interests and abilities; and (5) insure program continuity.

The *individual needs* of students may be determined in part by the health examination, upon the basis of which less fortunate students are assigned to restricted groups or special classes. Since individual needs of students vary widely, the issue cannot be settled adequately by the health examination alone. Even those without disease or obvious abnormality vary in skill accomplishment. Some swim; others do not. Some dance well; others scarcely at all. Some can throw, climb, jump, and run with ease and efficiency; others need instruction in these activities. Individual needs and total program objectives go hand in hand.

Classification to *promote fair competition* provides for equivalent groups of participants on the basis of skill or other qualifications. This plan is used in regularly scheduled classes and in athletics.

Classification to *facilitate instruction* refers primarily to the development of skills. Reasonably homogeneous groups enable students to progress faster than unselected groups when physical skill is the objective sought. Objectives of a social nature may favor reasonable heterogeneity, since normal situations in life present wide variations in the acquired abilities of participants.

Classification to *serve individuals of like interests and abilities* represents the basis for elective physical education. In many school systems students in the senior high school are permitted to elect, within a group of activities, the ones desired for a given season. This policy presupposes demonstrated competence in the range of experiences prescribed by the department.

Classification to *insure program continuity* refers to a graded program of physical education in which students are exposed progressively to more difficult standards of accomplishment. One of the greatest needs is a graded program established in each community which continuously challenges the interests and abilities of students toward successively higher levels of accomplishment in the objectives sought.

From the above discussion it becomes apparent that no single plan of classification will suffice in physical education. A classification system adapted to games and sports may not yield satisfactory results when applied to aquatics. In similar fashion, rhythmic activities may require abilities not essential to the same degree in stunts and tumbling. Further, one type of classification may favor the realization of certain objectives, while another system of grouping leads to success in others.

Since relatively low correlations exist among student abilities in different types of physical activities, and to facilitate school organization, doubtless the best single classification for class assignment is by grade— one grade to a class. Ability groupings within the class may be accomplished as necessary by squad organization.

The efficient teacher gives constant attention both to individual needs and to goals established by the department as he guides students toward worthwhile accomplishments.

SCHEDULING AND SIZE OF CLASSES

Scheduling physical education classes requires the same precise consideration that is given to scheduling academic subjects. Some building principals or persons charged with the preparation of schedules appear to be unaware of the true purpose of the physical education class. Thus attention may be focused upon careful assignment of pupils to academic classes, while physical education classes are often arranged on the basis of administrative convenience. In such instances, grouping by grade levels may be disregarded thus making it difficult if not impossible to conduct a progression program. Also, the class sizes may vary from ridiculously small to extremely large and overcrowded, and during some periods the physical education facilities remain idle. This process results in an uneconomical use of staff and facilities as well as a handicap to good instruction.

Available facilities and equipment frequently present problems in scheduling physical education classes. Limited indoor and outdoor areas lead to overcrowded classes. Spacious facilities with inadequate equipment may result in adapting the size of the class to the area, but time is wasted because of insufficient staff and lack of tools with which to work. Within limits the program offered should conform to available facilities and equipment, although sound administrative organization regards this problem as temporary with plans made to obtain the necessary means for implementing the desired program within reasonable time.

An interesting innovation affecting class size, as well as other matters of school organization and methodology, deals with *team teaching* or *teaching by teams*. Basically, the plan involves groups of teachers concerned with large subject areas—often cutting across traditional subject lines—and engaged in teaching a relatively large number of students. Hence there are no conventional classes of 35 students.

The plan further presupposes that some teachers function better in certain areas than others, and that individual teacher competence varies in working with larger or smaller groups. Thus groups up to 150 students may receive lectures or demonstrations by a qualified teacher, while small groups of approximately 15 students meet in seminars each with a teacher in charge. The innovation for physical education not only allows teachers in this field to demonstrate their individual competencies in activities which comprise the program, but suggests appropriate utilization of teachers from other subjects in physical education and, *vice versa,* physical educators may contribute their talents in broad areas outside their specialization. Perhaps interschool athletics has demonstrated the value of team teaching over the years. Several communities across the nation have established programs of teaching by teams in both elementary and secondary schools. Usually the plan starts on a limited or experimental basis and expands in response to growing interest and understanding by teachers and students.

PUPIL-TEACHER RATIO

Too frequently the pupil-teacher ratio for physical education is entirely too large to insure the best educational results. The practice followed in many school systems provides a limitation of 30 or 35 pupils assigned to one teacher for each academic subject class, while 60 or more may be assigned to one teacher of a physical education class. The physical education class is an instruction period in which attention is focused on individual differences in the development of skills and knowledge, and, as such, limited class enrollment is essential. Therefore, it is obvious that the pupil-teacher ratio in physical education should be the same as in other subjects.

In schools with large enrollments and adequate facilities it may be necessary to assign large numbers of pupils to a particular physical education class period. In such instances good departmental organization provides for specific teaching stations and sufficient staff to comply with the pupil-teacher ratio recommended above.

CLASS ATTENDANCE

A systematic and efficient plan for taking attendance in physical education classes represents one of the elementary technics of effective organization. The time-consuming practice of calling the roll has disappeared in most schools. Approved methods include: (1) the use of squad leaders; (2) having spots marked on the floor to which individuals are assigned, and upon which they stand at the beginning of each class; (3) having the roll checked by an attendant in the dressing room; or (4) having an assistant who records absences during the class period.

At the beginning of the term each class should assemble for instruction at the hour scheduled. Delay in starting classes until health examinations have been completed, or for other reasons, wastes time needed to orient students in the procedures to be followed, and often decreases the respect of other teachers for physical education. Modern practice which distributes the health examinations of students throughout the year, rather than scheduling them during the first few months of school, helps to solve the problem.

TIME ALLOTMENT

Standards recommended for time allotment provide for a daily period of 40 to 60 minutes for health instruction in grades 6 to 8, length of period to be consistent with the administrative policy throughout the school. One period per day is recommended for physical education, length of the period to be consistent with the established length of periods in the individual school. At the senior high school level a one-semester daily course in health in each of the tenth and twelfth grades is recommended. In physical education the standard calls for a daily period that is consistent in length with that established in the individual school.*

BASES FOR AWARDING MARKS

A satisfactory system of awarding marks in health education and physical education conforms to the policy and procedures established for the school as a whole. The only exception to the rule may be found in schools which have abolished all marking systems.

Customary practice in physical education indicates that marks are given according to some combination of pupil attendance, punctuality, effort, costume, achievement, and general attitude. Occasionally elaborate plans have been devised to record credit and debit marks for success or failure in each of the above items. Many of these complicated marking systems need revision.

It seems reasonable to propose that marks be awarded on the basis of *successful accomplishment in the objectives sought*. Some of these objectives lend themselves to evaluation by standardized testing procedures; and objective measurement obviates the need for subjective judgment. On the other hand, many of the more important objectives of physical education cannot be measured by current standard tests, and the instructor must rely on his personal and subjective judgment. Assuming that the objectives represent a satisfactory statement of desired outcomes, it is recommended that student achievement in those objectives forms the most appropriate basis for awarding grades at each scheduled marking period, even though many of the outcomes cannot be measured by standard tests and must be evaluated by subjective means. The day has passed, if it ever existed, when a single objective test of posture, strength, or cardiovascular endurance could be accepted as a satisfactory instrument for awarding marks in physical education.

In health education marks usually are given on the basis used in

* Because of the time consumed by dressing and taking showers in secondary schools, some administrators recommend scheduling a double period for physical education that approximates on a weekly basis the one period per day described above.

academic classes. Thus the pupil is marked upon what he *knows*. In view of the imperative necessity to stress the great importance of practice, it is desirable to modify the knowledge score by an evaluation of *habits* and *attitudes*. Pupils who succeed in applying the facts learned in the classroom should receive the highest marks, and those who consistently fail to practice what they know should receive the lowest ones. Efforts made to secure correction of remediable defects should be recognized by the final mark in health education for the year. As the importance of health practice is better understood, both promotion and graduation may depend upon the way a person lives and not only on what he knows.

CREDIT FOR HEALTH EDUCATION AND PHYSICAL EDUCATION

Closely associated with the problem of marking is that of *credit*. In some states the law specifies that credits and penalties shall be applied for success or failure in physical education as in other subjects. In many states without such legislation schools regularly give credit for health education and physical education toward promotion from grade to grade and for graduation.

The entire problem appears to depend upon the attitude of the board of education toward credit in general. If the board has adopted certain policies and procedures governing the issuance or nonissuance of credit for promotion and graduation, then these rules should operate in an equitable manner for all subjects or programs in the approved curriculum. The rapidly growing concept that the curriculum functions in improving the lives of children suggests the question: why should credit be applied only to certain traditional academic subjects? The advantage of age, alone, scarcely provides a safe criterion to follow in selecting the most productive school subjects for a changing world. Instead, each subject or program should be judged in terms of its contribution to the needs of society, and credit awarded in accordance therewith.

In any event the problem of credit rests on the attainment of carefully determined standards.

CREDIT FOR COLLEGE ENTRANCE

In recent years the decided trend toward acceptance of college entrance credit for health education and physical education illustrates the importance accorded these fields by institutions of higher learning. Most colleges accept 15 or 16 high school units for admission, some of which are required, others elective. One or two units of health education and physical education from approved high schools may be accepted on an elective basis. Doubtless the steadily increasing number of colleges and universities which award credit in health education and physical education toward the baccalaureate degree favorably influences the trend to accept high school credit for college entrance.

The responsibility to establish and maintain health education and physical education in schools and colleges on a level of proficiency worthy of credit, and the adoption of standards which facilitate the evaluation of instruction, represent a definite challenge to the profession.

PROBLEMS FOR DISCUSSION

1. Discussing program organization, a superintendent says: "When I was in high school, we had a physical training teacher who could teach large groups through formal command-response activities of a vigorous nature. I think we derived more benefit from that program than the youth of today get in play activities. Neither situation requires lesson planning and the teacher has no papers to grade or record to keep. Therefore, each physical education teacher should be able to teach 500 pupils per week if the academic teacher can teach 150." What are the issues involved?
2. A high school master schedule reveals that each of three different physical education classes contain many more pupils than existing facilities can absorb. The principal, reluctant to make any changes in the pupil assignments, requests permission to rent a nearby bowling alley to take care of at least one third of each class. This would result in two thirds of the class meeting in a gymnasium and recreation room respectively on a six-week cycle while one third would bowl. Assuming that you are the supervisor consulted concerning this matter, what would be your reaction?
3. The physical education teacher receives the following note from a parent: "Please excuse Johnny from gym exercises. He walks a total of two miles to and from school and delivers newspapers in late afternoon. Furthermore, he gets enough exercise playing ball in the street every day." How would you handle this problem?
4. Teachers are divided in their opinions about marking systems. One group states in effect, "It will be a glorious day when all grading can be discarded and youngsters may progress naturally in response to the stimulus each teacher brings to him." Other teachers hold to the belief that some sort of grading system is necessary. Explain your point of view in this matter.
5. Instructors and students may implement the above with problems gained from their own experience and observation.

REFERENCES

American Association for Health, Physical Education, and Recreation: *Current Administrative Problems.* The Association, Washington, 1960.

Joint Committee on Health Problems in Education of the National Education Association and the American Medical Association: *Health Education.* ed. 5. The Association, Chicago, 1961.

National Conference for City Directors of Health, Physical Education, and Recreation: *Administering City and County School Programs.* American Association for Health, Physical Education, and Recreation, Washington, 1960.

National Conference on Fitness for Secondary School Youth (Report): *Youth and Fitness.* American Association for Health, Physical Education, and Recreation, Washington, 1959.

National Conference on Interpretation of Physical Education: *Conference Report*. The
    Athletic Institute, Inc., Chicago, 1961.
Nixon, E. W. and Cousins, F. W.: *Introduction to Physical Education*. ed. 6. W. B.
    Saunders Company, Philadelphia, 1964.
Oberteuffer, D.: *School Health Education*. ed. 3. Harper & Row, Publishers, New York,
    1962.
Turner, C. E., Sellery, C. M. and Smith, S. L.: *School Health and Health Education*.
    ed. 4. The C. V. Mosby Company, St. Louis, 1961.
Vannier, M. and Fait, H. F.: *Teaching Physical Education in Secondary Schools*. ed. 2.
    W. B. Saunders Company, Philadelphia, 1964.

CHAPTER 8

HEALTH SERVICES

A POINT OF VIEW

The remarkable advances that characterize modern public school education—the improvement in plants, curricula, and personnel—seem no more significant than the transformed point of view that recognizes the needs and interests of youth in the choice of subject matter. Indeed, it may be argued that the shift in emphasis from subject matter to children is responsible for better plants, an enriched curriculum, and increased professional preparation of teachers. Out of the unprecedented improvement in education the idea has emerged that the school is concerned with the lives of individuals and not with a mere conquest of illiteracy. This viewpoint has stimulated the erection of modern plants, but of equal significance is the entrance of new educative forces that truly represent a broadening of the concept of educational purpose. These educative forces are represented by the physician, the nurse, the dentist, the dental hygienist, the psychiatrist, the nutrition expert, the guidance counselor, and others. Undoubtedly education is coming to believe in the development of the whole individual, and is seriously intent upon seeking ways to promote richer and fuller lives.

THE SCOPE OF HEALTH SERVICES

This view has transformed school procedure in dealing with the health problems of children. Early efforts in this direction in the latter decades of the nineteenth century have been expanded as their significance becomes apparent. Medical inspection, that arose in response to a demand for the control of communicable diseases in schools, now includes the detection of other health defects and the determination of health status. Progress has been halting and unbelievably slow. Too frequently it has remained an inspection service that only attempts to secure corrections and neglects the educational aspect of its opportunities.

One improvement is the substitution of the term *health services* for *medical inspection.* A mere change in terminology without substantial change in purpose cannot alone indicate progress. A change in name without recasting of purpose and procedure is an insidious temptation in the reorganization of any aspect of public administration. If the study of an administrative problem produces nothing more than a change in names of divisions or services, it is not likely to contribute greatly to the solution of the difficulty. The term *health services* implies at the outset a more distinctly significant and a more truly serviceable organization than ever did medical inspection.

Health services comprise the several administrative procedures designed to determine the health status of the child, to inform parents of disabilities that may be present, to educate parents and children in ways of preventing these, to aid teachers in recognizing early signs of disease and defect, and to assist in the correction of remediable conditions.

Health services include a periodic health examination; examination of pupils referred by teachers on the basis of their daily observation; measures to prevent the spread of contagion; follow-up services to secure correction of remediable disabilities; and the use of family physicians, clinics, hospitals, special classes, and other organizations for the care and treatment of children in need of special services.

ADMINISTRATIVE RESPONSIBILITY

In an increasing number of cities the responsibility for health services is placed with boards of education.

The Educational Policies Commission reports:

> The provision of medical and dental examinations at regular intervals during the the school career of each child constitutes a definite responsibility of school authorities. Physicians and dentists making these health inventories are employed either by the board of health or board of education specifically for this purpose; when making examinations they should be responsible to the school health authorities and through them to the board of education for the quality and completeness of their work in the school. The board of education is obligated to provide the services of physicians for the same reasons that it provides the services of psychologists and, at times, psychiatrists, for making mental health inventories, namely, to determine health status, facilitate removal of handicaps to learning, and to find out whether some special adaptation of the school program may be necessary (as, for example, the omission of some forms of physical education or provision of lip reading or sight-saving classes).

In some states the law delegates this function to boards of health, and in other states legal enactment places jurisdiction of health services with boards of education. The increasing tendency is toward board of education control and responsibility.

Arguments favoring board of health control may be summarized as follows: the board possesses legal power which is not delegated to the school (control of communicable disease); it serves the individual during his preschool life and after school is ended; it serves the individual during the entire year; and it employs personnel and provides facilities which should not be duplicated. In short, school authorities should cooperate with the board of health instead of instituting a service which parallels one already in existence.

Arguments favoring board of education control are based primarily on the principle that school health supervision is educational in scope. In such matters school authorities should have control, since they are in a better position than any other group to determine existing needs and satisfactory procedures. The control of communicable diseases is but a small part of the entire school health program which embraces many activities such as periodic health examinations, follow-up for the correction of remediable conditions, health supervision of plant and equipment, health instruction, and the like. Better cooperation may be secured from homes because parents are accustomed to dealing with the school, whereas the local health department may be looked upon as a police agency. That teachers cooperate better with school health authorities is proved by experience, since such authority places all under the same directing influence. Schools are conducted primarily for the education of children, a fact which implies the development of a child's physical potentialities as well as his mental aptitudes.

Cooperative Administration. Cooperative arrangements can be worked out at some levels and in some situations. At the state level cooperation is not difficult; at the local level city or county health councils may achieve excellent cooperation and this approach is recommended wherever there is strong disagreement on the placement of control and responsibility.

AUTHORITY OF THE SCHOOL PHYSICIAN

It is a sound policy of administration that *authority* should accompany *responsibility*. In matters of examination, exclusion from school, and assignment of work, the school physician has a precise responsibility. With the tactful school official, conflicts rarely arise, because he is interested primarily in securing cooperative home relationships and must, of necessity, work in professional harmony with his colleagues of the healing art. In some states parents may comply with the law requiring a health examination of school children by furnishing a health certificate from the family physician. A form is supplied by the school. The parents are given opportunity to waive this right.

In an increasing number of school systems administrative procedures encourage the periodic health examination of students by family physicians and dentists, with the schools making use of health data furnished by these specialists. Such procedures represent sound health education as students and their parents learn to regard the physician and dentist as family health advisers.

DEPARTMENT OF EDUCATION

BALTIMORE, MD.

---School

--Zone----------------

OFFICE OF THE
SCHOOL PHYSICIAN

Dear Dr.

_____, one of your

patients attending_____School,
has requested exemption from normal physical education.
The regular program consists of athletic games and
sports, gymnastic activities, lighter recreational
games, and dancing. Its purpose is to contribute to
the education of the child through physical activity,
in accordance with individual needs.

        If you believe your patient should not partici-
pate in a normal program please indicate on the
enclosed card the activities you recommend.

        Our school physician will review this case
and possibly confer with you, so that an ultimate
decision may be reached which is for the best interests
of your patient.

                        Sincerely yours,

_____   _____
     Telephone   School Nurse

Figure 6.   Form used by Baltimore Public Schools relative to request for pupil exemption from physical education.

    On the other hand, the family physician may not expect to excuse
children from school activities when a school physician is available to
perform this function. Arbitrary actions by family physicians can be
handled best by requesting a statement of the diagnosis and by using
forms that require the family physician to place himself on record (Figs.
6 and 7). Such an administrative technic prevents the ordinary, polite,
and goodwill excuse that the family physician often is called upon to
deliver, and tends to increase the physician's respect for the school
administration.

    In the control of communicable disease the board of health has jurisdiction and authority to isolate pupils and event to close the schools. The school physician will act in accordance with this fact and establish the closest cooperation to the end that such control shall be efficient, orderly, and agreeable.

THE HEALTH EXAMINATION

The several functions of the examination of school children are: (1) to determine health status; (2) to acquaint parents with the nature of deviations from normal; (3) to correct remediable conditions; (4) to acquaint school pupils with the purposes of health examinations; and (5) to develop a scientific attitude toward health.

To Determine Health Status and Abnormalities. Children have a great variety of disabilities: communicable diseases that range from impetigo to diphtheria, from scabies to scarlet fever; disabilities of the sensory mechanisms, such as vision and hearing; teeth, tonsils, and adenoids that present serious problems of oral hygiene; glandular disturbances, such as goiter, tuberculosis, and simple lymph-node enlargements; nutritional disturbances; spine and feet abnormalities; and numerous other unhealthful conditions of the skin, nervous system, heart, lungs, and other parts. To permit children to carry remediable conditions through the critical years of growth and development is to ignore the responsibility of the school to promote the education of the whole child and to neglect the school's rich opportunities to improve the health of future citizens.

To Educate Parents. Part of the value of such examinations is the education of parents in child care and protection. The fact that many children with serious health handicaps appear in school is adequate testimony to parental ignorance of, and indifference to, these conditions. Since the promotion of education is dependent largely on parental under-

---

DEPARTMENT OF EDUCATION - BALTIMORE, MARYLAND

Physician's Recommendation for
MODIFIED PHYSICAL EDUCATION

This is to certify that I have examined..
from school...and have found the following abnormal condition.
....

Therefore I recommend that participation in Physical Education be as checked below:
□ Normal program—all activities

MODIFIED PROGRAM

□ Relaxation—bed rest—quiet table games   □ Games like shuffle-board, archery, quoits
□ Mild exercises—done lying or sitting on mat   □ Ball skills without running
□ Target type games   □ Mild rhythmic activities
□ Body building exercises modified as to need   □ Social dancing   □ Square dancing

Duration: for.....................weeks, for...................months, until next examination ....

Date..   Signature ....M.D.

Telephone..   Address..

TO BE RETURNED TO THE SCHOOL NURSE

Figure 7.   Form used by Baltimore Public Schools to record physician's recommendation for pupil's physical education program.

standing and support, the value to society of the health examination in educating parents is apparent (Fig. 8).

To Correct Remediable Disabilities. Not all conditions are remediable but many of those that children have are readily corrected. Reports on corrections vary greatly in different cities because of the unstandardized procedures in examinations and classifications. In smaller cities, however, there are numerous examples of 80 and 90 per cent correction of remediable disabilities. These high percentages are possible where adequate facilities exist for treatment. In most cities free clinics are available.

To Instruct Pupils. The health examination provides an experience rich in opportunity to instruct pupils in the need for such examinations, how they are conducted, and the values of periodic consultation with the family physician or dentist. Attitudes formed by students toward medical and dental practitioners as a result of health examinations in schools often continue into adult life.

To Promote Scientific Attitudes. People have curious notions about health. When a disturbance arises, the uninformed are prone to rely upon mystical and magical sources for healing and to look upon the unwarranted claims of some cult with favor and approval.

The education of youth in scientific attitudes toward health is a vital part of the examination. This depends largely upon the pupil's respect for and confidence in the physician.

The school in general, and the medical profession in particular, should direct attention to the importance of medical consultation in relation to mental hygiene. The large number of persons without infection or abnormality who yet complain of illness represents a problem that is to be met in the early years of school and particularly in connection with the health services.

This kind of problem can be solved if the physician and teacher understand the nature of the difficulty, are competent to counsel the pupil, and give sufficient time to teaching the individual what he needs to know about his behavior. The above conditions seldom are fulfilled and, therefore, early correction of "mental illness" seldom is achieved. The solution depends upon the guidance of a psychiatrist who stresses the values of human relationships in which real values in life are derived through efforts of the individual concerned and do not appear to come through interference with the skills of another person or by the infringement of his opportunities. The solution is primarily educational rather than medical.*

Objections to Health Examinations. There are few objections to health examinations in schools, but occasionally some opposition is expressed. This is likely to arise, either from parental pride that is averse to the discovery by others of defects in one's child, or from religious belief that is

* Students and teachers interested in this problem will find the following reference informative: Thomas S. Szasz, *The Myth of Mental Illness.* Harper & Row, Publishers, New York, 1961.

in conflict with the scientific method regarding disease. The former can be overcome usually by sympathetic and kindly education; for the latter, nothing is very effective. When communicable disease is involved, neither pride nor religious prejudice may be permitted to obstruct what is clearly a social responsibility of the school, namely, the protection of the many from the contagion of the few.

BALTIMORE CITY HEALTH DEPARTMENT
Bureau of School Health

SPECIAL REPORT TO PARENT

To the Parent or
Guardian of .... Class ....

School No. .... Date ....

An examination of your child by the school physician shows the following condition:

....

....

....

....

You are asked to contact your family physician or dentist to get his advice and help. Your cooperation will safeguard your child's health and promote his future welfare.

If you wish to discuss this condition, you may visit the school physician by appointment or by calling ....

Your reply will be appreciated.

Signed ....
School Physician or Nurse

PARENT'S REPLY

....

....

....

Date .... Signed ....
Parent or Guardian

This Form is to be Returned to the School Nurse On or Before

....
Date

Figure 8. Form used by Baltimore Public Schools to invite parents to cooperate with health service and school authorities.

Education of parents where objections occur is an important responsibility of the school. The problem may be solved by presenting parents with the facts regarding health and disabilities, and their relation to school progress.

The seriousness of uncorrected conditions should convince parents of the necessity for health examinations of children and the correction of their remediable health disturbances. Modern education supports the principle that all children should have the opportunity to develop their optimum potentialities. Numerous special aids in the form of instruction and equipment are provided at public expense for children who exhibit slightly inferior intellectual qualities; in similar fashion, the needs of the physical organism are not to be neglected.

It is apparent that there are many impediments in the way. There is considerable suspicion of measures that seem to interfere with the private practice of medicine. The problem is real. In some communities the policy has been adopted that parents shall be *informed* regarding the existence of health handicaps among their children and *urged* to consult the family physician or dentist for further examination or correction. This represents a low minimum of responsibility for the school; it may become quite untenable in the future. Since public education is devoted to the promotion of social progress, and since it presupposes soundness in the whole child as a condition of soundness in citizens, it is not too much to expect that communities will provide medical and dental services for all school children in need of treatment who are not cared for by the home. Progressive communities that realize this expectation will establish clinics and hospitals along with schools and churches. The *whole child*, which is obviously the *real child*, will thus be cared for.

In some states laws prohibit the removal of clothing in the examination of school children. This makes effective examination difficult, if not impossible. Examinations conducted in public schools often are partial, inefficient, and wasteful of public funds. Laws that prevent an adequate examination are in part responsible for this state of affairs.

All Children Examined. All children in public schools should receive a periodic health examination by physicians and dentists. Those found with certain remediable conditions should be reexamined at intervals. Some districts adopt the policy of examinations for children entering kindergarten or grade one, grade three, grade six, and grade nine; those entering the school system from other districts or any children entering for the first time; those applying for work certificates; and those referred to physicians and dentists by nurses and teachers.

Parents at the Examination. The presence of parents at the examination of elementary school children is highly desirable. Many disabilities of children can be corrected only by the active cooperation of parents and child with school authorities or family physician and dentist. Moreover, the educational value of the examination is extended if attendance of a parent is secured, and public support for the school health program may be strengthened thereby. The attendance of a parent permits a better examination, since consent is usually obtained for removal of clothing. It favors opportunity to inquire into and instruct concerning the pupil's habits at home. It permits explanation of conditions found in a direct and personal manner. It is believed to favor a higher percentage of corrections. The attendance of parents at examinations has increased, but more remains to be accomplished in this direction.

If parents cannot attend, the educational aspect of the examination is still important, since the child remains the central feature in the procedure. Absence of parents never should mean a less careful examination.

The Teacher at the Examination.   Presence of the teacher at the examination of his pupils is important.* The advantages may be as follows:

1. It aids the physician and dentist in discovering the pupil's habits, mannerisms, energy levels, and other important signs.
2. It helps educate the teacher in the importance of certain aspects of the hygiene of instruction and in continuous observations.
3. It gives the teacher important clues for guidance of the pupil.
4. It fosters a cooperative spirit by emphasizing a joint enterprise.

It is not always possible to relieve a teacher so he may be present at the examination of an individual child, but arrangements sometimes can be made with other teachers or the principal.

The Standardized Examination.   A standardized examination is difficult to secure. It is quite impossible to get medical agreement, generally, concerning what constitutes such conditions as pathologic tonsils, adenoids, lymph enlargement, flat feet; and yet for practical purposes any school physician's staff may readily agree upon the classification of conditions found in school children. Standardizing the examination is of great importance, since otherwise some physicians tend to report a larger number of certain disturbances than others.

The examination should be standardized and, therefore, previous to the beginning of regular examinations in schools, meetings of school physicians and dentists should be held. At these meetings standards for diagnosis, referring of patients, exclusions, and readmission of patients should be discussed and established. Whenever more than one physician is engaged in health examinations a standardization clinic is essential.

Faults in Examinations.   Some of the common faults in health examinations, as now conducted in public schools, are:

1. Perfunctory examinations by physicians and dentists.
2. Neglect of children with obvious signs of health disturbances, such neglect resulting from a scheduled routine in which certain items are not listed.
3. Emphasis upon detection of disabilities and neglect, in whole or in part, of preventive and corrective measures.
4. Treating children as biological specimens, as tonsil cases, or adenoid cases, or the like, when the psychology of the situation requires recog-

* It is more important in elementary schools than in secondary schools.

nition of them as individuals, if wholesome educational influences are to operate.

5. Poor organization for the conduct of health services resulting from inadequate equipment, insufficient remuneration of physicians and dentists, and employment of examiners on a part-time basis with their main interests outside the schools.
6. Examination of only a few children instead of all children.
7. Lack of standardized examination.
8. Examination not given often enough.

THE HEALTH RECORD

Often it appears that the health examination is the only important act in determining the health status of the child. Are his teeth carious? Are his tonsils enlarged? These seem to be the vital questions. But obviously this emphasis gives only a partial picture of the child. It is also important to know what his past experiences have been, how his emotional reactions have shaped his attitudes, and what are his observable habits. His past is quite as significant as his present, not only in understanding his present but also in giving him guides for the future. Thus, his *health history* and his *health examination* comprise what may be called his *health record;* the former tells what he has been, the latter assays what he is now. Both are indispensable parts of the whole child as a person.

It is apparent of course that the extent of the health record may be restricted by the size of the budget and the ability of staff members. In some communities a few notes on children's diseases comprise the health history; and a brief survey of tonsils, teeth, vision, hearing, and adenoids constitutes the health examination. It is also obvious that few schools, and these mostly private institutions, conduct examinations that give a complete picture of the child's health status. For such a picture the combined services of teachers, nurse, psychiatrist, psychologist, dentist, and physician are required.

Health History and the Cumulative Record. In many public school systems there is a tendency to bring together in one folder all data referring to the pupil's health, scholastic, and social record. This practice is justified on several counts. First, the health of the child is to be interpreted in the light of all his functional performances. Second, it is important to bring together in one place significant data regarding the individual's responses in a variety of situations. Third, the level of intelligence and grade attainment may explain some health problems when glandular reactions, muscular development, or physical conditions fail to do so. This composite record may, therefore, contain data from six fields.

I. *Data from the environmental record* (Fig. 9).
    1. Items from the early environment, such as number of children

and place of examinee in order, breast- or bottle-fed, infancy record, prenatal care.

2. Items from the present environment, such as the "only child" problem, housing, work of father, occupation of mother.

II. *Data from the disease and health disturbance record* (Fig. 9).

1. Communicable diseases, such as diphtheria, scarlet fever, whooping cough, measles, meningitis, poliomyelitis, tuberculosis, influenza, typhoid fever.
2. Noncommunicable disturbances, such as broken bones, operations, malnutrition, rickets.

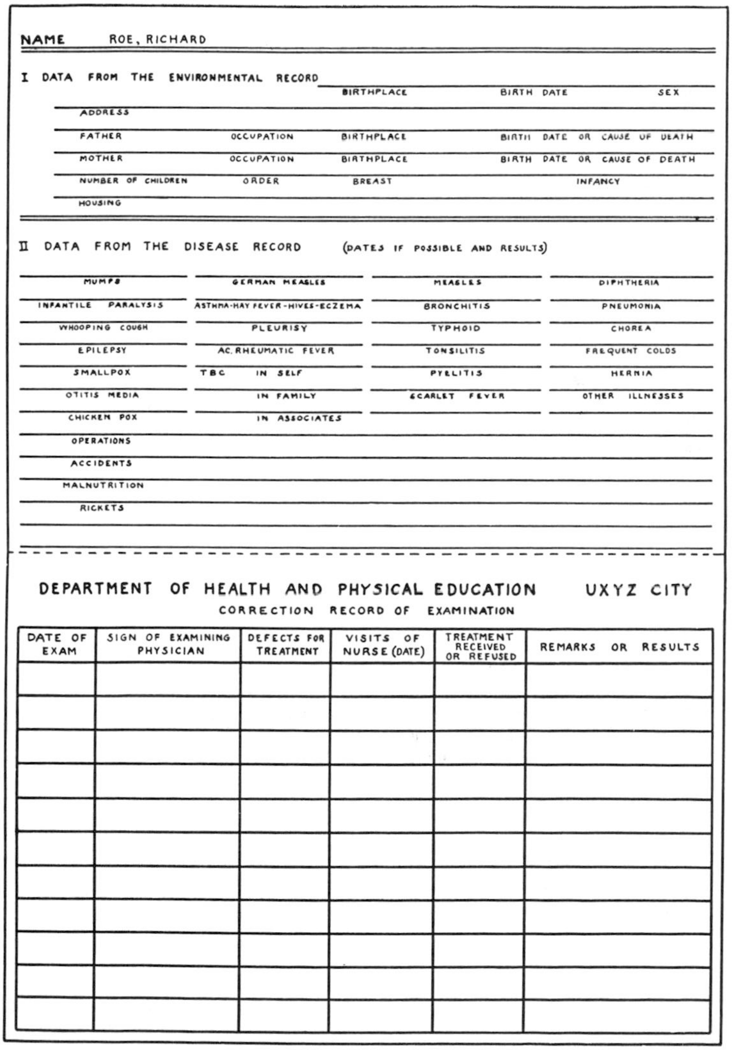

NAME ROE, RICHARD

I DATA FROM THE ENVIRONMENTAL RECORD

BIRTHPLACE BIRTH DATE SEX

ADDRESS

FATHER OCCUPATION BIRTHPLACE BIRTH DATE OR CAUSE OF DEATH

MOTHER OCCUPATION BIRTHPLACE BIRTH DATE OR CAUSE OF DEATH

NUMBER OF CHILDREN ORDER BREAST INFANCY

HOUSING

II DATA FROM THE DISEASE RECORD (DATES IF POSSIBLE AND RESULTS)

MUMPS	GERMAN MEASLES	MEASLES	DIPHTHERIA
INFANTILE PARALYSIS	ASTHMA-HAY FEVER-HIVES-ECZEMA	BRONCHITIS	PNEUMONIA
WHOOPING COUGH	PLEURISY	TYPHOID	CHOREA
EPILEPSY	AC. RHEUMATIC FEVER	TONSILITIS	FREQUENT COLDS
SMALLPOX	TBC IN SELF	PYELITIS	HERNIA
OTITIS MEDIA	IN FAMILY	SCARLET FEVER	OTHER ILLNESSES
CHICKEN POX	IN ASSOCIATES		

OPERATIONS

ACCIDENTS

MALNUTRITION

RICKETS

DEPARTMENT OF HEALTH AND PHYSICAL EDUCATION UXYZ CITY

CORRECTION RECORD OF EXAMINATION

DATE OF EXAM	SIGN OF EXAMINING PHYSICIAN	DEFECTS FOR TREATMENT	VISITS OF NURSE (DATE)	TREATMENT RECEIVED OR REFUSED	REMARKS OR RESULTS

Figure 9.

Ⅲ   DATA FROM THE SCHOLASTIC RECORD

	19 _ 19 _	19 _ 19 _	19 _ 19 _	19 _ 19 _	19 _ 19 _	19 _ 19 _	19 _ 19 _
I.Q. ___ ___DATE	TEST ___	TEST ___	TEST ___	TEST ___	TEST ___	TEST ___	TEST ___
	G.S. ___	G.S. ___	G.S. ___	G.S. ___	G.S. ___	G.S. ___	G.S. ___
STANDARD TEST SCORES	TEST ___	TEST ___	TEST ___	TEST ___	TEST ___	TEST ___	TEST ___
(G.S.=GROSS SCORES)	G.S. ___	G.S. ___	G.S. ___	G.S. ___	G.S. ___	G.S. ___	G.S. ___
	TEST ___	TEST ___	TEST ___	TEST ___	TEST ___	TEST ___	TEST ___
	G.S. ___	G.S. ___	G.S. ___	G.S. ___	G.S. ___	G.S. ___	G.S. ___
PROMOTION RECORD (P=PROMOTION R=RETAINED)							
ABSENCES (USE CODE FROM REGISTER)							
GRADE RETARDATION (USE CODE FROM REGISTER)							

Figure 10.

III. *Data from the scholastic record* (Fig. 10).
    1. Intelligence quotient
    2. Achievement quotient
    3. Promotion record
    4. Grade retardation
    5. Standard test grade scores.

IV. *Data from the adjustment record* (Fig. 11).
    1. Abnormal bodily movements, such as biting nails, twitching (tics), tapping feet, grimacing.

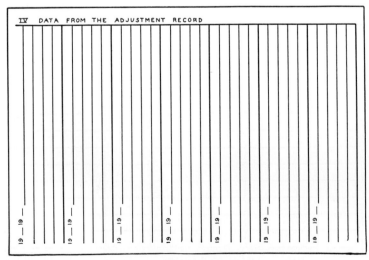

Figure 11.

2. Abnormal response to reasonable tasks, such as sullenness, tenseness, talking back.

3. Abnormal disagreement with group, such as playing alone, unwillingness to trust the group, resenting group action.

4. Abnormal use of practices to relieve emotional conflicts or tensions, shown in (*a*) behavior toward others, such as bullying, pushing, tripping, "taking it out on someone," (*b*) behavior toward self, such as failure to face the facts, proneness to seek alibis, wishful thinking and acting, excessive effort at justification, undue regrets, playing the martyr.

V. *Data from the social (intergroup relationships) record* (Fig. 12).

1. Abnormal treatment of other children, such as consistent bullying, nagging.

2. Unreliable, as shown by cheating, lying, stealing, truancy.

3. Disregard of common social standards as shown by neglect of social practices such as cleanliness of the person, orderliness of desk and school room, care of property, relations with opposite sex, sportsmanship.

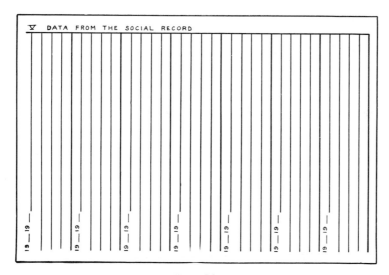

Figure 12.

VI. *Data from the health practice record* (Fig. 13).

1. Sleep, such as the number of hours, soundless, sleeping alone.

2. Food, such as the kinds of food habitually eaten—vegetables, fruit, cereals, sweets, meats, coffee, tea; frequency of eating—regular breakfast, luncheon, dinner, between-meal eating; and attitudes toward eating—appetite, liking food, thorough mastication, unhurried meals, pleasant experiences at the table.

3. Play and exercise, such as the kind of play and the number of hours daily out-of-doors.

VI DATA FROM THE HEALTH PRACTICE RECORD		19 _ 19 _	19 _ 19 _	19 _ 19 _	19 _ 19 _	19 _ 19 _	19 _ 19 _	19 _ 19 _
SLEEP	NO. HRS.							
	OPEN W.							
FOOD	VEGETABLES							
	FRUITS							
	MILK							
	CEREALS							
	C. OR T.							
PLAY								
CLEANLINESS								
REMOVAL OF DEFECTS PUPIL'S PART								
MENTAL HYGIENE PUPIL'S PART								
IMMUNITY	VACCINATION							
	TOXIN-ANTI.							
	SCHICK	POS _ NEG _	POS _ NEG _	POS _ NEG _	POS _ NEG _	POS _ NEG _	POS _ NEG _	POS _ NEG _
	T.B.C.	POS _ NEG _	POS _ NEG _	POS _ NEG _	POS _ NEG _	POS _ NEG _	POS _ NEG _	POS _ NEG _

Figure 13.

4. Cleanliness practices, such as relate to the teeth, hands (especially), general bathing, elimination.

5. Removal of remediable health handicaps, such as those removed by a single procedure as an operation, and those removed by a period of practice, such as underweight, carious teeth.

6. Use of immunity measures, such as vaccination for smallpox, toxin-antitoxin, inoculation for diphtheria, typhoid inoculation, poliomyelitis vaccine.

7. Attempt to preserve and express wholesome mental attitudes, such as consistently courageous, cheerful, and objectively minded.

These data give a clear picture of the individual, and many of his disturbances can be explained in the light of his history. The data sought in groups IV and V require comment.

In view of the many evidences of social and moral failure of persons in positions of great responsibility, it is apparent that schools must pay attention to pupil adjustment and social records. The time has arrived for a totally new emphasis upon character education. Such emphasis insists that social behavior, good manners, and ethical attitudes shall come first, and with these lacking no amount of scholastic achievement may win pupil promotion or graduation.

Minimum Limits of the Health Record. As suggested above, the health record may be limited by the budget or qualifications of the staff. A thorough and complete record may be impossible. The following items are recommended as a minimum list which all schools, unable to do more, should follow:

I. *Data from the environmental record* (as complete as possible)

II. *Data from the disease record* (as complete as possible)

III. *Data from the scholastic record* (all five)
IV. *Data from the adjustment record* (all four)
V. *Data from the social* (*intergroup relationships*) *record* (all three)
VI. *Data from the health practice record* (as complete as possible).

Items III, IV, and V can be supplied by the observant teacher; items I, II, and VI can be secured by the nurse at home visits and from the child.

Record Forms. Most record forms stress impaired functions, so that cards often relate to defects rather than to pupils. The record as described on the previous pages requires several cards; it may be desirable to have one large card that serves as a folder (Fig. 9) within which the other cards are kept. Moreover, the folder card should be the one first filled out and the pupil's name placed upon it to serve as an index of its position. The record forms should be large enough to provide space for the pertinent data regarding the pupil while he remains in school—a maximum usually of 12 years. It will be helpful to have the color of cards denote sex, to have a plate number so that additional cards can be easily ordered, and to have the insert sheets and cards of different color and of the proper size.

Health records should be made available only to authorized personnel. Usually the nurse is responsible for health records and for the interpretation of data contained therein. Certain information may be of confidential nature and should be regarded as such.

SCOPE OF THE HEALTH EXAMINATION

The examination (Fig. 14) should cover the following items:
1. *Vision.* Test of visual acuity using Snellen eye charts or the Massachusetts Vision Test, and test of color perception using yarns with younger children and Ishihara-type plates for older ones.
2. *Hearing.* Test of auditory acuity using the Pure-Tone Audiometer.
3. *Nasal Passages.* Test of freedom from obstruction in the passages from deviated septum, ridges, spurs, polypi, and blocking of posterior orifices by adenoids.
4. *Teeth.* Examine teeth for obvious caries using mouth mirror and explorer, and test for malocclusions.
5. *Tonsils.* Examine tonsils for size, signs of inflammation, and infection.
6. *Glands.* Examine lymph nodes in neck for enlargement and note locations as indicative of tuberculous adenitis, teeth or tonsillar infections, or pediculosis (posterior chain). Examine thyroid for enlargement and note related signs.
7. *Skin.* Examine for signs of communicable disease and particularly for impetigo, favus, trichophyton, pediculosis, ringworm, scabies, trachoma. Note presence or absence of vaccination.
8. *Lungs.* Examine for shape, size, and mobility of chest and condition

SCHOOL					
GRADE					
DATE OF EXAMINATION					
VISION — R. EYE					
VISION — L. EYE					
VISION — COLOR					
HEARING — R.					
HEARING — L.					
NASAL — R.					
NASAL — L.					
TONSILS					
GLANDS — LYMPH					
GLANDS — THYROID					
SKIN — ERUPT					
SKIN — HYGIENE					
LUNGS					
HEART					
BLOOD					
ABDOMEN					
BONES					
MUSCLES					
POSTURE					
FEET — R.					
FEET — L.					
PUBERTY					
NERVOUS SYSTEM					
HEIGHT					
WEIGHT					
NUTRITION					
REMARKS					
INITIALED DR.					

Figure 14.

of lungs. The condition of the lungs is best determined by x-ray: this method of testing for tuberculosis is more common today and the results are striking.

9. *Heart.* Examine for size and action of heart.

10. *Blood.* Examine for anemia.

11. *Abdomen.* Examine for hernia.

12. *Bones.* Examine for evidences of rickets, and general shape of bones.

13. *Muscles.* Examine for firmness, size, and deficiency in certain muscle groups.

14. *Posture.* Examine for symmetry of body, presence of abnormal spinal curves, and body balance.

15. *Feet.* Examine for structural and functional integrity of foot arches.

16. *Puberty.* Note stage of development and record findings as P1, P2, P3.*

17. *Nervous System.* Note mental and emotional reactions in the course of the examination.

18. *Height and Weight.* Measure height and weight. These two items have been extensively exploited as indices of nutrition, but studies fail to support claims that have been made. The height-weight relation is not a good measure of nutritional status. These measures are

* P1 denotes prepubescent; P2 marks the beginnings of hair on the pubes; and P3 signifies fully developed pubic hair.

helpful in guiding individuals when a continued loss in weight occurs or when normal growth increments fail to take place. The practice of using one child as a standard or the average of many children is fallacious, since individuals have their own growth pattern. Moreover, measurements other than height, particularly breadth of pelvis, chest breadth and chest depth, are better correlates with height. Height and weight measures are valuable when employed in the assessment of nutritive status by means of the Wetzel Grid.

19. *Nutrition.* Estimation of nutritional status is to be made by the physician after consideration of many factors, such as conditions of the tissues, weight, eating habits, infections.

Items 1 to 7 may be quickly and easily secured. Items 1, 2, 7, 14, and 18 may be tested by the nurse or even by the teacher; other items require a physician and dentist.

ADMINISTRATION OF THE EXAMINATION

It is desirable to avoid the cursory, routine inspection that so often passes as an examination. An honest effort to determine the health status of the child requires time. If it is impossible to provide a medical and dental staff to examine all children, it is far better to have the nurse make a rough screening for the purpose of selecting those children to be examined by the physician and dentist in addition to certain grades that may be selected, than to examine superficially all children. In any event teacher referral is important. Since it is desirable to have parents of elementary school children present at the examination, time should be taken to talk with the parent about the health problems raised in the health record. The following arrangement of duties will be found practicable:

1. Data for the health history secured by teacher and nurse before the examination.
2. Tests of visual acuity, for color perception, and auditory acuity and measurement of height and weight made by the teacher or nurse before the examination.
3. Letter sent to parent by the superintendent or principal before the examination, requesting attendance. This should be a friendly note that indicates the importance of what is being done by the school and a warm invitation to share in a worthwhile enterprise.
4. The parent is present at the examination and the room is screened so that physician, dentist, nurse, teacher, parent, and child have privacy.
5. The teacher gives valuable aid by recording, by helping to prepare the next child for the examination, or by keeping the waiting ones ready so that unnecessary delay is avoided.

In selecting a staff for school medical work the question arises concerning the type of physician to be chosen. Shall a corps of specialists or general practitioners be employed? There are reasons favoring either plan. It is commonly agreed that the general practitioner cannot make as thorough an examination as a corps of specialists, but it is not desirable in the great majority of cases that he do so. Moreover, when specialists are employed there is the danger that children will be considered as lungs, or hearts, or noses and throats, with consequent disregard of individual personalities. Also in passing the child from one physician to another the fear that many children have of the doctor is likely to be increased rather than decreased. One of the chief values of the health examination, properly conducted, is the development of an intelligent understanding of what a professional health service really is. The child needs to learn that the physician and dentist are his friends. If the decision is made to employ a corps of specialists, some one physician must be a real chief with a sound educational viewpoint who can summarize the diagnoses of the different specialists and conduct a good inservice education program for the school physicians.

PREVENTION AND CONTROL OF COMMUNICABLE DISEASE

The communicable diseases from which children so often suffer are well established clinical entities. Most of them have given up their age-long secret of causation and the life histories of the microorganisms involved are well known. The first administrative duty in preventing and controlling communicable disease is the organization of a procedure for the detection and exclusion of cases. Obviously the physician himself will be unable to inspect personally every child, and hence a plan must be devised that involves other agencies. Parents should be the first line of defense against the spread of communicable disease and should learn the early signs of disturbance. At school the homeroom teacher is logically the best person to prevent the spread of infection and should be regarded as the second line of defense against communicable disease. Supported by the physician and nurse, parents and teachers constitute an effective administrative arm of prevention and control.

Immunization. The use of immunization measures is essential in the prevention and control of communicable disease in schools. Smallpox, diphtheria, poliomyelitis, measles, tetanus, and whooping cough are readily controllable by these means.

The occurrence of epidemics in communities that have disregarded immunization is an indication of a widespread tendency to neglect this measure. Vigilance is the price of safety. Superintendents of schools should support public health officials in promoting immunization among school children.

Under the present organization of medical care for the community, the family physician should be requested to give these treatments. For those citizens who are unable to employ a physician, immunization should be made available at clinics and dispensaries.

Any program planned for the schools should be established after consultation with local health authorities, the local medical society, and the county health officer.

There is a sharp difference of opinion regarding the free administration to all children of immunizing serums. A policy has to be developed that insures local support. A policy of immunization for all school children may be established and if parents consent, protection for the school population, after considered effort, may be made complete.

ASSESSMENT OF THE PHYSICAL DEVELOPMENT AND CONDITION OF CHILDREN

A chief function of the school physician and dentist is the periodic assessment of the physical development and physical condition of school children. Children present a number of growth disturbances, developmental abnormalities, and remediable disabilities that should be detected and corrected.

In addition to the routine examination of all pupils, the school physician must examine boys and girls trying for places on school athletic teams. The physician's decision in these cases should be accepted as final.

Children seeking working certificates usually are required by law to pass a medical examination before the papers are issued. This examination is the duty of the school physician. The physician should know the hazards of different occupations and be prepared to advise and decide accordingly.

FOLLOW-UP AND TREATMENT OF PHYSICAL DISABILITIES

School health services contain procedures for the follow-up and treatment in cases of children with remedial handicaps. One purpose of the examination is the correction of remediable conditions. A policy regarding treatment of pupils should be established and plans evolved for handling indigent cases.

As a general rule the school does not give treatments beyond first aid. This policy is justified since the school is not equipped for therapeutic services, rather than because social effort of this kind is undesirable. Nevertheless, until a policy of medical and dental care is evolved that wins the support of public opinion, it is best for schools to refrain from treatments as routine procedure and to seek the enlargement of clinical services that care for those children unable to secure private medical and dental attention.

It is obvious that more than notification is required. Hence, there has developed the practice of following up these cases by the school nurse in home visitation, or by conducting parent-nurse conferences at school. Some communities yield as many corrections without home or school visitations as others do with them. The practice, however, has other justifications. Health and economic conditions are related. The nurse serves as an excellent contact for clinics and hospitals and is quite indispensable for those families that must rely upon charitable agencies. Close cooperation of the school staff with social agencies is vital in this connection (Fig. 15).

DEPARTMENT OF HEALTH EDUCATION
Evansville Public Schools
Evansville, Indiana

________________ Date

Dear Doctor ________________

This will introduce __________________________, a student at ________________ School, who is referred to you for an estimate on dental repair work needed, through the cooperation of Courier Charities, Inc., and the Evansville Public Schools.

In the space provided below, please itemize the work needed by this child, and the cost of this repair.

If this estimate is approved, authority to proceed with the work will be sent to you, and when the case is completed, your bill should be sent to Courier Charities, Inc., in care of Dr. Elmer W. Weber, Public Schools Office, 200 N.W. Seventh Street, City.

Your cooperation in this program will be appreciated.

Yours very truly,

Nurse-Teacher

- -

Date Estimate Given ____________________

Description of Work Needed	Cost

This form should be given to the student for return to the Nurse-Teacher.

Figure 15. Form used by Evansville Public Schools in cooperation with a social agency.

Correction through Public Health Agencies. This method, either free or at nominal cost, is an approved health services procedure. Through the school nurse these services are brought to the attention of families unable to pay for the attention of a private practitioner. The policy of ability to pay is exceedingly difficult to administer and requires the full cooperation of school, health, and welfare authorities. In many instances when mothers are working, are ill, or are detained at home for various reasons, the nurse takes the child to the hospital or clinic, often makes the appointment, and is always ready to bring confidence to the uninformed parent in matters of this kind. The hospital with a clinic service or a special clinic or health center comprises the usual type that furnishes free medical care. These may be endowed institutions operating on a budget supplied by private funds or public or semipublic institutions supported in whole or in part by public funds.

SUPERVISION OF THE HEALTH OF TEACHERS AND SCHOOL EMPLOYEES

Another function of health services is the supervision of the health of teachers and school employees. Those who return to school after illness should be examined, and this is particularly important in communities where the board does not permit sick leave on full or partial salary.

The active causes of health disturbance among teachers that are related to the vocation are many. Teachers as a group reflect the hazards of a sedentary group and, although well educated, exhibit generally habitual violation of many health laws. A relation may exist between the teacher's health and the temperature of the classroom, and fatigue may be a factor in some nervous disorders. Large classes and the strain of such situations doubtless impair the health of many teachers.

Boards of education in some cities offer assistance to teachers in the correction of physical handicaps. Usually this takes the form of examinations and advice. While assistance of this kind is important, much more could be done by: (1) thorough and more rigid examinations for appointment; (2) improving the living conditions through adequate salaries; (3) offering sickness insurance on a group basis; (4) providing adequate retirement allowances; and (5) furnishing some recreational facilities and encouraging outdoor recreational activities among teachers.

THE SCHOOL NURSE

The school nurse is a valuable member of the school staff. To perform her duties satisfactorily, she needs more than the nursing training given in a hospital. The latter is indispensable, of course, but not adequate for school work. In addition, the school nurse should be graduated from an approved public health nursing course which includes instruction in the teaching of health.

Duties. The duties of the school nurse vary in different communities, and depend upon the organization of the work, the service of outside agencies, and the coordinated relationship of the departments of health and the schools. The duties and functions of the school nurse have been clearly described in *The Nurse in the School*, a report of the Joint

Committee on Health Problems in Education of the National Education Association and the American Medical Association.

Administrative Considerations in School Nursing. The administrator should select a staff whose qualifications are adequate for the functions to be performed. Some means of certification should be required. At present all states do not offer certification for school nurses. There is great variability in this matter; the only uniform requirement in the states is registration.

After selection of the nurse personnel, the position of the nurse in the school organization should be made clear. This is particularly important if the nurse is employed by the department of health and gives part-time service in the schools. Regardless of the nurse's affiliations outside the school, nursing service in schools should be under the direction of board of education officials. This is particularly important with Red Cross nurses, tuberculosis nurses, and nurses from commercial or industrial groups.

The school administrator should select a competent supervisor and arrange for all nurses to have staff instruction and professional stimulation and growth through attendance at professional meetings. National nurse organizations recommend that nurses make and fulfill definite plans to extend their education. An organization that seeks high competence in its members should have the full cooperation of administrators.

The administrator should develop a policy regarding the nurse as a teacher. In the elementary school the problem rarely arises because of the general agreement that health teaching is the duty of the classroom teacher. In secondary schools the nurse often is called upon to teach home nursing, child care, growth and development of infants, care of injuries, prevention and control of communicable diseases, causes of illness, and accident prevention in home, school, and community. At times, teaching responsibilities are placed upon the nurse for which she is not prepared. It is the function of the administrator to determine whether or not the nurse is prepared for teaching, has time to do so, and has the necessary equipment.

In preparation, the nurse should possess qualifications comparable to those held by other teachers in the school. She should be judged as are teachers by the standards of good teaching.

The time factor is difficult. When the nurse is teaching she cannot carry on individual conferences with pupils that are such a substantial part of her contribution. Often she is not prepared for teaching and hence her efforts in this direction may be much less productive than her services in the work for which she is prepared.

Equipment is essential for much of the technical instruction that the nurse might give. In the subjects listed above which the nurse may be prepared to teach, technical equipment is necessary. Home nursing and child care are really laboratory courses.

There should be a written guide for the nurse which, in schools without a nurse, should be distributed to every teacher, that states clearly and in detail exactly the procedures to follow in the administration of first aid in case of accidents and sudden illness of pupils at school. This guide should have the approval of the board of education and contain directions regarding emergency treatments, notification of parents, medical services available, and other items determined by the board.

The nurse in a secondary school has a range of duties somewhat more extensive than a staff nurse assigned to an examination and follow-up schedule. Generally, her duties fall into six fields of service. She will:

1. Be in charge of the health suite, and hence responsible for the management of emergencies. This may involve only first-aid care or reference to home or hospital.
2. Aid in health examinations, arrange schedules, notify parents, and generally organize these services. She actually conducts some part of the examination herself, under the direction of the physician.
3. Advise the principal regarding school hygiene and the hygiene of instruction, and advise teachers with reference to health problems of certain students. In some schools she is selected as the health counselor, a position that involves centering the supervision of all health activities in one person.
4. Advise the principal, when the facts warrant her comment, regarding the effect upon pupil health of social functions, examinations, pupil load, the school lunch, and other general matters.
5. Establish effective measures for the control of communicable diseases.
6. Help according to her ability in providing instruction in health and be responsible for instruction in infant care, first aid,* and care of the sick.

THE PSYCHOLOGIST AND PSYCHIATRIC SERVICE

The school psychologist ordinarily is not considered a member of the staff of the health services, yet his duties and services often are of great import to those responsible for protecting and promoting the health of children. Psychological records should be available for this purpose.

Psychiatric service is a recent development in most schools. Its purpose often is restricted to special cases in which maladjustment has occurred. The mental hygiene program should be regarded as more comprehensive than mere control of problem children.

The school psychiatrist requires special preparation. The medical degree alone is not a sufficient indication of ability to diagnose disturbance and to guide youth in the perplexing problems of adjustment.

* Nurses should have a certificate to teach first aid issued by the American Red Cross.

This service doubtless will increase markedly in the future because of growing recognition of its usefulness in harmonizing individual adjustment problems, and because the number of children requiring psychiatric guidance will increase. The growth in mental and nervous disturbances in the adult population reflects a social condition that involves more children.

RELATIONSHIP OF SCHOOL ADMINISTRATORS TO HEALTH SERVICES

It is well established in practice that superintendents and principals are the chief administrative officers of schools. They correspond to the line officers of an army and have similar executive functions. Staff officers comprise those who are in charge of specific services–in the army, officers of the medical corps, nurses, engineers, supply, and transport officials. In schools, the staff officers are the physicians, dentists, nurses, supervisors, and others.

The work of the staff is expert in several fields, but the specialized character of expert service demands integration and coordination. This is one vital function of the school administrator. It is not his responsibility to determine the value of technical matters, but, as an executive of the line, to integrate efforts so that various units of school activity contribute to a common educational purpose. This policy is well established in the school with respect to various divisions. It should be thoroughly applied in the conduct of health services. Staff officers give expert technical and educational aid in the solution of health problems; line officers coordinate the efforts of various staffs and utilize the findings of the experts so that basic purposes for which schools are conducted shall be realized. To perform his functions a superintendent or principal requires competent staff officers. And likewise, the progress of the health work depends upon the executive activity of line officers.

THE HEALTH ROOM IN SCHOOLS

Regarding the broader aspects of the health education program and its relationship to the whole child and all his educational experiences, the location of the health room should be central, preferably near the main office and the guidance office.

In the modern school building, a room for the nurse where the health services can be cared for adequately is considered as essential as classrooms, laboratories, or gymnasiums. In size it should be approximately that of a classroom with a free space at least 22 feet long to provide an area for tests of visual acuity. For the latter function, good lighting, preferably on the north side, is required and, unless natural lighting is adequate, it should be artificially illuminated. A telephone connection is indispensable. Standard equipment of desk, filing cabinet, and chairs are provided.

In addition to these general items certain special equipment includes:

1. Snellen eye charts for testing vision or materials for the Massachusetts Vision Test. For children who do not know their letters, the Snellen E chart is desirable.
2. Yarns of different colors for testing color perception, and Ishihara-type color charts.
3. A Pure-Tone or 4-A Audiometer for testing hearing.
4. Scales of approved design and equipped with stadiometer for measuring the height. The scales should be placed so that it is unnecessary to move them after they are adjusted properly. In this way the chances of faulty action are minimized.
5. A full-length mirror for postural corrections. It should be attached to the wall, although movable mirrors may be used.
6. At least one cot. This should be of rattan construction to serve the purposes of an examination table. If the latter is available, the cot may be of the canvas type.
7. An electric heater for sterilizing.
8. Running hot and cold water.
9. A supply cabinet of sanitary type. It should contain the following: scissors, forceps, and tweezers; sterile gauze and sterile absorbent cotton; adhesive plaster in several sizes; gauze roller bandages of 1- and 2-inch widths; triangular bandages and splints; wooden tongue blades, wooden applicators, and toothpicks; three glass-covered jars (one for tongue depressor, one for sterile gauze, and one for sterile cotton); two clinical thermometers; several glass medicine droppers; tincture of green soap, and a saturated solution of boric acid; tincture of iodine or Mercurochrome in glass-stoppered bottles; Unguentine or petrolatum for burns; culture tubes and sterile swabs; Lysol and 60 per cent alcohol solutions; and white enamel basins.

THE REST ROOM

The rest room is to be regarded as a part of the health-services equipment and placed in the same suite of rooms assigned to this function. Surroundings should be quiet. A north room with little light but with good ventilation is desirable. Cots equipped with blankets and mattresses, several chairs, and a table with mirror constitute the movable equipment. There should be one cot for every 200 pupils in attendance.

PROBLEMS FOR DISCUSSION

1. A new public health director takes office in a city where school health services are under the direction of the board of education. He claims this arrangement fails to provide adequate health services to school children for the following reasons:

a. The director of health education and physical education is not a medical doctor.

b. The school nurses are *nurse-teachers* and do not make home visits.

c. The public health nurses are prepared in public health and their practice of home visits gives them a broader understanding of pupil health problems.

How would you handle this problem?

2. For several years the responsibility for a school health services program in a large city was vested in the department of health and physical education. For economical reasons the responsibility for the program was relinquished to the city health department. Responsibility for liaison was charged to the appropriate assistant superintendents and building principals. This resulted in limited cooperative endeavor and the program became less effective. In an effort to improve the situation the superintendent appointed an assistant superintendent "to coordinate all pupil personnel services, including health." What would be your reaction to this problem?

3. A school athletic policy requires that each boy receive an adequate medical examination before participating in an interschool sport practice or game. The school physician and nurse are not available until the third week of football practice. Health services personnel contend that examinations given the previous June assure reasonable protection. However, coaches point out that many candidates were not examined in June and several are entering the school for the first time. They express a real concern for permitting boys to participate without a good medical examination. What are the administrative problems involved?

4. Instructors and students may implement the above with problems gained from their own experience and observation.

REFERENCES

Cromwell, G. E.: *The Nurse in the School Health Program*. W. B. Saunders Company, Philadelphia, 1963.

Hanlon, J. J.: *Principles of Public Health Administration*. ed. 3. The C. V. Mosby Company, St. Louis, 1962.

Joint Committee on Health Problems in Education of the National Education Association and the American Medical Association: *Health Education*. ed. 5. The Associations, Washington and Chicago, 1961.

Langton, C. V., Allen, R. L. and Wexler, P.: *School Health Organization and Administration*. The Ronald Press, New York, 1960.

Massachusetts Department of Public Health: *Massachusetts Vision Test*. Boston.

National Committee on School Health Policies of the National Conference for Cooperation in Health Education: *Suggested School Health Policies*. ed. 3. National Education Association, Washington, 1956.

Oberteuffer, D.: *School Health Education*. ed. 3. Harper & Row, Publishers, New York, 1960.

Szasz, T. S.: *The Myth of Mental Illness*. Harper & Row, Publishers, New York, 1961.

Turner, C. E., Sellery, C. M. and Smith, S. L.: *School Health and Health Education*. ed. 4. The C. V. Mosby Company, St. Louis, 1961.

Wheatley, G. M. and Hollack, G. T.: *Health Observation of School Children*. ed. 2. McGraw-Hill Book Company, Inc., New York, 1956.

CHAPTER 9

HEALTH INSTRUCTION

THE THEORY OF HEALTH INSTRUCTION

Bacon proclaimed to the world that knowledge is power, and the favor accorded education since that time indicates that many have thought as he did. The dame schools, supported more by religious than educational purpose, were justified in their time, but no student of education today would accept the practices in education a hundred years ago any more than he would accept without question the pronouncement of Bacon.

Knowledge is power—but power to transform, to destroy, to build, to create, or to lay waste. To set knowledge apart from purpose is to miss the reason for its development and accumulation. There is no more justification for commending *knowledge* as power than there is for praising *habit* as power, or *skill* as power, or *attitude* as power. These have value only with respect to the purposes they serve and the results they produce.

Instruction in health may be organized and systematized into a respectable body of knowledge about how to live, but it has merit as education only to the extent that it influences living. Purpose and practice are the core of it all. The assumption that knowledge of how to live confers immunity upon improper purpose or foolish practice leads to error.

It is a weakness of educational method that much traditional subject matter is taught with nothing more than an optimistic hope that it will give power to the individual. Large areas of educational content have little chance of yielding power of any kind, but nothing could be more tragic that the development of the notion that hygiene is subject matter to be learned, rather than practices to be lived. The only justifiable theory for health instruction is based upon this principle:

117

knowledge of hygiene is defined in the lives of people—its content is their habits and attitudes, its methods are the routine of daily life, its results the happier and healthier citizens of the nation.

HEALTH INSTRUCTION TOUCHES ALL OF LIFE

Since the human organism is neither mind nor body but an individual with an enormous complexity of functions, it is apparent that the terms "physical health," "mental health," and "moral health" are only convenient and conventional phrases for referring to aspects of living. Moreover, these terms are most likely to be used when referring to deviations from normal functioning; they lose their peculiar appropriateness when the individual, as a whole, lives at a high level of action in all his important personal and social relationships.

Instruction in health touches the whole of living. It is not restricted to digestion, exercise, air, and sleep, or to such morbid matters as tuberculosis, heart disease, and diabetes. It relates to ways of thinking quite as surely as to the products of thinking, to superstitions equally with scientific facts. All the responses that an individual makes as a receiving, correlating, and responding organism constitute his *life* as it goes on, and it is with this living that health deals.

HEALTH TEACHING AND THE SOCIAL GOOD

Much health teaching is egocentric. The individual is to eat this food to be strong so he can run fast, to submit to vaccination to escape smallpox for himself. Such teaching doubtless contributes, with other major emphases in educational method, to the production of individuals who are selfish, greedy, and concerned only with direct personal outcomes. It is important to remember that education as a function of the state derives its power from the people who sanction the movement because they believe in its power to make life for all better, happier, kindlier, and more significant. In this view the state exists neither as an obscure theoretical concept, nor as a force aiming to promote individual selfishness, but as communities of real persons whose lives are better because education exists. Any education that promotes development of the individual, without regard for other individuals who are also members of the state, destroys the purpose that prompted and has even supported free public education in America.

The health of the individual is important. His and others' living is the only source from which community life springs. There is no attempt to ignore the importance of the individual in the community or to accord him less importance than his status deserves. Nevertheless, his health always should be interpreted in terms of what he does with it; his strength should be valued in accordance with the causes that it serves, and his powers should be ranked with respect to the purposes to which they are dedicated. The teaching of health offers the natural, logical, and strategic approach to the teaching of citizenship, concerned as something much more important than voting at elections and singing the national anthem. It would not seem necessary to urge this social point of view were the teaching of health and other subjects properly conducted in schools.

THE MEANING OF HEALTH HABITS, SKILLS, KNOWLEDGES, AND ATTITUDES

If the implications of the preceding discussion are accepted, then all the accomplishments in healthful living are to be interpreted with respect to both personal and social outcomes. Health habits and skills are largely, although not exclusively, personal. There are no watertight compartments in these matters. Attitudes encompass both personal and social outcomes in health, with varying emphases according to the attitude and its field of operation. Scientific knowledges provide the individual and social bases for developing sound attitudes, habits, and skills.

DIRECT AND INCIDENTAL HEALTH INSTRUCTION

It has been seriously proposed at times that all health instruction in the elementary school should be incidental in character, that textbooks not only were unnecessary but also were undesirable. As a proposal for broadening the concept of health teaching in the school this view was admirable in motive but, like some other good intentions, failed to evaluate all the factors in the situation.

Except for the unusual teacher—perhaps as rare as one in 2000—that which is left to chance is neglected and soon ignored. To teach health requires constant preparation. One does not prepare daily for the incidental or the extraordinary. It is daily, faithful preparation for the ordinary that gives one power to meet the unusual and extraordinary.

Incidental teaching of health never should be confused with correlation. If the plan calls for teaching health daily in connection with science, social studies, or other fields, there will be precise content to cover, known areas to investigate, and definite objectives to seek. Incidental health teaching means merely that the teacher teaches health when the teaching situation presents a problem with an obvious health concept, but since the teaching situation presents also many other problems, the ones for which the teacher has prepared in advance usually receive a major share of attention.

In the present state of educational methods, incidental health teaching is not recommended as a prominent or exclusive means of instruction in either elementary or secondary schools.

Direct health teaching requires a plan for teaching an organized and progressively arranged body of health content in habits, skills, knowledges, and attitudes. The efficient teacher attempts to unify the experiences of the child in school. Skills learned or tools mastered in English or mathematics are not allowed to be used improperly in other lessons, and likewise the health implications at one period are to be employed in various school experiences. To pay attention to habits of industry in reading and not in arithmetic is a poor method for promoting the habit; in similar fashion, the selection of proper food for growth in the classroom is a futile academic exercise if improper food is chosen at the school lunch. Direct teaching then does not exclude correlation, or render unnecessary wise and helpful supervision during the entire school day.

METHOD IN TEACHING HEALTH

The curriculum in health instruction may be organized as units of work. If this plan is used, several important points in method of teaching health should be considered.

If the unit of work emphasizes the child-interest approach, the material is related to the interests of the particular level. Method should be so closely knit with materials that the teacher has an opportunity to encourage pupil initiative in developing the unit and to direct the experiences of the pupil. Method may then enforce the material with which a teacher works.

If the unit involves considerable activity and individual participation by pupils, a formal method of handling the class fails in the purpose and may actually lessen the effectiveness of the material. If the material requires activity, the method of instruction must allow activity. The identification of particular method with particular material is a matter of common sense and should need no extended argument.

Method should be related to objectives. It is clear that modern principles of education give increasing attention to pupil participation. Thus objectives for children, as distinguished from those of the teacher, are not to be kept by teachers hidden in a formal report or locked in the syllabus for the subject. On the contrary they are to be known by children, at times even formulated by children, and always to be sought consciously by children.

Method in teaching health should employ the local situation for source material and to secure pupil participation and judgment. The school lunch, the health examination, the football team, or an accident in school may be used as real problems for the determination of satisfactory diets, the conquest of disease, training for fitness, or appropriate safety measures.

It will be apparent then that method in health education is good or bad according to the results it secures. If pupil participation is desired, the method that secures this is good. Method is not good or bad on an *a priori* basis but with respect to its effectiveness in realizing objectives.

Activities for Teaching Health. In addition to the systematic class instruction, there are many useful activities that aid in understanding health problems. They should be carefully planned and the outcomes checked. The selection of activities depends somewhat upon local facilities, but common opportunities are field trips to dairies, markets, public health laboratories, museums, and health exhibits.

SEX EDUCATION

Every teacher of health is at some time confronted with the problem of teaching social hygiene. Because of the widespread fear of and irrational notions about sex, the teaching of social hygiene in public schools is difficult indeed. Whatever plan is used should be developed in close cooperation and with approval by parents and the school administration. The plan should be matured after thorough examination of educational literature on the subject. Such material may be obtained from the Joint Committee on Health Problems in Education of the National Education Association and the American Medical Association, and from the American Social Health Association.

THE USE OF TEXTBOOKS

Direct teaching may or may not involve the use of textbooks. There should be printed materials for children to read, and good textbooks afford the best and most economical way of providing scientific content. It is not uncommon to find schools using health texts that are old and out-of-date as regards not only the method of presenting the material and the range of the content, but also in accuracy and appropriateness. Methods employed in the modern textbook are in accord with the procedures used in textbooks in other fields.

Other Materials in Health Instruction. In addition to textbooks, other materials may be used advantageously. The development of educational films has been rapid and today there are excellent films available. Instruction by this method is valuable, and the experience of the military forces in educating large groups in technical materials supports the contention that visual materials are essential for the most efficient instruction.

Charts, diagrams, and models are essential in the high school. There will be important physiology to present, and aids of this character are helpful.

Laboratory materials such as Petri dishes with culture media, tubes for throat cultures, and biological products such as antitoxin, are exceedingly valuable for demonstration purposes by those who know how to use them.

Scrapbooks, posters, and art materials prepared by pupils afford an interesting and instructive means for graphic representation of important health concepts.

Television, although in its infancy as an educational technic, suggests broad implications for this medium worthy of thorough exploration in the years ahead.

The use of commercial advertising material raises problems. In some school systems there is an administrative policy on this matter. If the department may do as it pleases, and chooses to use commercial material, it will find that some of it is authentic, presented in good taste, and readily acceptable. Such material may be used, but it seems unwise to open the classrooms to all commercial material.

IMPORTANCE OF COOPERATION IN THE HOME

Even the most casual analysis of the practices of children that relate to health reveals that the great majority of these are carried on in the home and only a few occur during the school day. The selection and eating of food, cleanliness, ventilation, care of the mouth, sleep, play and rest, listening to the radio and watching television, and numerous other practices with health implications are primarily home and not school problems. If habits are to be formed, the home must cooperate with the school.

The basic procedures for habit formation are well known, but the best steps to parental cooperation are not always clear. The school should assume, of course, that all parents wish for their children the best possible development and are willing to help in attaining this goal. The facts are somewhat at variance with this assumption. The plain truth of the matter suggests that there is a tremendous need for parental education in the hygiene of child care. To organize a home to meet the needs of growing children curtails or hinders many adult purposes and pleasures. Parents faced with the problem of harmonizing child need with adult desire often rationalize the problem and argue themselves into believing that it is not necessary for the child to follow the rules given by the school.

The parent-teacher association is a good organization to promote parental education in health matters. More adult education classes devoted to parent education would be helpful. It is important to plan for special programs presenting health education. Some associations have found parent study groups especially helpful in educating parents.

THE TEACHER OF HEALTH IN THE ELEMENTARY SCHOOL

In the elementary school, health should be taught by the classroom teacher. As yet, she is not as well prepared to teach health as she is to give instruction in other subjects. A thorough and continuous inservice preparation of classroom teachers can contribute a great deal to the improvement of health instruction. Although teachers' colleges are improving their curricula in health education, much remains to be done.

THE TEACHER OF HEALTH IN THE SECONDARY SCHOOL

The teaching of health in the secondary school is in a confused state due largely to the notion that health can be taught exclusively by incidental contributions from social science, biology, and household arts. Failure to provide solid and complete courses in health is an administrative weakness. Five full periods of direct health teaching are recommended for at least one semester during the ninth or tenth grade, and a similar provision of time during the eleventh or twelfth grade. The needs of youth for health instruction cannot be met by the incidental contributions from other fields.

It is clear that other areas may contribute to the health understandings of secondary school students. Thus, physical education should help in the formation of habits of cleanliness, in establishing training routines, in the use of safety measures and first aid, and in the practice of measures to prevent certain communicable diseases. Household arts, biology, social studies, and general science can make rich contributions to the students they serve; topics of health significance are nutrition and foods in their many aspects of buying, preparation and use, the school cafeteria, home nursing, household sanitation, the causes of communicable diseases, structure and functions of the body, public health measures, community sources for prevention of disease, and others.

A course of health instruction for all students in high school is essential. This course should have two purposes: to present scientific materials needed for wholesome living today, and to stimulate youths to practice what they learn. From this point of view the teacher of health starts with the basic premise that health knowledge is of little value unless it is practiced, that the personal effort of every individual is a tremendous force to be captured and used for self-improvement, and that achievement in health is to be evaluated, not only by one's grasp of health knowledge but also by one's efforts to live better.

Various departments have shown an interest in the problem of teaching health, but in the past most teachers have come from physical education, household arts, and general science.

The Physical Educator as Health Teacher. The average physical educator is not adequately prepared to teach health. He has something of a science background and may possess a rich literature of illustration that appeals to youth, but without additional preparation in health education he should not be given this teaching responsibility. His chief asset is likely to be found in his ability to arouse the interest of young people in the outdoors, in athletic training and conditioning, and to be himself a fine example of vitality and energy that youth may profitably imitate.

In the small high school this person may combine the work of the two areas, but most teachers of physical education carry heavy programs that demand their full time. In some schools the physical educator is qualified to be the health coordinator and serves admirably in this post, but the fitness is personal and not dependent upon professional preparation in physical education.

The Home Economist as Health Teacher. The teacher of household arts is sometimes a suitable novice in health teaching, but she too needs additional preparation in order to do justice to the work. Like the physical educator she has a specialized preparation that covers one of the important areas of health, but her qualification in nutrition, like his in physiology of exercise, covers only a portion of the basic material of instruction. She may be personally qualified to serve as health coordinator.

The General Scientist as Health Teacher. This person is well educated in science and is prepared to present the scientific facts that are important in hygiene, but the scientific method and scientific attitude of these teachers tend to a disrespect for motives, attitudes, and those emotional forces that are basic in the management of living. In teaching health it is never enough to rely upon mortality rates and the incidence of disease; to capture the interest and enthusiasm of youth for self-improvement, ideals and challenges are more moving than erudite but dull statistics.

The Nurse as Health Teacher. Efforts have been made to develop the nurse as the teacher of health. This plan proves successful if the nurse has been especially prepared for teaching. Her work in a hospital fits her to care for sick persons but not necessarily to teach. There is always a certain risk in giving persons with a background in pathology responsibility for such a normal matter as healthful living. If the nurse has been specially prepared for this work, she may make an excellent teacher. It should be noted that the nurse may be of great help to the regular teacher particularly in first aid instruction and home care of the sick.

PROFESSIONALLY PREPARED HEALTH TEACHERS

Specific courses in health are taught best by interested persons who specialize in health education. They are best qualified to give the necessary guidance and information to students in a competent manner. Just as there are certification requirements for teachers of other subjects, there should be certification requirements for health teachers.

THE CURRICULUM IN HEALTH INSTRUCTION

A definite and well organized curriculum in health instruction is essential. Without this important instrument the teaching is likely to be faulty with respect to the selection and organization of precise objectives, adequate materials, appropriate methods of presentation, sufficient references for both teachers and pupils, and accurate means of evaluating accomplishment.

PROBLEMS FOR DISCUSSION

1. A girl's high school physical education department receives a large number of parent requests to excuse students from physical education classes. The principal accepts all excuses without question. Physical education teachers protest his action and a conference results which includes the principal, physical education teachers, and the director of health education and physical education. At the close of the discussion the principal still favors accepting excuses from activity in physical education but recommends assigning all excused students to a health instruction class. What is your reaction to this decision?
2. A senior high school curriculum planning committee considers time allotment for health instruction. After discussion the committee agrees to allow three periods per week for health instruction in the second semester of grade 11. One committee member insists that this amount of time is exorbitant because:

    Teachers of physical education teach cleanliness
    Biology includes instruction in reproduction
    Civics and Modern Problems include community health
    Girls take household arts
    The doctor and nurse care for correction of defects.

    What is your recommendation?
3. Adolescents seldom realize that they have health problems and, as a general rule, they do not understand the effect of good health practices at this age. Therefore, health instruction for the adolescent is of little value. Do you agree?
4. Instructors and students may supplement the above with problems gained from their own experience and observation.

REFERENCES

Grout, R. E.: *Health Teaching in Schools.* ed. 4. W. B. Saunders Company, Philadelphia, 1963.

Humphrey, J. H., Johnson, W. R. and Moore, V. D.: *Health Education in the Elementary Schools.* Harper & Row, Publishers, New York, 1962.

Joint Committee on Health Problems in Education of the National Education Association and the American Medical Association: *Health Education.* ed. 5. The Associations, Washington and Chicago, 1961.

Kilander, H. F.: *School Health Education.* The Macmillan Company, New York, 1962.

Langton, C. V., Allen, R. L. and Wexler, P.: *School Health Organization and Administration.* The Ronald Press, New York, 1960.

Oberteuffer, D.: *School Health Education.* ed. 3. Harper & Row, Publishers, New York. 1960.

Schneider, R. E.: *Methods and Materials of Health Education.* ed. 2. W. B. Saunders Company, Philadelphia, 1964.

Turner, C. E., Sellery, C. M. and Smith, S. L.: *School Health and Health Education.* ed. 4. The C. V. Mosby Company, St. Louis, 1961.

Willgoose, C.: *Health Education in the Elementary School.* ed. 2. W. B. Saunders Company, Philadelphia, 1964.

CHAPTER 10

HEALTHFUL SCHOOL LIVING

THE SCOPE OF HEALTHFUL SCHOOL LIVING

The conditions under which children experience schooling affect their total education. These conditions may be classified into three groups: (1) school environment including such items as building codes, building location and construction, fire protection, and custodial services; (2) classroom experiences including such items as discipline, fatigue, success and failure, reading, noise, and excitement; and (3) school organization including such items as length of the school day, divisions of the school day, home study, schedules, and school feeding.

CONDITIONS OF THE SCHOOL ENVIRONMENT

A factory-like building could be erected that provides for all the essential hygienic requirements of lighting, ease of cleaning, ventilation, and safety; but health alone is not enough. The school building should inspire young people, not only with its program but also with its form. "Magic casements opening on the foam" depend in part on how the windows open. There must be light; that is a good reason for windows. In short, the demands of hygiene and the demands of architectural beauty do not inevitably clash. To bring them together is the task of administration.

There are valid reasons for making the school plant both hygienic and beautiful. In the first place, children spend the major portion of their working hours in this environment and it is important that the school be as healthful as the skill of man can produce. On the other hand, such an environment offers unique possibilities for the education of youth. When one recalls that for many children this is the only safe and enjoyable place where they may play and experience proper sanitary

126

conditions, or where grass, flowers, and shrubs may be seen and loved, one is impressed with the need for attractive surroundings.

It is apparent that the construction and maintenance of school buildings involve both the canons of good architecture and the principles of modern education. The two are closely interwoven. Realization of this condition has been responsible for the rise of a group of architects especially qualified in planning school buildings, and a consciousness on the part of superintendents that schools are to be erected and conducted in such a manner that the various attributes of education may be realized more adequately.

State and City Building Codes. Indeed, the problems of construction have become so important educationally that numerous states and cities give consultation and advisory service to boards of education. Standards are available dealing with such matters as the size of the school plot, type of building materials to be used, adequacy of water supply, size of classrooms, amount of window area, desirable methods of heating, lighting and ventilation, and approved methods of fire protection.

Function of Experts in Recommending Standards and Supervising Maintenance. In planning new buildings, the competent school superintendent seeks the advice of those who are experts in various fields. He expects the director of research to determine the geographical centers of population which are to be served. Principals and supervisors are consulted with respect to rooms needed for types of education peculiar to the community. Experts in health education render service in recommending hygienic standards which are to be observed. School architects assume responsibility for drawing the plans and in matters pertaining to mechanical stress and strain.

Supervision of the hygienic and sanitary aspects of school maintenance is a function properly delegated to those responsible for the school health program. That this is a relatively new administrative procedure is evidenced by the fact that only in the more progressive school systems have such persons been called upon to exercise this responsibility. Reasons for this state of affairs are obvious. As the public school system develops, numerous specialists are employed to improve the effectiveness of an increasingly complex organization. Each department is expected to render the type of service for which it is best fitted. In the better teacher-education institutions, especially in graduate schools, administrators of health education and physical education receive special instructions in health supervision. These administrators are not only conversant with the health standards of building construction and operation, but they are also informed about the relationship of such standards to the educational program as a whole.

THE SCHOOL SITE

Insofar as the health of children is concerned, the two most significant factors associated with choosing school sites are: (1) the location of the building, and (2) the size of the playground area.

Location of the Building.   Upon first thought one might conclude that schools should be placed in close proximity to geographical centers of population. Careful analysis of this problem results in the generally accepted policy that whereas definite population areas are to be served, centrality may be sacrificed for adequate size and hygienic environment, or the safety of children. In the interests of enonomy, land might be purchased near large manufacturing plants, railroad yards, aviation fields, swamp land, or municipal dumping grounds, although newer concepts of education indicate that schools are to be situated where there is freedom from noise, dust, unpleasant odors, improper drainage, insufficient natural light, and safety hazards.

Size of the School Site.   In recent years the size of playgrounds has become an important factor in school planning, and support for this point of view has grown rapidly. First, automotive transportation makes possible the consolidation of small schools into larger and more efficient regional units. Second, the expanding curriculum based upon the belief that the school must educate pupils more fully and completely suggests an environment which is artistic and beautiful for the richer life experiences of youth. Third, extention of the physical education program by the addition of games and athletics for all requires adequate play space.

CLASSROOMS

A number of items must be considered in providing for the hygienic aspects of classrooms.

Size.   Health standards for the size of classrooms are based upon three factors: (1) the number of pupils to be accommodated; (2) the number of square feet of floor area per pupil; and (3) the cubical contents of the room. The average classroom is planned for 35 to 40 pupils. It is approximately 28 feet by 30 feet by 12 feet. Primary classrooms have approximately 1000 square feet. Besides taking into account the health needs of children, these standards aim to facilitate academic instruction.

Walls and Ceilings.   It is desirable for walls of classrooms to be treated acoustically, either with acoustic board, cinder block, or plaster. The type selected should permit painting of the walls.

Oil paint, giving a dull finish, is recommended because of its durability, light-reflecting quality, decorative effect, and ease of cleaning. When using oil paint, a slightly roughened plaster is preferable to a smooth hard surface, since the latter reflects light without diffusion, often resulting in a glare which is harmful to the eyes of students.

The color of walls and ceiling is important. While neutral tones of gray are frequently recommended, rooms thus treated present a drab and unattractive appearance. The most luminant neutrals are obtained by combining the primary colors red, blue, and yellow with white. A trace of yellow with white gives the egg-shell tint approved for ceilings, whereas a slight touch of green, blue, or yellow with white represents a satisfactory covering for walls. An abrupt contrast between the color of walls and ceilings is to be avoided. Under average conditions each classroom needs to be repainted every fifth year.

Floors. Some persons believe that hard-wood floorings are best for classrooms. When properly fastened to a sound foundation and attached to felt-lined screeds, the wood flooring is resilient, easily cleaned, attractive, practically noiseless, and forms a satisfactory base for school furniture. Advocates of asphalt tile and linoleum find great merit in the smooth surfaces produced, the absence of dangerous splinters, and the ease of cleaning. It is important to lay these coverings firmly and tightly.

Kindergarten floors covered with battleship linoleum or similar material insure a comfortable and sanitary play surface for younger children.

School Furniture. Adjustable and movable school seats and desks are recommended. The next best plan, in the interest of cleaning economy, is to select the single pedestal combination desk and seat which can be adjusted to the desired height.

Common faults in school seating are: (1) seats too high and too deep for pupil; (2) desks too high; (3) desks too close or too far away from pupil; and (4) the unit not adjusted to the growth changes of the pupil. The rule for adjusting desk height to seat height is: *When the pupil is sitting erect, with arms in writing position, the desk top should be in the plane of the under side of the forearms.* In adjusting desk to seat the edge of desk next to pupil should overlap front edge of seat by 2 inches. A desk slant of 15 degrees is preferable to a flat top.

Some one person in each school must be charged with the responsibility of properly adjusting classroom seats. In the correct sitting position, the feet rest easily on the floor with no pressure under the knees.

Chalkboards. In the modern school "board-work" is greatly minimized. As an instructional technic, use of the chalkboard by children is not only time-consuming, but numerous disciplinary problems arise as a result of this activity. Quite apart from its teaching value, extensive use of chalkboards is condemned for hygienic reasons. Millions of chalk dust particles are breathed into the lungs of children. Herein lies an important health hazard readily appreciated by educational or industrial hygienists. Moreover, the old-style blackboard absorbs great quantities of light; or if improperly cleaned, it may become shiny and reflect the sun's rays directly into the eyes of pupils.

The trend in schoolroom construction is to install chalkboards in light pastels in place of blackboards. Whatever the kind of material used, boards should not be placed between windows; they should be fastened to the front wall or attached to the wall separating the room from the inner corridor. In some schools chalkboards have been replaced with tack boards. They serve well the limited uses made of them and are free from chalk dust and glare. For children to use the board while maintaining a normal standing position, it is recommended that the chalk tray be 24 inches high for the first and second grades; 26 inches high for the third and fourth grades; and 28 inches high for the fifth and sixth grades.

REST ROOMS

Rest rooms for each sex are essential in all school buildings of four or more classrooms. Some states have legislation or codes regulating this item. They should be placed within the health suite or located conveniently to toilet and first-aid facilities. Supervision may be provided from the administrative office if full-time health services personnel are not available. Rest rooms are desirable for teachers as well as for pupils.

CORRIDORS

The width of corridors usually is governed by state or local regulations. As a safety precaution these regulations need rigid enforcement. A satisfactory standard provides main corridors from 8 to 10 feet wide in elementary schools; main corridors approximately 12 feet wide, and subsidiary corridors of 8 to 10 feet in width in secondary schools. More space is desirable where lockers for clothing are arranged along or in the walls.

LAVATORIES

As used here, the term "lavatory" refers to provisions for washing the hands and face; toilet facilities are discussed in the section which follows.

Contrary to popular opinion, few health standards relating to lavatories have been established which are based upon scientific investigation. In fact, this problem does not lend itself to experimental technics now available. For example, it is difficult to determine the incidence of communicable disease transmission traceable to washing the hands in a bowl that has been used improperly by others.

There are, however, principles of personal cleanliness which enjoy the support of leading health educators and sanitarians. It is upon these principles that the following standards are based.

There is practically unanimous agreement that lavatories should be placed near all toilet rooms. Recommendations advise one lavatory in each primary classroom and in each kindergarten room. In new buildings it is recommended that both the lavatories and toilets be incorporated in a single unit with the seats and urinals on one side of the room and the wash bowls on the opposite side. Hot and cold running water, liquid or powdered soap kept in easily operated containers, paper towels, and a mirror are essential. The use of common towels is not permitted in most states. Paper towel disposal cans should be open. In elementary schools one lavatory to 30 pupils, and in secondary schools one to 50 pupils, are considered adequate. The recommended heights of lavatories are: kindergarten 18 inches; elementary grades 18 to 21 inches; junior high school 21 inches; and senior high school 30 inches.

As a part of the health instruction program, children should form the habit of washing the hands thoroughly with soap after using the toilet, before eating, or whenever the hands become unclean from handling art or physical education equipment.

TOILETS AND URINALS

Practically all standards now available represent opinions of sanitarians and hygienists who have given careful thought to this important problem. That few schools constructed years ago embody these principles is evidenced by the critical writings of health educators who survey existing conditions in many cities.

DRINKING WATER

In most communities the purity of drinking water is safeguarded by the board of health. If there is any doubt in the matter, bacteriological tests should be made and steps taken to rectify unhealthful conditions.

Some rural communities still have the pump and bucket problem. The use of paper cups removes some of the danger of contagion but attention to the source of water is an important obligation of local authorities. The selection of well designed fountains, correct installation, and the proper use of this equipment present educational problems worthy of consideration by school authorities.

HEATING AND VENTILATION

Two important factors of health supervision are heating and ventilation. Partly owing to tradition, but more especially to the interrelationship of these two items, they have been considered together in most of the recent literature.

Acceptance of the policy favoring public education led quickly to the formulation of standards* pertaining to the heating and ventilation of school buildings. In their evolution, these standards have undergone numerous modifications. At first, chief consideration was given to the thermal aspects of the problem; second, speculation with respect to the deleterious effect of carbon dioxide caused a shifting of emphasis from temperature to the chemical composition of air; and third, scientific investigation has shown that physical qualities associated with air movement and humidity, especially the former, are quite as important as

* State and local building codes give proper standards.

temperature and much more significant than the amount of carbon dioxide present.

Scientific investigation of the problem of heating and ventilation of school buildings discloses certain facts. First, variations in the heredity and environment of individual children complicate the problem. Thus differences in metabolism, blood composition, the distribution of blood supply to the body surface, and clothing make one person too cool, another person comfortable, and still another person too warm, even though all of them are exposed to identical conditions of heating and ventilation. Since it is impossible to accommodate each individual, the best procedure is to strive for conditions most comfortable and healthful for the majority of children. Second, it is helpful to remember that similar effects can be produced by different combinations of air factors. It is common knowledge that a high temperature may be modified by greater air movement; that a high temperature is accentuated by increased humidity which prevents normal evaporation, or neutralized by decreased humidity; and that at intermediate temperatures air movement and humidity are less important.

Viewed from the preceding discussion, modern science indicates that the prime factors of heating and ventilation are temperature, humidity, and air movement. In general, the carbon dioxide content of the air can be ignored.

Although expired air is not poisonous, in an unventilated room it may possess an esthetically unpleasant odor which diminishes appetite and arouses personal discomfort. For this reason the problem of sufficient change of air is important.

More recently the old problem of bacteria in air has become prominent, and the behavior of viruses in air raises the question of how to control air purity. The use of aerosols is promising; the administrator should follow developments in this area so that possible application to school conditions may be made.

In general there are two plans of heating classrooms, direct and indirect, and two plans of ventilating them, mechanical and window-gravity. *Direct heating* consists of locating radiators in the classrooms. *Indirect heating* involves placing the heating surfaces outside the classroom, usually in the basement, and conducting warm air to rooms by means of ducts or flues. *Mechanical ventilation* is obtained when fresh air enters the basement and is forced into the room through flues by means of fans or blowers. Sometimes the same flues are used for mechanical ventilation and indirect heating. *Window-gravity ventilation* consists of admitting outdoor air through windows and dispelling it through exhaust flues located in the opposite wall of the classroom.

No single standard code for heating and ventilation has yet been developed and approved for all schoolroom conditions. Special problems associated with the local environment may suggest one system as being superior to all others for that community. Nevertheless, it is possible to suggest certain general principles based upon experimentation and accepted generally by sanitarians and heating experts. These should be adapted to local conditions.

During the cold season of the year the most desirable temperature of the classroom ranges from 65° to 75° F. Experimental evidence indicates that a temperature deviation of 2° or 3° above or below 70° F. fails to cause a measurable influence upon the incidence of respiratory diseases, and in fact fluctuations between these limits are preferable to uniformity. Even though thermostatic heat regulation is provided, each room is to be equipped with a thermometer placed at the sitting height of pupils.

Humidifiers infrequently are found in modern school buildings. Doubtless excessive moisture or dryness are uncomfortable, especially when combined with unusual temperatures, although under normal conditions it is not apparent that humidity makes much difference. In fact, unhumidified rooms often are more agreeable, probably because of greater fluctuation in the moisture content of air and unhumidified air approximates outdoor conditions.

With respect to the amount and change of air in classrooms, research fails to support the claim that mechanical ventilation is essential, except in schools where outdoor noise, dust, or odors prevent opening the windows. It appears to make little difference, insofar as respiratory diseases are concerned, whether children are supplied with 15 or 30 cubic feet of air per minute, or whether this air is supplied by fan, a unit ventilator, or by the window-gravity system. A slight fluctuating air motion probably increases personal comfort, although drafts are to be avoided.

AIR CONDITIONING

In recent years problems of *air conditioning* confront educational administrators. Success of this venture in theaters, public buildings, railway cars, airplanes, offices, stores, and homes has led to its use in schools.

Doubtless the best results will be obtained by installing a central heating, ventilating, filtering, and humidifying plant. In winter the apparatus provides heat and the proper humidity. In summer the same central plant cools the air and controls the humidity. During both winter and summer adequate circulation and filtration of air insure correct ventilation. Standard commercial concerns guarantee desired temperature and humidity within the limits of 1° F. and 1 per cent humidity, respectively.

Appropriate recognition should be given to the contributions of engineers in this field. Continued interest and cooperation in the development and refinement of air-conditioning processes will greatly benefit society in providing a larger measure of happiness and comfort to those who are compelled to spend long hours in an environment of unregulated temperature.

LIGHTING*

The lighting of schoolrooms is an important factor in the comfort and efficiency of occupants. Increasing attention is being given by architects, illuminating engineers, and school administrators to the construction and equipment of school buildings to provide proper illumination for the widely varying visual tasks encountered in the classroom. There are so many variables in site location, orientation of the building, type of construction, and equipment that no simple formula is possible that insures proper illumination. Certain basic facts, however, may be stated.

If daylight is to be used efficiently, the window area should be one-fifth to one-fourth of the floor area, the windows should extend as near to the ceiling as structurally possible, and the room width should not exceed twice the window height. With the trend toward lower ceilings and wider classrooms, the usefulness of daylight is rapidly diminishing. Furthermore, no shading device which requires manual manipulation by a room occupant can be considered desirable. However, since most classrooms today are equipped with window shades or venetian blinds, the satisfactory control of sky and sun glare depends on the diligence of the teacher.

The problem of classroom lighting should include consideration of the amount of light necessary for the visual tasks and the uniformity of its distribution over the desk area. Even more important is the quality of light which includes a minimum of direct glare from fixtures and windows, maximum reduction of reflected glare, and the reflectance of room surfaces including ceiling, walls, floor, chalkboards, and trim. This will determine the brightness differences to which the eyes will be exposed in the total visual field.

The total visual field extends from the visual axis approximately 50° upward, 70° downward, and laterally about 180° (Fig. 16). With in-

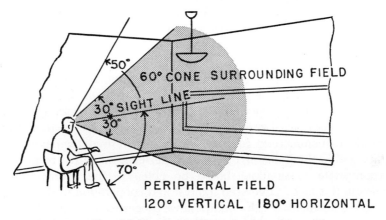

Figure 16.   Visual fields, showing line of sight and cone of vision.

* Credit for this section belongs to Wilson Younglove, Senior Engineer, Baltimore Gas
  and Electric Company, Baltimore, Maryland.

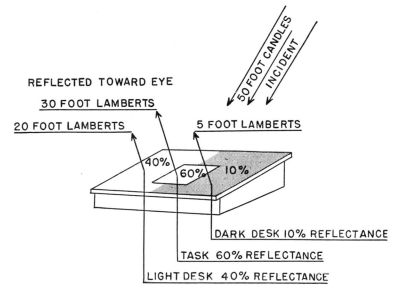

Figure 17.   Footlamberts are the product of footcandles multiplied by the reflection factor. They indicate the effectiveness of illumination on a task.

formal seating which permits the most efficient use of the classroom space, every surface in the room must be considered as part of the visual field.

The ability of a surface to reflect light which is incident upon it is called reflectance and is expressed as the ratio of the reflected to the incident light. Therefore the reflectance determines the brightness of a surface. The unit of brightness measurement is a *footlambert* and is equal to the incident light (footcandles) multiplied by the reflectance (Fig. 17). Brightness is a dominant factor in seeing.

The reflectances of room surfaces for a comfortable visual surrounding should conform to the values shown in Fig. 18 (reflection factor is reflectance expressed in per cent). All finishes should be nonglossy. With these values (Fig. 18), and with proper design of lighting fixtures and control of daylight, the brightness differences in the visual field should conform to the brightness ratios shown in Table 1. Therefore, the eyes

Table 1. *Limits of Brightness Ratios in Schoolrooms*

	RATIO
Between the central field and adjacent surfaces such as between task and desk top	1 to $\frac{1}{3}$
Between the central field and remote darker surfaces such as between task and floor	1 to $\frac{1}{10}$
Between the central field and remote brighter surfaces, such as between task and ceiling	1 to 10
Between luminaires and windows and surfaces adjacent to them in the visual fields	20 to 1

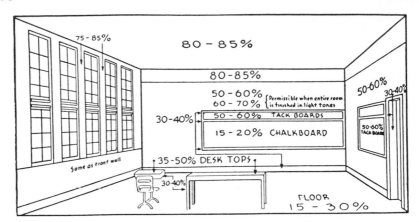

Figure 18. Reflection factors desirable for schoolroom surfaces. (*American Standard Guide for School Lighting.* Illuminating Engineering Society, 51 Madison Ave., New York. Courtesy of publishers.)

do not have to adapt for widely different conditions and the physical energy wasted in the process of adaptation is minimized. The ceiling should be flat white. The walls should be in pastel shades, the specific color being a matter of taste. The floors should be at least as light as freshly finished oak. It is important that desk tops have a nonglossy surface to minimize reflected glare.

The design and placement of lighting fixtures is an engineering function and requires considerable experience to provide maximum visual comfort. The viewing zone of the fixtures in the angles from 45° to 85° above the nadir, which is at the observers feet, is particularly important to reduce direct glare. Artificial illumination should be adequate for daytime use of the school and for community purposes at night which comprise a large part of the service required in a modern plant.

The quantity of light or footcandles which is required varies with the difficulty of the task. Studies indicate that the greater part of a student's visual time is spent on tasks which require 60 to 100 footcandles for comfortable, efficient seeing. Duplicated material and pencil writing are probably the most difficult tasks in standard classrooms. Special rooms used for sewing, lip-reading, drafting, and others require more light for equal visual efficiency.

Lighting systems are divided into five categories depending upon the amount of light directed above and below a horizontal plane through the fixture (Table 2). Each system has qualities which may match the requirements of a given situation. The first consideration should be whether the system meets the requirements for visual comfort and efficiency in the given situation.

Indirect lighting is dependent on a ceiling of high reflectance and produces diffused, practically shadowless lighting. However, for illumination levels above 40 to 50 footcandles the ceiling may become uncomfortably bright.

Table 2.   *Percentage of Light Distributed*

	UPWARD	DOWNWARD
Indirect	90 to 100	10 to 0
Semi-indirect	60 to 90	40 to 10
General diffuse	40 to 60	60 to 40
Semi-direct	10 to 40	90 to 60
Direct	0 to 10	100 to 90

Semi-indirect lighting is also dependent on high ceiling reflectance. Because of the translucency of the fixtures, they blend with the ceiling and are more comfortable and less conspicuous. Unless repainting can be scheduled on at least a five-year basis, which is seldom possible on a school maintenance budget, indirect and semi-indirect lighting systems are not practicable except in special applications such as classrooms for the visually handicapped.

General diffuse or direct-indirect systems are most generally used with fixtures suspended on at least 12-inch stem hangers in order to spread the upward light as evenly as possible over the ceiling. If egg-crate louvers are used on the bottom of the fixtures they should be designed so as to shield the eyes from view of the lamps at an angle of 45° above a horizontal sight line. Reflected glare is more of a problem and it is very important to avoid glossy tasks and desk tops.

With ceilings as low as 8 feet it is impracticable to suspend the fixtures. They are mounted directly on the ceiling and semi-direct lighting results. Brightness ratios listed in Table 1 generally will be exceeded, and reflected glare is an even greater problem. The ceiling is generally dark and the brightness of the fixtures exceeds the ceiling brightness by more than 20 to 1 and may go as high as 100 to 1.

Direct lighting results when troffers are recessed in the ceiling or when industrial fixtures without up-light are used. Shadows are harsh and both direct and reflected glare increases.

Fluorescent lighting is generally used in classrooms because the tubes give more than twice as much light per watt of electricity used, although the first cost is considerably higher. Also the tubes have rated life expectancy of more than 10 times that of incandescent lamps and therefore reduce maintenance cost.

FIRE PROTECTION

The huge toll in human lives, not to mention enormous economic losses, stands as a stark reminder of the need for school buildings constructed of fire-resistive material. Legislation in most states governs this factor as well as the erection of fire escapes and the provision for fire drills and instruction.

Efficient school administration contributes to the safety of children by the strict observance of such laws and by cooperation with the local fire department in abiding by its ordinances.*

Most school buildings of any size, in addition to being fire resistive, are equipped with one or more standpipes of at least 3 inches in diameter extending from the basement to the roof. On each floor there are two valves attached to the standpipe, one containing the standard thread for connecting the fire department 2½-inch hose, the other for the 100 feet of 1½-inch hose which is folded on a rack adjacent to the standpipe, or wound around the reel in a permanent fire cabinet attached to the wall.† In addition, each cabinet should be equipped with a chemical fire extinguisher. In fact, at least one fire extinguisher should be provided for every 2000 square feet of floor area. Extra equipment, such as wool blankets, preferably flame-proofed, should be in evidence in laboratories, woodworking shops, or other rooms where easily inflammable materials are used.

On account of the large number of school fires which start in basements, storage closets, and shops, rigid regulations should be in force regarding the disposal of oily cloths and the storage of turpentine, paint, and other inflammable materials. As an additional safety measure, automatic sprinklers are frequently installed in these rooms.

All outside doors leading to the street or to fire escapes are to be equipped with panic bolts which permit exit by a slight pressure such as would be produced by the weight of the average child. Clearly marked and illuminated signs should indicate the fire exits. Self-closing fire doors situated at points of greatest probable danger and especially near the heating plant are added safeguards.

Every school building should have an electric fire-alarm system attached to a circuit which is separate from the ordinary call bells. Responsible persons shall sound the alarm for drills or in case of a real fire. In addition, the school should be equipped with a signal for calling the local fire department. Each school principal should be held accountable for determining a plan whereby all classrooms and laboratories may be vacated in the quickest time compatible with safety. Even in large schools the maximum time for leaving the building is three minutes. Every pupil and teacher should know exactly what he is to do or where he is to go in case the fire gong rings at any time throughout the day.

Fire Drill Regulations. It is important for every school system to practice fire drills and to adopt precise directions regarding them. The following include the important items in the administration of fire drills; fire drills monthly during the school year; fire-alarm signal distinctive and uniform; half the drills to be obstructed, with the obstructed exit changed each time; drills called at different and unusual times; directions for procedure in drills posted in every classroom; ready access to the fire-alarm key by all teachers, custodians, and clerks as well as prin-

* Fire drills: see Chapter 11, Safety Education.
† Local or state fire regulations may require different standards.

cipals; during drills exit doors to be opened by children who reach them first and held open by them, both doors of double doors opened; absolute control of the drill by teachers; teachers and pupils pass without hurry; pupils not permitted to talk; and school personnel assigned to inspect basement and toilets when alarm sounds in order to secure complete evacuation of the building.

Special regulations are essential to govern the exit and safety of pupils engaged in physical education activities. Those clothed in physical education uniforms should proceed immediately to the nearest exit when the alarm sounds. Pupils who are in the dressing area or swimming pool should clothe themselves in any available garments and proceed to the nearest exit. An allotment of towels, twice the number of the largest class, always should be available on the pool deck, in close proximity to the exit.

It is desirable to alert physical education teachers whenever a fire drill is to be called so that they may not require students to leave the building during inclement weather. When the alarm sounds and no notice has been given, physical education teachers should comply fully with fire drill regulations. In these instances safe shelter areas should be provided in close proximity to the school. These may consist of annex buildings, churches, business establishments, and private homes.

CUSTODIAL SERVICES

Viewed from the standpoint of providing a healthful environment for children, the custodian is one of the most influential members of the school personnel. Sometimes incumbents of this position, both men and women, possess few qualifications for the office except that they work for a miserly salary, have a friend who will "speak a good word for them" with some member of the board of education, or belong to the political group which controls the community. This kind of custodian, whatever else his qualifications, is not apt to render good service to the school.

Altogether too frequently the custodian has "good connections" with as much authority in school matters as the principal or the supervisor of school building sanitation. Even superintendents have been known to resign because of disagreements with the man who has charge of the school furnace or mows the school lawn. Fortunately this extreme condition is not widespread.

Attempts have been made to elevate the custodian to a position of some educational prominence, and to make him feel that he is a part of the school personnel. To this end standards are available for school custodians, and courses in the subjects are given in several teacher-education institutions. Most counties in California conduct annual workshops for school custodians.

Approximate standards have been proposed for custodians, as follows:

Education. To read printed instructions and reports carefully, all employees shall have completed the eighth grade or its equivalent.

Preparation. This may be obtained by pursuing summer courses, laboratory courses, or lecture courses, or by serving an apprenticeship.

Health. Employees should be free from chronic or communicable diseases and frequent colds, maintaining such robust health that they seldom are absent from duty.

Moral Character. Association with children during the period of great habit formation, makes it imperative that employees demonstrate desirable traits of moral conduct.

Personal Traits. Every custodian should be courteous, obliging, tactful, self-controlled, and able to cooperate with teachers and pupils with varying dispositions. He recognizes the principal as the responsible person for that building. In his dealings with school personnel he must be congenial but avoid familiarity.

Personal Appearance. He gives close attention to cleanliness and neatness.

Scientific Attitude. He develops a scientific attitude toward his work, and by experimentation and sound judgment seeks continually for improved methods of serving the school efficiently.

Square Feet of Area per Custodian. This approximates 15,000 to 17,000 square feet.

CLEANING

There are standard procedures for cleaning, and public opinion supports an administrative policy that maintains clean and attractive buildings and grounds. In the maintenance of a wholesome and sanitary school plant, the cooperation of students is most important and both precept and example should be used to develop in students an attitude of respect for property, cleanliness of buildings and grounds, and sanitary practices in the use of them.

Care of Floors. The technic of caring for floors varies with the kind of material used in their construction. Schools equipped with a vacuum cleaner system can maintain excellent conditions of cleanliness in classrooms by daily cleaning after school. In the installation of the vacuum cleaner system, inlet valves are placed so that a 40-foot hose reaches all parts of the classroom. Strenuous use of corridors and stairs indicates that they need cleaning twice daily, or more often in inclement weather.

Washing Windows. Under normal conditions windows should be washed on the outside during vacation periods and on the inside at least once a month.

Care of Chalkboards and Erasers. With a reasonable amount of use chalkboards need to be cleaned thoroughly at least once each week. Chalkboards should be cleaned by custodians, not by teachers or children.

In the average classroom it is necessary to remove the chalk dust from erasers at least twice each week. Many school systems have found it desirable to supplant hand methods by a combination rumbling, brushing, and vacuum machine. The latter method removes a much higher percentage of chalk dust, especially near the bottom of the grooves. Teachers should not be expected, or children allowed, to clean erasers.

Cleaning Gymnasium Mats.   Strangely enough, few teachers of physical education or custodians realize the importance of keeping canvas-covered gymnasium mats free from dirt or unsightly spots. It is not uncommon to find teachers who allow students to drag this equipment across the floor, or custodians who take pride in sweeping and dusting classrooms but who allow mats to remain in a deplorable condition. Cooperative effort on the part of these two persons is essential. First, a well qualified teacher will insist that mats be carried to and from the place where they are needed or that they be transported on trucks provided for this purpose. Second, an efficient custodian will vacuum them frequently. Plastic-covered mats or those of foam-rubber composition clean easily. Use a damp cloth on plastic surfaces, and a special detergent, recommended by manufacturers, on foam-rubber types.

Lavatory and Toilet Sanitation.   A superintendent of schools once remarked that the efficiency of custodial service can be judged by the sanitary condition of the toilets.

Experts agree that the floor of the lavatory-toilet room should be composed of some impervious material and sloped toward a convenient drain. Whereas the floors of classrooms are cleaned daily, it may be necessary to flush the floor space in front of urinals more frequently. In addition to the flushing process, toilet rooms need to be scrubbed at least once a month with hot water containing a strong solution of an effective cleansing agent.

All wash basins, toilet bowls, seats, and urinals must be cleaned thoroughly at least once a day; the toilet bowls, seats, and urinals with a good disinfectant. The use of a deodorant is a lazy way of covering up inferior work; this may destroy the unpleasant smell but the unsanitary conditions which cause the odor still remain. Sanitary conditions of locker and shower rooms in many public schools are extremely bad; there is no excuse for the gross neglect of simple sanitary rules.

CLASSROOM EXPERIENCE

Experiences in the classroom may stimulate and strengthen a child or depress and impair his functions. Matters of discipline, fatigue, reading, writing, noise, excitement, and sedentariness have large implications for health.

Discipline.   The teacher may succeed or fail in developing healthful and wholesome attitudes among children toward their tasks and responsibilities. Much depends upon the philosophy of the teacher. What is he trying to do? Are there continual efforts to correct faults according to adult-conceived and promulgated standards or is there the purpose to help children develop standards of behavior which they themselves help to form and for the enforcement of which they assume responsibilities? The latter viewpoint helps to create in the classroom an atmosphere of cooperation, joy, and satisfaction, and results in the development of a wholesome and responsible personality.

It is good hygiene for children to learn early in life to be responsible for their acts, to face frankly their failures, and to react on the basis of facts. Since the proper end of all discipline is self-direction, the constant goal for the teacher should be self-discipline.

Fatigue. Many factors enter into the production of fatigue in children. The teaching may be uninspired, the program monotonous, or outside activities too many and too strenuous. Signs of fatigue are outbursts of anger or crying, irritability, pallor, cold hands or feet, and digestive disturbances. In older children excessive home study and late hours from whatever cause contribute to the condition.

Success and Failure. Accomplishment has direct relationships to the emotional life of the individual. Classroom experiences should provide satisfaction, but it is a mistake for the individual to develop the notion that he must always succeed and that failure is intolerable. Some failure at some time is the experience of every person. One must learn how to meet it. Failure tends to destroy self-confidence and consistent failure is unwholesome, so that placement of pupils and assignment of tasks have large meanings.

Noise and Excitement. The classroom should be a quiet and orderly place with an atmosphere of happy purpose. Noise tends to produce excitement and voices are raised in the effort to be heard. To control noise in school, music and typwriting rooms should have double partitions, windows should fit tightly, hydraulic door checks should prevent slamming, movable furniture should have noiseless gliders, teachers should wear rubber heels, and the handling of all objects should be done quietly.

Sedentariness. It is desirable for growing children to be active. The necessity to sit still is artificial without value in itself. Free movement of children in school lessens the chance of boredom that may result from too little activity.

The Hygiene of Reading. Vision is used so intensively in the classroom that special attention must be given to its hygiene. With reference to reading, good lighting, size of type, length of line, kind of print, and quality of paper are important.

The following items may be considered in the selection of textbooks: (1) the size of type should be large enough to enable children to read easily without eyestrain—sizes of type* recommended are:

---

* Size of type is expressed in points—the printer's measure of the height of letter. There are 72 points to the inch; the more points the larger the letter.

AGE OF READER	SIZE OF TYPE
Under 7	24 point
7–8	18 point
8–9	14 point
9–12	12 point
Over 12	10 or 11 point

(2) kind of print—plain black type is best; (3) length of line—a long line causes fatigue of the eye muscles; for accuracy and eye comfort a line of 100 mm. is best; (4) kind of paper—it should be slightly off-white, without gloss, and heavy enough to be opaque.

Individual Differences. In addition to the preceding factors, methods of teaching affect the health of school children. Each child is to be studied as an individual personality, and not only in relation to statistical averages obtained from intelligence or achievement tests. Provisions for individual differences compatible with personal emotional traits, intellectual capacity, and physical status are indications of efficient instruction. In the interests of developing a healthful personality, children must be allowed to progress in school at varying rates of speed. Gifted children may be encouraged to choose extra work; and in the same manner curtailed programs should be advised for those with certain health limitations.

Fear is a destructive emotion and often is the underlying cause of maladjustments in children. It is the responsibility of every teacher and administrator to teach and to organize so that fear associated with failure, ridicule, sarcasm, and punishment is prevented. Some children show fear very readily and are unusually sensitive to the surrounding conditions of the classroom.

CONDITIONS OF THE SCHOOL ORGANIZATION

Any arrangement of the school day must be regarded as unhygienic if it overtaxes children either mentally or physically, or fails to provide satisfaction by a proper balance between work, play, rest, and the taking of nourishment.

School Food Service. Health factors associated with the school lunch are both singularly important and relatively numerous. Quite apart from matters of child growth and development, the school lunch program is of interest to the administrator because it represents one of those marginal activities between clearly defined functions of the health services, healthful school living, and health instruction. As a means of correcting conditions of underweight among school children, the school lunch becomes primarily a matter of the health services, since this division is concerned with things done to the child to improve his health. On the other hand, the school lunch is like heating or ventilation in that each of them represents a factor in the child's environment which vitally affects his well-being. Insofar as the school lunch deals with environment, it pertains to healthful school living. Moreover, it is known that one of the best ways to develop correct eating habits among children is to use the school lunch as a *life experience;* hence the food service becomes a teaching aid in the program of health instruction.

Practically all health experts agree that a hot lunch at noon is desirable for every child, although there is some doubt about allowing everyone to partake of the *mid-session* lunch. As planned originally the mid-session lunch, consisting of milk or chocolate milk and crackers, was supposed to assist undernourished children to gain in weight. In many communities the venture became so popular that a large percentage of children in the lower grades availed themselves of the opportunity offered. Opinion is divided regarding the desirability of this practice, but it is agreed that mid-session lunches are desirable for those who have been recommended for this service by the examining physician.

The educational potentialities of the school lunch are several: (1) the food served; (2) the lunchroom itself; (3) the time allowed for eating; (4) the economics of the project; (5) the facilities and character of the furnishings; (6) the student participation in rules of conduct; and (7) the health supervision of lunchroom employees. If normal health is to be encouraged, the food must be of good quality, properly prepared, and served attractively—not purchased from questionable sources, cooked in a haphazard manner, and "thrown" at children. Only food suitable for the growing child is to be used. Some variety is essential in order that the pupil may develop skill in the selection of a balanced diet. There should be close correlation between the classroom instruction in nutrition and the selection of food by children at lunch time.

Plans for new buildings usually provide a suitable room for school lunches; occasionally the lunchroom is located in the basement where inadequate artificial light, plain concrete floors, unfinished walls and ceilings, rough tables, and long coarse benches produce an altogether unsatisfactory environment. The advocacy of "all-purpose" rooms to serve the needs of assemblies, dramatics, music, physical education, and cafeteria is a tragic blunder. Acceptable standards demand a well appointed lunchroom which is bright and sunny, and equipped with modern conveniences such as up-to-date cooking utensils, attractive display counters, sanitary trays, small tables, and individual chairs so that the child may eat his food seated comfortably without crowding.

The school program is to be planned in such a way that every child is given at least 20 minutes for the noonday meal. This is a minimum and provides only for time to select and eat an adequate lunch. For passing to and from the cafeteria and for use of the toilet and washing of the hands another 10 minutes is required. Moreover, supervision is necessary to prevent pupils from hurriedly eating their food and leaving at once for the playground or study hall. Various types of supervision may be employed: (1) teachers assigned to table groups; (2) one or more teachers assigned to each lunch period; and (3) student monitors supervised by the student council. The school lunch should be a place where desirable eating habits and table manners are formed, although too often the child is allowed to develop food habits disapproved by society.

Under present standards of public education pupils are expected to pay for the food they consume. This does not mean that the project is to be conducted for profit, but prices are fixed to cover the initial food cost, with employees and upkeep paid out of regular school funds. In most schools there are a few children who have no money for food; provision should be made for them inconspicuously, by providing tickets or other means of letting them appear to pay, the cost being assumed by the board of education, a local voluntary organization such as the parent-teacher association, or a luncheon club.

Participation by students in the formulation of rules of behavior in the lunchroom is important for their own development as citizens as well as for success in maintaining an orderly and happy place.

It is essential that all food handlers employed in the school lunch be examined to eliminate those with communicable diseases.

In large schools the noon lunch should be managed by a woman qualified in nutrition, in the preparation and service of food, in business management, and in education. In small rural schools a good housekeeper may be acceptable.

The manager in charge of the school lunch in each school should be a member of the health council, a member of the social committee of the school, and a member of the household arts staff if this field is represented in the curriculum.

Length of the School Day. For the elementary school, one session is recommended in kindergarten and primary grades. Beginning with the third grade two sessions may be held. Whatever the length of day, there should be play and rest periods in accordance with pupil needs.

Division of the Day. It is common knowledge that children are more efficient mentally in the morning than during the afternoon, hence the need for scheduling those subjects demanding more diligent application early in the day, or subjects requiring painstaking academic preparation may be interspersed with those permitting free movement and exacting less mental effort. In elementary schools, a class devotes 20 to 30 minutes to a specific task; in secondary schools 45 to 50 minutes comprise the time allotment for a single class period. No child in the elementary school should be expected to engage in study at his desk for more than 60 minutes at one time, probably less.

Health of the Teacher. One condition of the school that the pupil never escapes is the health of the teacher. Therefore, it is important to have well qualified teachers of pleasing personality and robust health, and then to protect them from overwork, anxiety, improperly equipped rooms, poor living conditions, or other influences which result in nervous tension, low physical vitality, or illness. In brief, the health of the teacher reflects, in no small measure, the success of the school.

Several state departments of education require health examinations of all teacher-education entrants. Such examinations and others given throughout the college years are based upon the principle that only persons of good health should be allowed to teach children. A more recent venture is the commendable policy of numerous boards of education which makes thorough health examinations a condition of employment.

School administrators should know the extent of absence among teachers caused by ill health and the nature of illnessses for which excuses are sought. If it is possible to determine the effects of such absences upon the promotion or efficiency of pupils, detailed studies of this problem should be made.

In the interests of academic efficiency as well as for personal health reasons, all factors of the health services are as applicable to teachers as to children.

School Schedules.   No one can be aware of the mood and manner of modern life without asking what the school does to promote peace and calm of spirit. School administrators often seem unaware of the problem, and as the curriculum becomes enlarged they appear to cram the schedules full to overflowing. Children run to class to avoid being tardy, or hurry through the lunch period to fulfill some extra assignment. School life on the whole contributes not to peace and calm but to tension, worry, and distress. This is a matter that needs urgent correction.

Home Study.   Many children are kept from needed and desirable activity by unreasonable homework assignments. Below junior high school homework never should be assigned as a regular practice, and in secondary schools homework should not interfere with a reasonable amount of social and physical activities.

STATE CODES FOR SANITATION OF THE SCHOOL PLANT

Several states have developed codes covering many of the items included in this chapter. It is the duty of the person charged with the responsibility of supervising the hygiene and sanitation of school plants and processes to familiarize himself with these codes and to use them in the performance of his work. Such codes, however, represent *minimum* standards to be attained and sometimes fall short of *desirable* standards approved by experts in the respective fields.*

PROBLEMS FOR DISCUSSION

1. A city council proposes, as an economic expedient, to transfer responsibility for school construction and maintenance from the board of education to the municipal department of buildings and grounds. Educational authorities object to the proposal, contending that this aspect of healthful school living provides

* Health environment factors pertinent to physical education are discussed in Part III.

valuable experiences in the total education of youth. How should the problem be resolved?

2. A school superintendent, in conference with the director of health education and physical education, suggests that the director assume administrative responsibility in a democratic manner for the entire program of healthful school living. At present, such responsibility is divided among the business manager, the custodian, and individual school principals. What arguments support and oppose the superintendent's suggestion?

3. A duly elected fire inspector in your district reports to the superintendent that many schools in the community constitute a fire hazard. The superintendent authorizes you, as the director of health and physical education, to prepare a set of fire regulations for use in the construction and maintenance of buildings. How would you proceed in formulating and gaining official approval of these regulations?

4. A problem of long standing exists in your community about the lunch period. Each school has a good lunchroom where wholesome food is served at a reasonable price, but certain conditions, as the following, are bad: students choosing improper food; many lunches brought from home and eaten in the cafeteria; loud and boisterous deportment by students during the period; bits of food and paper strewn about; bolting of food and racing to the playground or gymnasium. One principal elects to conduct a pilot study in his school aimed to make the lunch period a sound educational experience for youth, and requests the assistance of your department with the pilot study. Outline the essential administrative details in making the lunch period a sound educational experience.

5. Instructors and students may implement the above with problems gained from their own experience and observation.

REFERENCES

Butler, G. D.: *Recreation Areas, Their Design and Equipment.* ed 2. The Ronald Press, New York, 1958.

Greider, C., Pierce, T. M. and Rosenstangle, W. E.: *Pubic School Administration.* ed. 2. The Ronald Press, New York, 1961.

Joint Committee on Health Problems in Education of the National Education Association and the American Medical Association: *Health Education.* ed. 5. The Associations, Washington and Chicago, 1961.

Joint Committee on Health Problems in Education of the National Education Association and the American Medical Association: *Healthful School Living.* The Associations, Washington and Chicago, 1957.

Langton, C. V., Allen, R. L. and Wexler, P.: *School Health Organization and Administration.* The Ronald Press, New York, 1960.

Report: *High Schools 1962.* Educational Facilities Laboratories, Inc., 477 Madison Avenue, New York.

U.S. Department of Health, Education and Welfare: *Environmental Engineering for the School.* Superintendent of Documents, U. S. Government Printing Office, Washington, 1963.

CHAPTER 11

SAFETY EDUCATION

SAFETY IN AMERICAN CULTURE

Safety slogans and warnings in America have become as common-place as blueberry pie. Some of these pronouncements enjoy long and traditional acceptance. Others must await the passage of time. Such phrases as SAFETY FIRST and WATCH YOUR STEP are familiar to young and old; and who has not encountered the sign STOP, LOOK, AND LISTEN? While most persons get accustomed to THE LIFE YOU SAVE MAY BE YOUR OWN, their forebearers lived in an age of PLAY IT SAFE. In fact the last warning no longer applies only to the avoidance of accidents, it also refers to business ventures and professional activities in which humans engage.

The average citizen seldom realizes that concerted attention to safety represents a social and economic development of the present century. Great progress has been made, especially in the past 25 years. Industry forges ahead with protective and automatic machines and with safety directors appointed from the staffs of skilled engineers. Mining has one of the strongest safety organizations. Transportation moves rapidly forward with traffic regulations, ingenious safety devices, and competent men pursuing research in accident prevention. Each military unit appoints a safety officer who may have this assignment in addition to his other duties. Homes become safer, constructed of fire-resistive materials, and with the moving parts of household equipment protected by guards. The manufacturers of farm machinery work diligently to make their products "fool proof" because few agriculturalists can afford to employ safety experts. And throughout the entire process scientific discoveries in medicine reveal improved treatments for the injured, while numerous departments of government and voluntary agencies increase their efficiency in safeguarding human lives.

The phenomenal development of safety in this country comes as a result of fusing many interdependent forces. One might call it an evolutionary process of social progress designed to benefit mankind. Such progress occurs when economic, social, and political forces are blended together into a distinctive pattern. An enlightened civilization can have the kind of culture it wants and will support. This country has enjoyed marked economic benefits during the past half-century. Social forces demand the extension of resources to affect a larger segment of the population. Political forces establish laws and regulations that protect and enrich the lives of citizens. In a narrower sense, labor unions insist on safety protections in many kinds of occupations, and management finds that saving lives and preventing accidents represents sound business practice, with reduced loss of time by workers and less need to train new men for machine operation.

THE ROLE OF EDUCATION

Within every cultural movement education serves as a great common denominator that gives direction and fixes limits to an enterprise in terms of man's knowledge, attitudes, habits, and skills. Complete education includes all experiences that affect a person in schools and elsewhere. Likewise, many subjects or programs currently found in schools were literally forced upon them by outside pressure groups. This truism applies to safety education. Until comparatively recent years, educational institutions gave limited attention to safety instruction. In fact, safey education began as an accepted school program about 1922. Since that time and, doubtless partially due to education, the death rate from accidents among children between the ages of 5 and 14 shows a remarkable reduction, a favorable comparison with a lower incidence of motor vehicle accidents among secondary school youth who have completed driver education courses.

Few accidents can be attributed to chance. Human error and undisciplined conduct probably account for 85 per cent of such injuries and fatalities; hence education for safe living becomes a sound approach to the problem. Most accidents result from: (1) inadequate knowledge of safety rules; (2) insufficient skill wherein persons attempt acts beyond their ability levels; and/or (3) improper attitudes of carelessness.

Most public schools and many colleges now conduct safety programs of some kind. Many of these programs are restricted largely to *service* activities dealing with the safe construction and maintenance of school plants, bus transportation, and the like. Other programs combine the above service activities with planned *instructional* experiences for elementary and secondary school youth. Probably driver education for students in secondary schools has progressed faster, according to the number of schools involved, than any other program within the present generation. Nearly half the states have passed special legislation that allocates certain funds to secondary schools for driver education, and at least one state requires a passing mark in driver education before the adolescent may obtain his license to operate a motor vehicle.

Numerous colleges and universities offer professional preparation in safety. Some states require limited preparation in safety as a condition of certification for elementary teachers. Other states contemplate special certification for safety teachers in secondary schools. Nearly every state has standards for licensing driver-education teachers. Colleges and universities assume responsibility for the various types of preparation outlined above and, in addition, a respectable number of them offer a major or minor for persons desiring professional careers in safety education. Colleges of engineering and departments of psychology conduct needed safety research, law schools give attention to affairs of the traffic court, and at least one university has a series of courses for policemen aiming to become better traffic officers.

Thus safety problems involve huge numbers of schools and colleges in one way or another. Perhaps one significant feature deserves attention here: safety education constitutes an excellent example of cooperative activity between educational institutions, homes, departments of government, voluntary organizations concerned with safety, and private enterprise. In these days when professional leaders turn their attention to the "functional curriculum," safety education ranks high as a program that functions in the lives of people at all ages and functions as an integrating agency for the school and community.

ADMINISTRATIVE DIRECTION

Since this text deals with administration, readers may be concerned at this point with the different ways school authorities determine responsibility for the conduct of safety education. The type of administrative direction frequently conforms to program scope originally envisioned by its founding fathers. Thus the person in charge of physical education, or health education and physical education, often has safety education assigned to him as an additional duty.

This plan of organization follows a common pattern. First, more accidents occur in physical education activities than elsewhere in the school curriculum. Hence the competent physical educator has better preparation in and closer contact with safety problems than most other persons employed in the system—except the specialist in safety education, a recent addition in some schools. Second, health education long has been closely associated with safety; nearly all courses of study and texts in health emphasize accident prevention and first aid, and teacher preparation in this field nearly always includes safety. Third, superintendents and principals favor the combination of similar programs into a single administrative unit, without establishing additional departments unless the procedure seems absolutely necessary.

Two other plans of administrative organization deserve mention. Sometimes the program of safety education acquires such breadth and scope that a director does become necessary. In this event, either a director is employed who has specialized in safety education, or the appointee who has demonstrated abilities in this field comes from the ranks within the system. At other times, the program starts with driver education and, as the program develops, this teacher finally becomes the director of safety education.

The best administrative policy for most school systems, under present conditions, seems to favor associating safety education with health education and physical education with a single director for the combined programs. Of course there will be departmental staff members whose major functions deal with safety, just as one finds numerous specialists in health education and physical education.

A COMPREHENSIVE SCHOOL SAFETY PROGRAM

Broad concepts of this program bring together its two major aspects of *services* (to insure a safe environment) and *instruction* (planned curricular experiences that promote wholesome attitudes and skills based upon accurate knowledge). Competent educators recognize the close association of services and instruction, with both of them collectively strengthening the total program of safety education.

Safety education in public schools is required by law in 16 states. State education departments in more than half the remaining commonwealths recommend the adoption of such programs by local districts. Thus most elementary schools accept safety education as a functional part of the curriculum. Fewer secondary schools follow the example set by the lower grades. Many secondary schools, however, have focused attention on traffic safety and driver education with excellent results.

The real scope of safety education embraces all areas of human activity in the home, school, community, farm, or industry. Most effective programs extend beyond the school and, by means of adult or continuing education, affect parents and other adults. Cooperation is essential between the work done by schools and similar efforts performed by out-of-school agencies.

BASIC OBJECTIVES

The list and interpretation of objectives which follow, with free adaptations from documents prepared by the National Commission on Safety Education of the National Education Association, may serve as guides. The person educated in safety:
1. Possesses understandings, attitudes, habits, and skills that enable and encourage him to protect himself and others.

2. Recognizes and practices the difference between true adventure and recklessness; between bravery and bravado.
3. Accepts self-responsibility in respecting his legal and moral obligations in the prevention of accidents.
4. Protects natural resources against damage or loss as a moral and social obligation.
5. Lives by that great principle of democracy—the supreme worth of the individual.

INSTRUCTIONAL AREAS AND ENVIRONMENTAL FACTORS

Because of its relative infancy, no set pattern of program activities fits all schools. State education departments, school districts, and individual schools usually adopt their own programs. The following 25 items illustrate the various responsibilities of educational institutions:

1. *Construction and maintenance of buildings and grounds:* buildings constructed of fire-resistive materials, located on spacious and safe plots, equipped and maintained in accordance with established safety rules.
2. *Corridors and stairways:* wide enough to accommodate free passage at peak load; rules enforced that inculcate habits of safe living and social acceptance.
3. *Gymnasiums, locker rooms, and shower rooms:* furnished with good equipment, kept in repair, and carefully supervised; recognize that more accidents occur in connection with physical education than elsewhere in the school program, attributed to such causes as faulty equipment, inadequate leadership, risks inherent in certain activities, irresponsible students, and poor physical condition. Keep in mind that most activities in this program present a challenging adventure for youth who learn to accept the wise challenge without fear.
4. *Swimming pools:* equipped with the usual safety tools known to qualified persons in this field and instruments to insure sanitation; used only with competent persons in charge, certified by the American Red Cross or other recognized authority; rules enforced to protect swimmers; life-saving techniques taught as part of regular instruction.
5. *Playgrounds:* (same as items 1 and 3 above).
6. *Shops:* equipped with standard machinery of modern design manufactured by responsible firms; staffed by licensed instructors; dangerous materials kept in a safe place; avoidance of inflammable or explosive litter; rules enforced to prevent accidents.
7. *Laboratories (general science, household arts, agriculture, chemistry, physics):* (same as 6 above).
8. *Fire drills:* arranged for each school to permit egress of all students in three minutes or less; held at reasonably frequent intervals as recommended by the local fire department; each student knows the

route to follow irrespective of his location in the building; alarm system separate from other circuits; rules carefully established and rigidly enforced.

9. *Civil defense plans:* organized by each school district and each school in accordance with programs established by community, state, and the Federal Civil Defense Administration; recognize that civil defense is the business of all people and refers to natural disasters or wartime attacks; involves evacuation and survival knowledge and plans for youth and adults; program should include appointment of a civil defense coordinator for each school.*

10. *Pedestrian safety:* reliable estimates indicate that two-thirds of all traffic accidents involve pedestrians; most injuries and deaths to pedestrians result from crossing the street against traffic signals, diagonally, between intersections, stepping into the street from behind parked cars, walking carelessly on highways, playing in street, hitching rides.

11. *Traffic safety:* organized instruction in schools along with suggestions contained in items 10, 12, 13, 14, 15, and 16.†

12. *Safety councils:* used to instruct, direct, and control members of the student body in crossing streets and highways at or near schools; assist teachers and parents in the instruction of students in safe pedestrian practices at all times and places; help to develop civic responsibility; serve as a clearing house for school safety problems.

13. *Bicycle safety:* planned instruction in the safe use of bicycles, since most of these accidents occur because of traffic violations; inspection of bicycles owned by students as an essential part of this program; demonstration of bicycle skill tests to determine the capabilities of children; instruction for parents who often permit children to ride on streets and highways before youth has acquired sufficient skill and knowledge.

14. *School bus safety:* rigid inspection of vehicles at frequent intervals; only qualified drivers employed; inservice preparation of drivers including elementary first aid, sound driving practices, and emergency problems; students instructed in the proper use of school buses as a public means of transportation.

15. *Public transportation safety:* refers to vehicles other than school buses used in going to and from school; also refers to day coaches in railway trains, pullman coaches, dining cars, street cars, interurban buses, airplanes, steamships, and others.

16. *Driver education:* such courses are now organized in more than half the senior high schools of this country. Here adolescents acquire

* See especially *Civil Defense Education Thru Elementary and Secondary Schools,* National Commission on Safety Education, National Education Association, Washington, 1960.

† Complete information on the subject may be obtained from such sources as the American Automobile Association, the National Commission on Safety Education of the National Education Association, and the National Safety Council.

skills and knowledge related to motor car operation, and should form attitudes about the obligations they have to drive carefully and efficiently as prescribed by traffic regulations and the social code; under the leadership of certified instructors, driver education becomes an important element in functionalized education for both personal safety and civic responsibility.

17. *Home safety:* acceptance of the unpleasant fact that, despite partial success in other forms of safety, home accidents increase; with growing interest in the do-it-yourself movement and power tools, the problem may become ever more acute. Home accidents are due to environmental hazards and human failure; the program acquaints students with common home accidents and their avoidance, such as falls, fires, burns, cuts and bruises, suffocation, poisoning, and others. Successful achievement means reaching the adults in the community—student check-lists of such hazards for use at home, and adult education classes may help to focus attention on this important matter.

18. *Farm safety:* realization that more and more persons spend a part of their lives on farms or in rural areas, and that more accidents occur in agriculture than in any other occupation; ranked order of accidents shows falls topping the list followed by machinery and livestock, and then fires (including lightning), hunting, poisons, and heat exhaustion; authorities recommend painting all danger spots with a vivid and contrasting color, plus identification of first-aid equipment and fire-fighting apparatus in similar fashion.*

19. *Vocations:* vocational courses and guidance departments in secondary schools can furnish materials on safety associated with different occupations; visits to nearby industrial plants and other places of employment give first-hand information on the subject; progress made by industry, commerce, and transportation in the prevention of accidents sets a standard for homes and schools to follow.

20. *Fires:* include a unit on fires in all general safety courses and in related courses as they apply; most fires are caused by careless individuals or faulty construction; fire hazards in the home and on camping trips naturally belong within household arts courses, defective wiring in science classes, lightning in farm management.†

21. *Fireworks and other explosive materials:* (approximately the same as 20 above); follow local ordinances pertaining to the subject.

22. *Firearms:* more persons engage in hunting than in any other sport with the possible exception of fishing; safety instruction in the use of firearms is sorely needed because of the frequent remark, "I didn't

* Valuable information on farm safety may be obtained from the United States Department of Agriculture, the National Safety Council, the Future Farmers of America, manufacturers of farm equipment, the local 4-H club, and state colleges of agriculture.

† For complete information on fires, obtain materials from the National Board of Fire Underwriters, or consult the local fire department.

know the gun was loaded!" Records indicate that young people who have learned to handle weapons properly have fewer accidents than those deprived of such instruction.*

23. *Vacation safety:* vacation accidents assume major proportions because persons often pursue unaccustomed activities; instruction in the application of suggestions described in this total list of items could help make the vacation a joyous and safe adventure.

24. *Reporting accidents and hazards:* develop a systematic procedure in each school for handling all accidents and illnesses that affect students and employees; do the same for reporting hazards; arrange for a clear understanding of these procedures by everyone connected with the school.

25. *First aid:* several persons in each consolidated school should be qualified to render first aid, with proper assignments made to insure adequate coverage at all times when the school is in operation; provide a sufficient amount of first-aid materials to meet emergencies, store them in cabinets located in convenient places; give first-aid instruction to students in health or safety classes.†

METHODS AND MATERIALS IN SAFETY EDUCATION

Students should learn to accept safety as a way of living happily and serviceably in a democratic society. This means that youth: (1) recognizes the hazards associated with daily activities; (2) develops wholesome attitudes that encourage him to adjust properly to his environment—wholesome reactions not motivated by fear and timidity, nor reactions that confuse courage with fool-hardiness; (3) masters skills and acquires knowledge to enable him to meet potentially dangerous situations; and (4) makes use of these attitudes, skills, and knowledge to protect himself and others.

This means, further, that teachers need to guide youth in developing a philosophy of safety that emphasizes *positive* rather than *negative* elements. One might draw a parallel with health education in this respect. For some years the precise data revealed by vital statistics (frequency and cause of illness and death) focused teacher attention on the morbid or negative aspects of health. More recently health teachers stress "living at one's best" as a positive force leading to happiness and success. In like manner the publication of injury and fatality rates due to accidents often lures the unsuspecting teacher into channels of negative attitudes toward safety rather than using safety experiences as a positive influence to enrich lives.

Safety education can make important contributions to the fulfillment of democratic ideals. A democracy offers to members both freedom and

* For valuable information on the safe use of firearms, consult the National Rifle Association of America.
† School physicians and nurses, or the local board of health, will advise on first-aid equipment and procedures; or the local Red Cross chapter may be consulted.

responsibility. Within the safety program students learn to respect authority and the rights of others; they learn that private good and public good have much in common. Few schools thus far fully realize the medium of safety education as a functional laboratory in the social sciences. The extent to which safety contributes to the realization of democratic ideals depends somewhat on the school organization for instruction.

Communities differ in the kinds of organization used for safety instruction. Most elementary schools follow the plan in operation for other areas of education; either separate courses or large blocks of work wherein safety experiences receive attention along with others—such as the study of transportation, communication, work, government, or leisure. An increasing number of secondary schools offer separate courses in general safety along with planned integration of accident prevention in nearly all subjects, especially in physical education, health education, shop courses, household arts, courses in agriculture, and the general and social sciences. Driver education in secondary schools is always a separate subject and this precedent may well affect other features of safety in future years as communities better understand the potential worth of this program.

Audio-visual materials in safety education have increased by leaps and bounds. These include various types of motion pictures, filmstrips, slides, and posters. The person in charge of such materials in the school system, or the state education department, can furnish information that guides the administrator or teacher in the choice of helpful media—for purchase, for rental, or without charge.

Few textbooks in safety education for students thus far have been produced. As the program becomes more prominent this field may be an interesting one for prospective authors. Written materials in the form of guides, bulletins, and pamphlets are published by the American Red Cross, the National Safety Council, the National Commission on Safety Education of the National Education Association, the American Automobile Association, the United States Department of Agriculture, the National Board of Fire Underwriters, numerous insurance companies, state education departments, and many other commercial and voluntary agencies.

SCHOOL ORGANIZATION FOR SAFETY

Effective action with any program depends largely upon the proper organization of resources. In safety education one might categorize these resources as those belonging to the school, to the community, and to state and national groups. A basic concept of organization is worthy of repetition here for emphasis: *the three types of resources should operate in harmonious relationship to each other.* This means that administrators must strive to develop attitudes of "desirable working togetherness" rather than "grudging cooperation."

School Resources.   First consideration belongs to the selection of a competent administrator or director to help plan and coordinate program activities among the various schools. He may be the director of health education and physical education, as previously noted, or another person with administrative vision and wisdom capable of unifying activities throughout the school system and utilizing community and state agencies. Next in importance comes the appointment of one person in each school who serves as a safety coordinator or consultant. Quite obviously, both director and consultants function with greater efficiency when supported in their efforts by the school superintendent, the person in charge of buildings and grounds, and school principals.

Principals, teachers, and students make significant contributions to the program. Until more principals receive safety instruction in undergraduate and graduate preparation, their primary role may rest with giving sanction and support to activities recommended by authorities in this field. Most other instructors need inservice education to qualify them for their respective duties, except for teachers in elementary schools, health educators and physical educators whose preparation includes a course or two in safety education.* Too often administrative expediency places safety instruction in the hands of teachers whose chief qualifications are that they have unscheduled periods in their regular assignments, or that a place must be found for them because of demonstrated incompetence in other classes. Under these conditions the unfavorable results seem rather obvious.

Students contribute to the program in many ways including membership on junior safety councils and junior safety patrols. Many schools have a safety council either as a part of or separate from the school health council described in Chapter 7: Program Organization in Health Education and Physical Education. School safety councils are represented by the principal's office, teacher groups concerned with certain aspects of safety, students, custodial and bus services, and possibly one or more community groups involved in accident prevention.

Community Resources.   Success of the school safety program depends largely on community interest. Coordinated efforts between the school and community yield the best results. Like health education, safety precepts learned in school by young people without parental and community support often fall by the wayside of neglect and nonconformance.

Municipalities establish codes, ordinances, and regulations affecting the welfare of all citizens. These enactments and their implications furnish on-the-spot material for safety education. Cooperation between the schools and police departments, fire departments, departments of buildings and grounds, park departments, civil defense, and numerous voluntary agencies helps to objectify and actualize classroom instruction. The municipality may have a commissioner of public safety whose activi-

* Nearly all states require special certification for teachers of driver education.

ties are closely related to the elementary and secondary schools as the child of today becomes the adult citizen of tomorrow with broader responsibilities to his family, community, state, and nation.

State and National Resources.   State laws and regulations adopted by the legislature and by departments of state deal with accident prevention. These laws and regulations become an essential part of the school safety program. An increasing number of states have established a state safety commission and a state safety council. Further, state units of government and many voluntary organizations with state offices publish materials and render services that strengthen the school program.

National resources of extreme value have been listed at times throughout the chapter and appear in the selected references. Letters addressed to these organizations (preferably written by students) bring prompt and efficient response. Use them whenever national organizations can render service.

A SUMMARIZING STATEMENT

Thus safety education throughout the country assumes the characteristics of big business. Everyone has a part in this great enterprise. The child in school has his obligations to protect himself and others. The school has its opportunity to use safety as a powerful force in education for good citizenship. Parents and other adults have their significant responsibilities. Community and state governments must devote their efforts to saving lives and increasing the happiness of people. The national government must do its part in keeping with the Constitution which extols the rights of life, liberty, and the pursuit of happiness but delegates certain functions to the respective states. Other agencies, such as industry, commerce, transportation, and voluntary and professional groups should continue their activities in research and publication of materials, their example, and their help in producing qualified leadership that promotes the tenets of safety education. All are dedicated to insuring the normal growth and development of the comparative infant, safety education, as they figuratively surround the cradle and contemplate the growing-up that lies ahead for the program.

But society must not forget another side to the picture of optimum living in a democracy. While the nation extols the virtues of safety, it seems clear that life should be lived as well as contained. Continuous adherence to the slogan "safety first," admirable as it is, can promote undue caution and carefulness. The dangers of childbirth, saving a drowning person, burning the midnight oil in a worthy cause, or preserving national security are accepted as a matter of course by those who give priority to life rather than to safety. An established custom may develop timidity in a people when exigencies of the times demand courage and self-sacrifice.

PROBLEMS FOR DISCUSSION

1. Several community pressure groups want the schools to utilize more resources of the community and state to improve the existing program in safety education. Over the years school authorities have resisted such pressures on the bases that (a) educational experts themselves know best what kind of education is needed, (b) some of these resource groups might try to gain control of the school safety program, and (c) if successful in item (b) pressure groups might try to assume control of other school programs. What should be done?
2. Five years ago safety education was placed within the department of health education and physical education. Separate classes in health education and physical education are arranged in the secondary school but, except for driver education, all safety is taught incidentally as part of various subjects. The departmental staff believes that safety education in secondary schools should receive attention on a basis comparable to other subjects—scheduled time, competent instructors, credit, adequate equipment. Principals and higher administrative authority point out that an already crowded curriculum does not permit adding another subject. How might a director handle this problem?
3. Driver education is to be offered in a high school for the first time and it is decided that the instruction be given during school hours. School officials, expressing the belief that driver education is a physical activity, recommend that it be substituted for physical education class instruction. What would be your reaction to this recommendation?
4. Owing to retirement, a vacancy exists as director of health education and physical education. Several candidates in the department present their credentials for the position, along with the man in charge of driver education who thus far has reported directly to the assistant superintendent for secondary education. The board of education and superintendent favor extending the department to include driver education. What should be done in selecting a new director?
5. Instructors and students are encouraged to include other problems for discussion based upon their own experiences and observation.

REFERENCES

American Automobile Association: *School Sportsmanlike Driving.* ed. 4. McGraw-Hill Book Company, Inc., New York, 1961.

Florio, A. E. and Stafford, G. T.: *Safety Education.* ed. 2. McGraw-Hill Book Company, Inc., New York, 1962.

Halsey, M.: *Let's Drive Right.* ed. 2. Scott, Foresman and Company, Chicago, 1958.

Heinrich, H. W.: *Industrial Accident Prevention.* ed. 4. McGraw-Hill Book Company, Inc., New York, 1959.

National Commission on Safety Education: *Checklist of Safety and Safety Education in Your School* (1953), *Civil Defense Education Thru Elementary and Secondary Schools* (1960), *Our Schools Plan Safe Living* (1956), *Minimum Standards for School Busses* (1960), and *Patrols* (1961). National Education Association, Washington.

National Rifle Association of America: *N.R.A. Basic Rifle Marksmanship* (1960), *N.R.A. Hunter Safety Course* (1956), and *N.R.A. Hunter Safety Handbook* (1959), Washington.

New York University Center for Safety Education: *Man and the Motor Car.* Rev. ed. Prentice-Hall, Inc., Englewood Cliffs, 1962.

Stack, H. J. and Elkow, J. D.: *Education for Safe Living.* ed. 3. Prentice-Hall, Inc., Englewood Cliffs, 1957.

CHAPTER 12

SPECIAL EDUCATION*

THE PRINCIPLE OF INDIVIDUAL DIFFERENCES

Human beings vary tremendously, not only in structural patterns but also in functional powers; not only in habits and reflexes but also in emotional reactions. The principle of individual differences is well established in science although much lawmaking, education, and general social effort proceed as if equality rather than inequality prevails.

Wide differences are readily apparent. The blind child is recognized as different from the one that sees, the crippled child exhibits clearly his handicap, and the feebleminded child reveals through the agency of exact tests his mental age. In each of these groups, however, and in others as well, there are individual differences. No two blind children are alike in all other respects; no two normal children exhibit identical reactions in response to widely varying physical, psychic, and social stimuli. Many differences in children never are recognized; indeed for such qualities as endurance, vitality, adaptability, social intelligence, and similar ones there are no adequate tests and no acceptable classifications.

It is sometimes difficult to draw the line between what is normal and what is abnormal. The diagnosis of abnormality, however, depends upon drawing such a line. Where norms exist as they do for numerous qualities, the diagnosis must be made and then the attempt to correct abnormalities is justified. For example, although a certain posture may be classified as a family trait, and although the operator has no delusions about restoration to a norm, still the effort to compensate for its inadequacies by muscle reeducation is justified in precisely the same way that approval is given for a therapy that seeks restoration of normal vision, or

* This chapter is included for two reasons: (1) directors of health education and physical education sometimes have administrative responsibilities for special education; and (2) close relationships should exist among these fields.

improvement in speed, or strengthening the heart muscle. Under such conditions, the objective is to help the individual achieve the most possible within the limitations of the disability.

When experience proves that social effort to remove handicaps is a waste of money and human energy, then realities are to be faced and the problem solved in terms of the best procedure for all concerned.

At times the missionary in people takes curious turns in dealing with the handicapped. For example, in the treatment of delinquency human effort and wealth spent in elaborate buildings and equipment appear excessive. But social approval in which sentimentality bulks large is given for such expenditures. However, for those appearing on the other end of the scale—accelerated children endowed by nature with superior gifts—public approval is slowly and haltingly accorded for a kind of education compatible with their potentialities. The blind beggar with sores is apt to arouse pity more readily than the "poor" boy or girl with superior intelligence who is denied an adequate opportunity for education and development. Society may soon be compelled to deal realistically with this problem.

INDICATIONS OF NORMALITY

Ruth Moore reports that the human body is composed of 1,000,000,-000,000,000 cells.* This enormous number, many times greater than the total population of the earth, presents numerous opportunities for something to go wrong; some groups of cells may fail to develop properly, others may secrete too much or too little, while the coordination of all functioning processes in harmonious action presents a picture of chemical and physical balance that always amazes the student of physiology. The human individual, however, built of these myriad cells, each a chemical laboratory where life processes go on, more frequently attains to normality than to abnormality.

Within the fertilized ovum (which in reality is an individual in a one-cell stage) are contained the powers, capacities, abilities, and functions that are to develop. In this cell are found the potentialities of heredity. During the period of its development within the uterus certain conditions may affect the welfare of the embryo so that at birth or even later imperfections occur which are recognized as congenital. To a certain extent the chemicals of the maternal blood may be deficient with a resulting disturbance in growth or development that appears at birth or later.

DEVELOPMENT OF POWERS AND FUNCTIONS

As the single-celled individual gradually but surely assumes a polycellular form, the powers and functions of cells, now specialized as they

* Ruth Moore: *The Coil of Life.* Alfred A. Knopf, New York, 1961, p. 380.

arise, come into existence. The first functions to appear are called *fundamental*. They come first and are the last to go. Nature provides for their development by impulses within the protoplasm itself. Thus, nature is difficult to defy, for even the most serious obstacles are surmounted by the hereditary impulse to develop functions that maintain the life of the organism. The circulation of blood, the digestion of food, the elimination of waste, breathing—these and other fundamental functions arise in persons castigated by nature as well as in those favored by the tides of opportunity.

In addition to these fundamental powers, nature produces specialized functions of the nervous system which, unless exercised in education, may be partially or imperfectly developed. These higher abilities are dependent upon the fundamental functions and since these come first in nature they should come first in education.

Precociousness in nature is a mistake; in education it is a disaster. Many of the emotional and adjustment problems of children arise out of the effort of parents and occasionally teachers to develop abilities in the child long before he is prepared to make the advance desired. In elementary schools the chief purpose of nature is growth and development of the motor and circulatory systems; the same purpose should dominate education. The selection of developmental tasks for which the individual is ready and to which he is stimulated to respond is a proper problem for both parents and teachers.

GROWTH AND DEVELOPMENT

Growth is an increase in mass. It represents merely size and it tells nothing of the powers and functions of the mass. *Development* is an organization of the mass with respect to certain powers and abilities.

In the early years of childhood growth is a measure of the normal progress of the individual. Growth in cells and tissues comes first; later these structures develop special functions. This relationship holds also for individuals, although less rigidly. In the elementary school years the stress of nature is on growth; in the high school years the stress is on development.

The growth of a child is an indication of vitality. Causes which impair growth frequently interfere with the development of functions later. This is one of the axioms of child nature.

Feeding may affect growth. Japanese children born and reared in America are larger, age for age, and heavier than children in Tokyo. American-born children of Italian and Russian stock are 4 to 5 inches taller than their parents. Australian-born children of English stock are taller and heavier than their parents.

Communicable diseases interrupt normal growth. Numerous reports show the effects of retardation caused by whooping cough, influenza, rickets, and other diseases.

There is a considerable body of opinion to show that bright children are taller and heavier than dull ones, and retarded children are shorter and lighter than children in grade at normal age, but the exceptions are so numerous and outstanding that this view should be held quite tentatively.

And this growth and development of the individual are mental and emotional as well as physical. Efforts to rehabilitate the handicapped should take into account the whole person, and therefore should encompass for the handicapped, as well as for others, the socializing experiences of play, and other social experiences in the ordinary patterns of everyday life that the normal individual knows, often quite unconsciously and without planning, but which require careful planning to insure them for the one who is different.

PERIODS OF NORMAL DEVELOPMENT

Kerr describes three aspects of normal development (Fig. 19). The first is *nutritive*, the second *motor*, and the third *intellectual*. It should be understood that there are no sharp lines dividing these stages, nor are the qualities manifested exclusively in any one period. Nature has no water-tight compartments; only man so conjures with such data.

In the *nutritive* stage, prominent from 1 to 5 years of age, the organism is feeding, digesting, and sleeping a great deal. Vegetative growth is nature's purpose. Teeth appear, and usually at the end of 2½ years the child has the complete temporary set. Normally he walks at 14 months and his motor activity, while increasing gradually, does not dominate until after the age of 5 years. He talks, saying simple words at the age of one, and completes sentences at two years. The heart increases in size rapidly and doubles its volume between 18 months and 4 years of

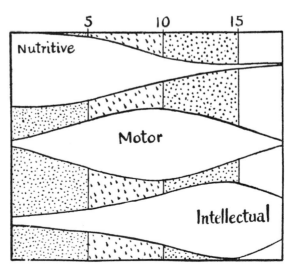

Figure 19. Scheme of relative rates of development of various nervous functions at educational ages. (From Kerr, *Fundamentals of School Health*. George Allen & Unwin, Ltd.)

age. This is the period for growth and nothing should be permitted to interfere with its normal rhythm.

In the *motor* stage, prominent from 5 to 10 years of age, the child wishes to climb, slide, and run. He seems inexhaustible in his energy for play. In this stage his interest is in big-muscle activity, although in the later years of this period he may wish to use his hands in construction. His speech is clear, and by the end of the period he has neared the end of his second dentition which begins at 6 and normally is completed at the age of 12 with the exception of the third molars (wisdom teeth), which appear at 18 to 20 years of age.

The third stage, the *intellectual,* begins at about the age of 10 years. It begins earlier, of course, but typically accompanies a flowering of the individual in adolescence. In this period a group of emotions arise which are gradually refined and ordered, giving a wider outlook and an intellectual grip of the universe.

These periods or stages of emphasis describe in part nature's plan. They suggest that milk and sleep are more important for babies than anything else; that "games are better than grammar" for the 9 year old; and that intellectual sources are to be made available in adolescence.

PHYSIQUE

By physique is meant a general structural fitness of the individual for functioning. It is physical in its outward aspects but nervous and chemical in its inner manifestations. Muscular exercise is nature's way of developing physique, and nothing invented by man can replace the racial, natural activities of play and combat for this purpose.

The items that comprise physique include vital capacity of the lungs; muscle development, hardness, and strength; postural adjustments; heart action; and other functional powers and abilities to engage in activity and to pursue it vigorously.

HEALTHY PERSONALITY

The essential characteristic of the normal mind is integration of personality. Integration implies unity, wholeness, and wholesomeness; it is the opposite of a state of "going to pieces" or of being "scatter-brained." Influences in nature that make for unity in competition with those forces that produce conflicts mark the area in which problems arise for the individual in his effort to adjust to his world and to find meaning for his life. The healthy personality is not one that is perfect and free from defects but one that is able, when difficulties occur, to adjust, to integrate its wishes, its achievements, and its failures.

The handicapped individual faces a serious problem unless he can develop a rational concept of his worth as a person. It is often far easier to live with a physical defect than with the accompanying psychological sense of inferiority. The crucial task confronting those who work with the handicapped is to guard against psychological injury, to repair its damages when they arise, and to teach a system of values by which the handicapped individual can live with satisfaction.

TYPES OF ABNORMALITY

In the previous pages some characteristic features of normal development have been discussed. Abnormalities in children occur in great number but vary in severity. From the viewpoint of educational policy and social planning, there are many slight abnormalities that must be ignored; others are so widespread, or so handicapping to development, or so serious to society, if neglected, that they deserve attention. Indeed, modern social philosophy holds that the handicapped child must have an opportunity in accord with his possibilities.

The services of education vary considerably as applied to different types of abnormality. Its functions are discussed here with respect to atypical children for whom health education and physical education are of some service, and for whom special class or school organization of some kind is essential. It is obvious that although children with tonsillar hypertrophy or carious teeth are handicapped, they are not placed in special classes or in special schools. Such children are to be treated in the routine of the health services. This chapter deals with the handicapped who require special organization either of class or of school in order that the appropriate type of education may be possible.

SPECIAL TEACHERS AND SPECIAL CLASSES

Teachers need special preparation to instruct handicapped children. In addition to the preparation required for teachers of the conventional curriculum, the special teacher must possess abilities and skills peculiar to the types of defect for which the service is intended. The usual preparation of the physical education teacher is quite inadequate to conduct exercises for even the mild forms of orthopedic defect. In teaching the handicapped, the physical therapist, prepared in the intricacies of isolated muscle contraction, is the proper person to preside over the exact requirements of therapy. For the important development in general coordination, however, and the utilization of adjusted activities, the physical educator can give excellent service, which explains in part the use of many physical educators in the rehabilitation programs of veterans and armed forces hospitals. With adequate preparation, the physical educator can give valuable instruction in modified group games; many handicapped persons are able to participate in such activities as bowling, table tennis, shuffleboard, and others.

THE HANDICAPPED CHILD AND THE SPECIAL CLASS

There is considerable difference of opinion concerning the segregation of handicapped children. All agree that it is desirable to enroll the handicapped child in regular classes as soon as it is profitable for him, but it is apparent to those who have worked with the handicapped that many important aspects of the curriculum injure the handicapped child when he attempts the activities of normal children. Physical education is a good example. The development of a spirit of fair play, the ability to take defeat gracefully, and the ability to engage courageously in competition come from participation in actual situations demanding these qualities are not by keeping score or passing a ball with the teacher or another child (Fig. 20). If the handicapped child attempts to play with children of a normal group, continual failure may develop a feeling of self-pity and self-depreciation. In competition with others who are handicapped, success is possible and growth in desirable traits of character results. Experience of the William S. Baer School in Baltimore strongly supports the view that a special school for those who need it removes feelings of inferiority, reduces to a minimum personality failure, and aids in their complete adjustment to a normal group.

Some groups of handicapped children can be taught successfully in special classes, but this arrangement usually limits greatly the rehabilitation features of the program. A regular school with a special class for crippled children, for example, often does not have the facilities for physical therapy and other rehabilitating services.

Figure 20. A physical education class for crippled children at the William S. Baer School, Baltimore. (Courtesy of Baltimore Public Schools.)

In rural areas not even special classes normally are possible, and handicapped children of rural areas generally are neglected.

CLASSIFICATION OF ATYPICAL CHILDREN

With slight modifications the following classification seems appropriate:

Physically atypical children may be grouped into five categories:
1. Orthopedic disabilities
    a. Postural
    b. Crippled
2. Visual disabilities
3. Hearing disabilities
4. Speech disabilities
5. Respiratory–cardio disabilities.

Socially atypical children may be classified in four groups as those requiring:
1. Custodial service
2. Remedial service
3. Preventive psychiatric service
4. Developmental service.

Mentally retarded children.

ORTHOPEDIC DISABILITIES

Children with orthopedic disabilities may be classified in two groups: (1) those so severely handicapped as to require special schools, such as schools for crippled children; and (2) those with minor handicaps who attend regular schools and are assigned to adapted physical education classes. A wide variety of bone, muscle, and nerve disease occurs in such cases, but the most common cause probably is cerebral palsy. Other causes are poliomyelitis, epilepsy, congenital deformities, muscular dystrophy, Legg-Calvé-Perthes disease, improper body mechanics, psychic and emotional distortions, and trauma. Doubtless many postural disabilities diagnosed as weak muscles are the product of unrecognized and mild infections of poliomyelitis.

Postural Disabilities. A great variety of muscular and skeletal conditions occur. Some are suitable for correction; others are not. Muscle tension, various types of round shoulders, mechanical unbalance, weak feet, and similar conditions may be improved markedly by expert prescription of exercise and faithful practice by the pupil. The bony deformities accompanying rickets and certain severe scolioses are beyond the service of individual physical education.

Diagnosis. Diagnosis of the postural condition should be made and treatment prescribed by an orthopedic physician. Following a period of individual physical education conducted by a person specially prepared for this work, the physician should reexamine the patient. The frequency of this supervision will depend upon the case. He may wish to see some pupils every two weeks; others may be referred for special services without seeing them again during the school year. If the orders have been placed in the hands of an expert, the physician will need to give less time to supervision of cases; some operators are more skilled in the practical aspects of these matters than the average physician.

Adapted Activities. The pupil assigned to physical education may or may not be enrolled in classes with restricted activity. The adapted program is arranged for individuals not vigorous enough to engage in strenuous activities or with handicaps of function that prevent full participation. Some pupils assigned to this program also should engage in group activities. Obviously, it may be possible for a pupil by individual work to attain nearly a perfect physical structure and be quite uneducated in the use of it in various types of activity. A functional physical education program does not seek structural form alone but strives also for functional ability that serves the individual.

Size of Classes. Pupils assigned to individual correction assemble at stated periods, but there is considerable latitude in the arrangements. Thus, the size of the class varies according to the type of case and the ability of the instructor. The type of case is even more demanding of flexibility than class size. Hence, a child with cerebral palsy may require the entire time of the instructor in any one period. On the other hand, the average instructor can manage four or five children with infantile paralysis disabilities, and a group of 20 with flat feet or muscular underdevelopment can be taught efficiently as a class. This gives no priority to type of case. All are important but it does indicate how the type of case controls the size of class.

Number of Periods per Week. This procedure of organization also should be flexible. Some groups, such as those with foot disorders, if they require only instruction in how to use the mechanism, may attend one period in the adapted class and other periods in the regular class. If they are assigned to the special group of those suffering from serious fatigue, a daily period may be indicated and some of this may be spent in rest. Muscle training for a child with cerebral palsy or "polio" demands daily attention.

Many periods should be assigned for Saturday mornings and, if a clinic is held, this is the best time for consultation with the doctor, parents, and special teachers. It is important, of course, to have the doctor present at the clinic and this may afford the best time for a check-up on individual children.

Length of Periods. The periods will vary in length and great flexibility is desirable because of the type of disability. In general, short, frequent periods are better than long, and less frequent, ones.

Exercises for Use at Home. Some exercises may be practiced at home, but usually the task of supervision is quite beyond the ability of parents. The daily admonition of the mother to "do your exercises" may be spoken kindly and with admirable purpose, but it is apt to degenerate into a form of nagging. The home must cooperate, but such aid is best given by parental supervision of hours of sleep, diet, rest, and other matters of practical hygiene that are clearly recognized by the child as within the scope of parental authority and responsibility. Care to prevent psychological friction between child and parent is important in all school administrative methods.

Education in Postures. It becomes increasingly clear that the profession must use the word *postures* rather than *posture* to avoid the misunderstandings that cluster around the singular form of the word. The word *posture,* and particularly the term *good posture,* carries the impression that there is *one* correct posture. Obviously, such is not the case. There is not *one,* there are *many* good postures. That posture is good which is good for something and hence the posture good for bricklaying may not be good for violin playing, whereas the one good for football may be quite unapproved for the soldier on parade. Unfortunately, it is this "military" posture that so often is taken as a model of goodness for all postures in the standing position.

It also should be clear that good use of the body should be the concern of every teacher in the school. When there was one posture for the child to acquire, it seemed reasonable to expect his physical education teacher to train him in it, but since he uses his body in many ways in the classroom and has many postures to control, it is imperative that every teacher in the school understand and be interested in the problems involved.

Moreover, it is recognized that use of the body implies much more than muscles, bones, and ligaments. Emotional, nutritional, and activity factors are involved. A feeling of self-respect and courage is reflected in bodily adjustment just as fear and self-consciousness are. Lack of energy, fatigue, and other physiological states together with habit and probably heredity, reflect themselves in postural patterns. Any plan for education in postures that neglects these factors fails to account for vital elements in the problem.

The modern principle of behavior, that describes the individual in relation to his environment, finds a good illustration in the way the body is used. Classroom seats, clothing, and weights to carry need careful supervision. Particularly is it the responsibility of the supervisor of health education and physical education to secure proper adjustment of seats as pupils are assigned to classes.

Equipment. The adaptive gymnasium should be equipped with necessary appliances and apparatus for effective work. The equipment will vary somewhat: just as painters wish to select their own brushes, so technical experts have their preferences for tools. But just as all painters use brushes, so all teachers in individual physical education will require mats, stools, mirrors, apparatus for reclining such as plinths or tables, apparatus for hanging such as rings, horizontal bars, or stall bars, and some means for recording the conditions found. Some will use the silhouettograph, the foot-o-print machine, and other mechanical aids; others will use cameras for simple picture-taking or in connection with more elaborate recording devices.

Crippled Children. It has been estimated that there are about 500,000 crippled children under 16 years of age in the United States. Their handicaps are the results of a variety of causes. Many are the results of anterior poliomyelitis. Special work* for crippled persons began in 1863 with the establishment in New York City of the Hospital for Ruptured and Crippled. Interest in the problem of the crippled child increased, and in 1921 the International Society for Crippled Children was formed.

Location of the Problem. The local community, aided by the state and even by the federal government, must face the problems of: (1) discovering the number of crippled children in need of care; (2) determining the type of service to be rendered; and (3) financing the cost of special education.

This threefold aspect of the problem is greater than the board of education can face alone. The assistance of other agencies must be sought. Two groups should be interested in and are necessary for the success of such an undertaking. One group of lay persons provides the opportunity (facilities and means); and the other, a professional group, provides the technical skill. This is sound advice for any community. The local medical, nursing, and social agencies are interested and in most communities share in the work. The form of cooperation varies, but if the board of education assumes responsibility for the supervision of the physical condition of children, most lay and technical agencies outside the schools readily cooperate. For this reason, the board should employ as one of the school physicians an orthopedic surgeon competent to supervise any therapy carried on in the school for those who are crippled.

Definition of the Crippled Child. The definition includes children whose activity is, or because of progressive disease may become, so far restricted by loss, defect, or deformity of bones or muscles as to reduce their capacity for education or self-support. In state legislation dealing with the matter the term is defined rather broadly as it should be, emphasizing the child's inability to profit by attending regular class instruction. Under the definitions used by some states, children with cardiac defects could be classified also as crippled children. For proper administrative procedures the definition should be precise enough to include children with orthopedic disabilities.

Preschool Children. The reported experience of experts suggests that at least 50 per cent of crippling conditions that occur before 6 years

* Many of the suggestions for postural disabilities apply in caring for crippled children.

of age are curable if treated promptly. Obviously, the thoroughness with which the preschool population is canvassed, and the responsibility which is felt for those who are soon to be in school, affect the success of the whole program.

Administration of Public School Special Classes. In large cities where work with crippled children has passed the experimental stage, the administration is well established. Boards of education provide special classes in regular schools and in convalescent homes and hospitals, and home-teaching for those unable to attend school. Some cities have special schools; the Spalding Crippled Children's School in Chicago is one of the best known.

Recreation for Crippled Children. The crippled child needs recreation and every effort should be made to supplement the excursions, picnics, and other entertainments that comprise the usual program for handicapped children.

Periods of free play are essential, and these should be provided so that success in overcoming obstacles and in competition with others is to a certain extent assured. The crippled child often is sensitive, and unless the valuable education obtained through play is available there is grave danger of personality disturbances arising which blight the life of the child. The tendency toward daydreaming to compensate for a sense of inadequacy in real situations requires ingenuity of the teacher to provide real play and to treat all efforts with respect and consideration. In some ways, free play is more important for crippled children than any other one feature in the school program because in groups outside of school this need of the crippled child often is neglected.

Cerebral Palsy. In cerebral palsy muscular control is impaired or lost. The disability may affect any of the motor muscles and results from some injury to the brain; most cases are caused by brain injury at the time of birth. Much can be done to improve these children but the outcome depends upon the extent of brain damage, medical care given, personality of the child, educational program available, and character of the home.

Although the brain is injured, it is estimated that two-thirds of those with cerebral palsy have normal intelligence. Programs for these children may require special educational methods.

VISUAL DISABILITIES

Two problems arise in dealing with visual conditions: (1) the education of the blind, and (2) the establishment of sight-saving classes for those with seriously impaired vision. With respect to the first problem there are state-supported special schools for the blind. Special sight-saving classes for children with impaired vision together with special medical aid are maintained by boards of education.

Prevention of Blindness. Although the Credé method of instilling silver nitrate in the eyes of the newborn to prevent gonorrheal infection and resulting blindness was developed in 1881, for many years thereafter its adoption as routine technic was delayed. Such social lag is to be expected, since it takes at least 25 years for any new scientific procedure to gain wide acceptance. It is obvious that birth infections can be prevented, except for the occasional accident that represents failure of the attending physician to use properly the antiseptics available.

Blindness may result also from smallpox, trachoma, tumors, congenital defects, sinusitis, and syphilis. Smallpox is preventable today although approximately 50,000 cases occur annually in the United States. Fortunately few cases develop serious injury to the eyes.

The role of trachoma as a cause of blindness varies in importance in different countries. In some localities it is responsible for about 15 per cent while in others it is the causative agent in 30 per cent of the cases. It occurs most frequently among the poor and is widely distributed among inhabitants along the Mediterranean, Caspian, and Black Sea coasts, and the Asiatic and African coastal settlements. The cause is a virus; dirt and poverty favor its transmission. The contagion is readily carried from person to person using the same towels and handkerchiefs.

Tumors and congenital defects may produce disturbances in different parts of the eye mechanism with resulting blindness. In some instances sinus infection in the ethmoidal cells extends to the eyes, seriously impairing vision.

Syphilis is a common cause of blindness, although treatment of the disease has improved greatly in recent years. Prevention of the disease rests more, however, in the successful work of education in schools promoting modern health education programs and in society through the activities of boards of health and such organizations as the American Social Health Association.

In addition to these causes of blindness, accidents produce a certain number of cases. Safe and sane Fourth of July celebrations for children, industrial hygiene in factories, and health instruction in schools are the chief avenues of preventing blindness from this cause.

Sight-Saving Classes. Franz von Gaheis of Austria in 1802 proposed that children with partial vision be placed in special classes, and Kerr in 1908 established a myope school in England. Similar schools were provided in Germany and Austria. In 1913 the first sight-saving class was organized in America. Various methods were developed by independent workers in these early efforts. There was little coordination. Each pioneer had to experiment with problems already solved by others because there was no available body of knowledge regarding procedure. In the summer of 1921 Teachers College, Columbia University, offered the first course for the preparation of teachers in this field.

The Examination for Sight-Saving Classes. Established administrative procedures admit children to sight-saving classes only after an ophthalmologic examination has determined the need for such service.

The ophthalmologist also recommends the amount of work which may be permitted and the frequency of reexamination.

From the standpoint of conservation of vision, every school system should consider three groups of children: (1) those with normal vision; (2) those with remediable defects of vision or diseases of the eye that may be cured; and (3) those with serious eye difficulties who, after proper refraction or treatment, cannot be educated profitably in the regular classroom. It is for this third group that sight-saving classes are intended.

In the New York City schools visually handicapped children learn to live and work with their visually normal companions. Candidates for sight-saving classes are selected from those children of normal mentality who have 20/70 or less vision in the better eye after refraction. A child with better vision than 20/70 may be admitted if a progressive condition is present, or if there is temporary need for special eye care.

Upon receipt of an ophthalmologist's recommendation to place a child in a sight-conservation class, the following administrative steps are followed.

1. The sight-conservation office sends an official notice to the principal of the school in which the candidate is registered, requesting that a transfer be issued to the child to the sight-conservation class indicated on the form.
2. Parents of the child are notified of the transfer to be made and the visiting teacher calls at the home if further explanations are needed.
3. The principal of the school to which the candidate is assigned also receives a notice from the sight-conservation office requesting that the child be admitted to the sight-conservation class in his school.

If the vision of the child improves he may be recommended by the opthalmologist for discharge from the sight-conservation class. Books used in sight-conservation classes are printed in 24-point type.

Rooms for Sight-Saving Classes. Visually impaired children should be taught in rooms with excellent lighting. The walls should be painted a light buff, ceilings should be white, and all furniture should be of a dull finish. The hygiene of instruction demands, for these as well as for other pupils, books printed on unglazed paper in clear and large enough type.

HEARING DISABILITIES

Over one-half the states have laws that require annual examinations of vision and hearing of school children. The ability to hear spoken words has a profound influence upon the development of speech. Children with defective hearing may range in defectiveness from slight impairment of hearing to complete deafness. Great variation in this condition requires special treatment for the different degrees of deafness.

The totally deaf are placed in schools organized for that purpose.

NAME _John Smith_

AGE _13_

GRADE _6 A³_

DATE _Jan. 26, 1926_

DO NOT MAKE ANY NOISE
AS IT WILL SPOIL THE TEST

INSTRUCTIONS

You will hear numbers spoken by a person who is moving away
from you. The voice will get weaker and weaker. Listen
carefully and write as many numbers as you can.

Hearing Loss	1	MASTER SHEET RECORD No. 1 TEST 1	TEST 2	LEFT EAR 5	6	7	8	Hearing Loss
30	526	526	538	483	853	541	466	30
27	948	348	363	525	436	285	868	27
24	414	414	318	624	841	115	543	24
21	111	111	868	482	218	821	225	21
18	648	648	338	856	414	118	262	18
15	526	526	182	416	483	491	444	15
12	826	826	548	638	441	284	622	12
9	369	363	351	463	18	491	415	9
6	528	528	341	844	298	123	668	6
3	614	634	588		664			3
0	131	124	565		448			0
-3		858	134					-3

He...

Hearing Loss _0_

TEST 3	TEST 4
863	646
224	662
546	648
288	624
883	331
416	462
813	452
345	126
588	831
133	833
461	554
165	636

...ORY

Did you ever ...n in your ear? _no_ Which Ear? _—_

When? _—_

Did you ever ... _no_ Which Ear? _—_ When? _—_

Does it run ...

Do you ever ...ear, like buzzing, hissing or

roaring? _Yes_ ...hen? _In swimming._

Figure 21. Record sheet and test sheet used with the 4-A audiometer. (From Philips and Rowell, *Your Hearing*. D. Appleton-Century Company. By permission of the Graybar Electric Co.)

Most states maintain state schools for the deaf. There are four classes of deafened children who should be in state institutions: (1) those whose home conditions are unfavorable for their proper development; (2) the incorrigibles and the mentally deficient; (3) country children without opportunity to attend day schools; and (4) children incapable of learning speech.

The hard of hearing should receive lip-reading instruction. These children may attend regular classes. If the teacher recognizes the hearing problem of these children, if hard of hearing children progress normally, and if the group as a whole is not impaired by their presence, such attendance in a regular group by the handicapped child is highly desirable.

Physical Education for the Deaf. Most schools for the deaf provide a systematic course in physical education for pupils. In practically all residential schools for the deaf, sports are available, with baseball and basketball the most popular. For boys, football, tennis, track and field usually are offered; for girls, basketball, tennis, swimming, and other sports. Public day schools for the deaf provide regular programs of physical education.

Deaf boys and girls have interests in physical activities similar to those of other children and the need for developmental and educational experiences is equally apparent.

The Examination of Hearing. Rough screening of children may be made in the usual health examination but, unless special attention is given to the hearing function, partial defects in hearing will be overlooked. For the special test, the audiometer is preferable to a watch or whisper test; moreover, from 75 to 150 children can be tested in an hour by using this instrument.* If the examination reveals a loss of 6 sensation units§ for children in the higher grades, or 9 sensation units for children in the lower grades, reference of the case should be made. An otologist should then reexamine the child and the aural efficiency should be exactly determined, the condition of the nose, throat, and sinuses ascertained, and the history of the child and the family recorded. Figure 21 shows the record sheet and test sheet used with a 4-A audiometer.

SPEECH DISABILITIES

Speech defects develop early in life, usually before the age of 6. The majority arise out of a psychic disturbance; a few have a physical basis.† The common types are stuttering, articulation and voice disorders, retarded speech development, cleft palate, cerebral palsy, and impaired hearing.

The Speech Mechanism. Speech is the production of sounds by the vibration of air passing from the lungs. In this act numerous parts of the throat and head contribute to the sound, shaping, modifying, and giving it quality. The vocal cords, the tongue, the soft palate, the lips, the head passageways, and the sinuses all share in the mechanics of the act. But these parts are not wholly adequate for speech; other mechanisms are required.

When an individual desires to speak any particular word, impulses pass from the brain directing the speech mechanism to operate in such fashion that the word is produced. When a speech disability of psychogenic origin exists, the disturbance lies in some interference with the normal passage of nerve impulses from the brain to the speech mechanism. Various causes have been assigned to explain the disturbance, but

* Many state departments of health furnish the audiometer free of charge for use in the schools.

§ A sensation unit is a notation of hearing loss.

† Speech disability may follow trauma of the larynx, postlaryngeal diphtheria, intubation of the larynx, or tracheotomies.

there is no general principle involved, and doubtless many factors may act to upset the relationship between the central control for speech and the actual mechanism.

Speech Disabilities and Special Classes.   There is not the same need for special classes in caring for speech conditions that exists for certain other physically atypical children. It is common practice, therefore, to find these children enrolled in regular classes and engaged in the regular program of the school. They should have, however, special attention which provides a number of services.

First, there should be a diagnosis of the condition. Since these disabilities usually occur before the age of 6, the kindergarten teacher should be alert to detect abnormality. The child then can be referred for diagnosis. In arriving at a diagnosis it may be essential to secure the cooperative services of physician, psychologist, and special teacher of speech, but in most cases one of these is adequate. In large cities speech clinics may be established and parents encouraged to bring preschool children for diagnosis and treatment. In recent years great progress has been made in speech correction by teachers especially prepared for this work.

TUBERCULOSIS

The care of children with tuberculosis has improved as the nature of the disease has become more clearly understood. Tests have shown that practically all adults are or have been infected with the tubercle bacillus.

The Health Examination and Tuberculosis.   The routine health examination is worthless for the early diagnosis of this disease. Any case discovered by the routine method would be active in lungs, bones, or glands. Discovery of early tuberculosis in children requires a special procedure. The x-ray examination now represents standard procedure.

If this reveals the presence of a focus of the disease, steps are taken to combat the infection. Owing to the development of microfilms the expense of x-ray examinations is reduced. In fact, many school systems now conduct routine x-ray examinations for tuberculosis, assisted by voluntary or official health agencies in the community.

The Care of Tuberculous Children.   A reactor to tuberculin may have an active case of the disease, a recently arrested case, or a healed lesion. Children who give x-ray evidence of a healed lesion may be considered normal and well, and may engage in the normal activities of children of similar age without danger. Children with recently arrested cases may be permitted to enroll for classes in school but they should be carefully watched to note their ability to live normally without a reappearance of symptoms.

A child with any form of active tuberculosis should not be permitted in a general classroom; he should be under treatment in a hospital or at home. Open-air schools and outdoor classrooms have been abandoned; they have no important place either in the prevention or treatment of tuberculosis.

CARDIAC DISABILITIES

Heart injury in children may follow diphtheria or scarlet fever or be congenital in origin, but the commonest source is acute rheumatic fever.*

The Care of Cardiac Children.   Not all children with cardiac disease require special attention. Many should attend regular classes. Emerson estimates that in not more than 8 per cent of the 20,000 cases in New York is it necessary to deny any of the normal activities of childhood. Those with slight defects free from infected foci are not included in such classes; they may be treated as normal children with only the limitation of competition imposed.

Children, unlike adults, seek their exercise level and operate at it continuously. Physical exercise does not precipitate heart failure, which is always associated with infection. When infection is not present and there is no evidence of impairment of functional activity of the heart, a child can be trusted not to exercise to excess under ordinary conditions. Disinclination to exercise on the part of any child, as well as shortness of breath on exertion, always call for careful examination. Care must be taken to exclude from athletic competition those with serious cardiac conditions. Frequently the plaudits of the crowd stimulate boys and girls to continue vigorous activity in spite of nature's warning that rest is necessary.

Beyond this supervisory service, the "cardiac" needs thorough medical attention directed to the relief of conditions (of tonsils, teeth, and so forth) that may be the source of infection. Children with cardiac disease need to learn to recognize their limitations; and care must be exerted to avoid pampering and unduly arousing fears and inhibitions that often are worse than the disease itself.

NUTRITION DISABILITIES

The nutrition of an individual is an expression of the chemical activities of his body cells on the one hand, and his food supply on the other. Basal metabolism is the activity of body cells when the individual is in a state of rest and without food. This can be measured accurately and portrays the level of chemical activity existing in the cells. Boys and girls have about the same metabolic rate until the age of 14 when girls show a lower one.

Nutrition Classes.   It is generally agreed that there are six essentials

* Diphtheria rarely leaves a permanently damaged heart. In these cases of heart injury following diphtheria the children usually either completely recover or die.

for the health of the growing child: (1) absence of physical impairments; (2) sufficient amount of nourishing foods at proper times; (3) outdoor air; (4) prevention of fatigue and adequate rest; (5) developmental physical activities; and (6) cooperation of the home in the first five of these essentials.

Well organized nutrition classes set for themselves the realization of these six essentials. In such a program, to feed children who suffer from serious defects is apt to be disappointing in its results—rest periods are essential and activity must be curtailed temporarily.

Children for nutrition classes should be selected by the physician, although the teacher should be alert to observe lack of ambition, flabby musculature, appearance of anemia, underweight, lessened resistance to disease, and early fatigue, referring those with such conditions to the proper medical authority.

SOCIALLY ATYPICAL CHILDREN

When the gardner transplants a shrub or young tree, growth during that season is apt to be less than usual. It is remarked that the plant needs to adjust itself to the new environment. If the tree is moved from poor soil or from a crowded to a free site, it may show in the first season distinct improvement. These are common observations upon plants. Man now recognizes more and more the problems of adjustment that confront him, particularly the great variety that present themselves to children.

The children of any community represent a group that faces strenuous and highly complex adjustment problems. These arise in the home, in the social life of school and other institutions, in the street, and in the play life of children. Adults, of course, have adjustment problems, but for many the formulas have been worked out, the protecting reactions developed, or the philosophy matured that harmonizes the conflicts that arise. There are adjustments to be made to physical and chemical influences; these take place in relation to the phenomena of growth and development. Often of more profound import are the adjustments of personality, the emotional and psychic orientations that increase during childhood and find their maximum in adolescence.

In the attempt at adjustment of the individual to his world, the problem may be increased because of a defective nervous system, inadequacies of early training, or extreme harshness of the environment. Thus, individuals may need one of four types of service, which follow:

Custodial service: the care of those feebleminded and mentally disabled persons who cannot be allowed free in society.

Remedial service: the care of individuals in institutions where special workers seek to correct the defects that have developed. In this group are the delinquents and others maladjusted to society.

Preventive psychiatric service: aid to adjustment, which is rapidly developing in schools. The problem boy or girl is today studied as a phenomenon of maladjustment and not classed merely as obstinate, mean, or "ornery." Child guidance clinics and school psychiatric service comprise progressive measures aimed at the prevention of more serious disturbances.

Developmental service: the efforts by various agencies to make the community environment a wholesome place for the development of happy, healthy, young people. Fundamentally, this involves adult education. There must be better homes, recreational and play centers, music organizations, festivals, and all the allied arts that minister to opportunity for action and expression.

State governments and private enterprise provide custodial and remedial services. Public opinion is becoming alert to the necessity for preventive psychiatric service, but the great importance of wholesome environments, not merely sterile environments, is as yet quite unappreciated.

CUSTODIAL SERVICE

The feebleminded, unable to develop intellectual powers sufficient for living as free and responsible members of society, often require the care of the state. To determine the mental condition of these unfortunates, the intelligence test and the medical examination are the two most important measures. In general, those children to be assigned to custodial service are idiots, imbeciles, feebleminded persons, and moral imbeciles.

Custodial care should be adequate for the simple needs of inmates; it is a mistake to spend an excessive amount of time, effort, and human energy in attempts to educate or reconstruct the wasted products of humankind. Care in the colony where some may do work to contribute to their cost to the state should be humane but without delusions and surely without sentimentality. These individuals, however, usually are the responsibility of the state.

REMEDIAL SERVICE

Children who require remedial service may have adjusted adequately for a number of years in school, but with the storms of adolescence find their problems too difficult. Often they become delinquent and are committed to state institutions. Their delinquency arises, however, during school age so the problem bears directly upon the administration of public education.

The Nature of Delinquency. Boys and girls who break out of the established social patterns of behavior may be classified as uncontrolled, problems, truants, incorrigibles, or delinquents. The degree of their variation determines their classification.

The child unable to adjust is the problem child of the classroom. This inability is a condition of the nervous system which is called *neurosis*. The neurotic individual may exhibit various outward manifestations. He may show a lack of muscular tone. He may be average or above in intelligence and yet nothing in the school challenges his interests. Daydreams and fantasy carry him into a world of the imagination so that attention is poor. He becomes self-centered, especially if an only child. He feels misunderstood, becomes sensitive to criticism, and may develop a sense of inferiority or, as a compensation for inadequacy, adopt a bullying and boasting manner.

Various postural attitudes and muscular movements may appear— stammering, curious attitudes of head and shoulders, twitchings, vision disabilities, nail-biting. They represent the strain on the neurons of the neurotic child, hard pressed by his environment, often undernourished, and quite unable to find unity for himself in the total situation.

It is obvious that the world for children as well as for adults has become more complex. The ox-cart civilization was an easier world for children as it was for grown-ups. To the new world produced by inventive genius, the older members of society have not brought adequate social controls, so that the child is catapulted into a society of frequent divorce, nervous parentage, religious conflicts, and emotional problems of various kinds.

In the face of this background of neurosis it is obvious that the problem of delinquency is not to be solved by whipping, scolding, or moral lessions. A study of the child is required and full recognition must be given to the kind of nervous system inherited as well as to the various environmental factors of the home, school, and companions that affect personality.

Delinquency increases markedly in early adolescence. The median age for boys is 14 to 15 years and for girls 15 to 16 years. Police reports cite the youth of criminals. Forty-five per cent of the inmates at Sing Sing are under 25 years of age. Beliefs regarding the influence of nationality and of physical condition in the production of delinquency have not been borne out by studies made. Problem children exhibit a physical condition that is no worse than the general run of children, nor does good condition aid in the success of treatment.

It is important to note, however, that physical defects may be a factor in personality disorders. Especially in girls, protruding upper teeth, facial scars, or other deformities may help to produce excessive shyness, objectionable mannerisms, sullen moods, and similar personality traits.

The problem is complex. In addition to the inheritance factor, exciting causes of delinquency are: (1) bad companious, often a by-product of broken homes or working mothers; (2) poor recreations; (3)

adolescent instability frequently associated with economic insecurity; (4) early sex experiences; (5) motion pictures; (6) school dissatisfaction; (7) mental conflicts; (8) extreme social suggestibility; and (9) love of adventure. Lack of intelligence is not a factor.

These factors indicate the importance of wholesome interests and partially explain the prophylactic influence of playgrounds upon adolescent youth. In many communities there are churches and schools which interest themselves too little in the promotion of normal social life. The former are concerned largely with formal religion and the latter with formal education. Even today, the school is very slow to apprehend its social function. It is so much concerned with units of credit, college board examinations, and other academic traditions that it neglects the problems confronting children as they face the demands of a society that often are exacting and even unreasonable. Instead of trying to soften the shocks of an imperious demand for adjustment, teachers too often are engaged in making school life difficult, doubtless in the expectation that if children can stand that, they can endure anything.

In some school systems certain problem children are placed in special classes. In some cities there are special schools of the farm type. In both classes and schools physical education is a basic part of the program.

PREVENTIVE SERVICE

Diagnois of children's difficulties may lead into the field of emotions or intelligence. In the former are found truants, incorrigibles, wanderers, delinquents, criminals; in the latter, the mentally retarded and those with more serious impaired intellectual capital. The role of the school in dealing with emotions has been discussed; the function of the school with respect to the mentally retarded also is important.

Mentally Retarded Children. Special classes for mentally retarded children are organized in most large cities. The physical education program for these handicapped children presents a difficulty. Retarded children usually are awkward, with coordination much impaired. They need to be encouraged to try different movements. Singing games and simple dances may be used to advantage; music helps considerably in these activities. Rhythm is a rather fundamental quality in all humans and although some retarded children appear to be devoid of even the most remote traces, others may develop a good sense of rhythm. The large body movements should be taught first of course; there will be better success with them. Fine coordinations such as those involved in tap dancing will be acquired very late if at all.

Certain games involving recognition of color, name, or number may be used helpfully in these classes. Obviously the problem is dual: to give as much help as possible in developing the powers of mind that the child has, and to develop and educate him in motor activities. There should be no delusion about the product. The best of opportunity can yield no more than nature gives at the start.

SUMMARIZING STATEMENT

To find opportunity in life that calls forth one's best efforts is to find a way of living in which the individual can be satisfied and the community can be proud. The conflict that tends to develop between the needs of the individual and the needs of society gives rise to all sorts of stresses. These produce ill health or result in maladjustment. Many of the disabilities of children arise out of accidents that leave the individual crippled in some respect. The good society provides rich opportunities for the development of the individual and gives needed supervision to his activities. Moreover, it is the business of wise parents and good citizens to reduce the conflicts that arise between the individual and society. If they unavoidably do arise, the larger good of society of course is to be protected; but it should be remembered that there is no community good existing as a state apart from the welfare of individuals who compose the community.

The disposition to separate the community from individuals who compose it is as fallacious as the purpose to make a distinction between the organism and the environment. Such a distinction is wholly artificial, and serves only the convenience of language. The environment and organism are merely two aspects of one phenomenon: the individual in a total situation. To improve the environment is to enrich child life, and to impoverish it is to drain away national resources. As schools and other social institutions engage in the leadership of people, teaching them how to live, these agencies must conceive of their functions as related to human behavior and the development of the individual. When this happens the academic allegiance to remote and traditional ends will decrease, but so powerful is the influence of custom that the pace to better living in the world must of necessity be slow.

PROBLEMS FOR DISCUSSION

1. A director of health education and physical education recommends a full time physical education teacher (with special preparation in rehabilitation) for the school for handicapped. The superintendent opposes the recommendation on the basis that, "Our handicapped children are different. They are not athletically inclined. A good recess period each day is sufficient." Do you agree?
2. The gifted child is often regarded as a small, weak, uncoordinated and studious individual. In reality he is larger, stronger, and healthier for his age group. Because he is often accelerated in school, he is not as physically mature as his classmates. His knowledge and understanding of the game is often far superior to his physical ability. What considerations must be made to keep this child interested in physical education activities?
3. Programs of adapted physical education vary in philosophy from the remedial to the strictly recreational. What is physical education's role in working with the exceptional child?
4. A junior high school, located in an average community, has an enrollment of 1,500 pupils of which 200 are mentally retarded. The chairman of the physical

education department requests that these pupils be scheduled in separate physical education classes with a maximum enrollment of 25. The principal disagrees and holds that they should be scheduled with normal children so that they may learn from them. What position would you take in such a situation?

5. Instructors and students may implement the above with problems gained from their own experience and observation.

REFERENCES

American Public Health Association, Committee on Child Health: *Services for Handicapped Children—A Guide to General Principles and Practices for Public Health Personnel*. The Association, New York, 1955.

Clarke, H. H. and Clarke, D. H.: *Developmental and Adapted Physical Education*. Prentice-Hall, Inc., Englewood Cliffs, 1963.

Daniels, A. S.: *Adapted Physical Education*. Harper & Row Publishers, New York, 1955.

Hagman, H. L.: *The Administration of American Public Schools*. McGraw-Hill Book Company, New York, 1956.

Hunt, V. V.: *Recreation for Handicapped*. Prentice-Hall, Inc., Englewood Cliffs, 1955.

Joint Committee on Health Problems in Education of the National Education Association and the American Medical Association: *Health Education*. ed. 5. The Associations, Washington and Chicago, 1961.

Pelone, A. J.: *Helping the Visually Handicapped Child in a Regular Class*. Bureau of Publications, Teachers College, Columbia University, New York, 1957.

Rathbone, J. L.: *Corrective Physical Education*. ed. 6. W. B. Saunders Company, Philadelphia, 1959.

Stafford, G. T. and Kelley, E. D.: *Preventive and Corrective Physical Education*. ed. 3. The Ronald Press, New York, 1958.

CHAPTER 13

INTRAMURAL ATHLETICS

WHAT ARE INTRAMURAL ATHLETICS?

A definition in keeping with the derivation of the term would limit intramural athletics to those activities, competitive and noncompetitive, conducted within the limits or boundaries of a particular school. Frequently, contests between teams or individuals representing various schools of a community, held without an admission fee, are regarded as intramurals. The term "extramural" appears more appropriate to designate this type of activity.

PURPOSES OF INTRAMURAL ATHLETICS

Intramural athletics provide an opportunity for all students to engage in many types of athletic activities regardless of skill. Members of intramural teams enjoy the thrills of success which crown achievement, learn to take defeat intelligently and graciously, develop worthwhile habits of leisure, and form a permanent interest in sport.

Thus the objectives of intramural athletics may be summarized in terms of their educational values:

To Promote Leisure Education. A part of each person's leisure should be devoted to wholesome physical activity. Without the specialization required for interschool competition, intramural athletics promote skills in various games and sports intended for use in leisure time while at school and in life after school.

To Enrich Social Competence. Intramural athletics establish group relationships in situations of vital interest to students. Proper organization and conduct of these activities facilitate the development of such desirable qualities as sportsmanship, cooperation, self-reliance, and friendliness.

To Develop Group Loyalties. Devotion to a cause enables a person to put forth his best efforts, subjugating individual interests to the welfare of the group. Interschool athletics restrict this privilege to the limited number who comprise the team, intramural competition provides opportunity for large numbers to enjoy this rich experience.

To Provide Healthful Exercise. Since health is associated with wholesome living in which exercise constitutes an essential part, intramural athletics contribute to health by developing interests and skills which all but guarantee continued participation.

Since intramural athletics serve the mass of students, whereas interschool competition restricts participation to the few possessing superior skill, the intramural program is superior to interschool athletics for the general purposes of education. It should be remembered that interschool teams are a great incentive to the successful operation of an intramural program. Many participants in intramurals who never can develop sufficient skill for the school team find in intramural athletics the realization of values which to them represent a desirable goal. For the favored youth of high potential capacity, the intramural program provides opportunities to develop skills which later enable him to join the interschool squad, thus helping him to realize one of his highest ambitions. The fact that many players on interschool teams are recruited from the ranks of intramural athletics should be regarded as an associate rather than a direct value of intramural sport. An intramural program conducted primarily as a *feeder system* for interschool teams fails to comply with sound educational purposes.

ORGANIZATION OF INTRAMURAL ATHLETICS

Several important factors deserve consideration in the organization of intramural athletics.

Elective Basis. Although physical education may be required, it is recommended that the intramural program be placed upon an elective basis. Boys and girls should be encouraged through appropriate guidance to elect some form of intramural participation. Success in securing a large elective participation depends upon the initiative and leadership of the director.

The danger always threatens that an overemphasized intramural program may restrict free elective participation; further, that emphasis on group activities may discourage the student who prefers individual participation. In these respects intramural athletics often create problems similar to criticisms leveled at interschool competition.

The Intramural Director. In large schools one person in the department, called an intramural director, may organize and direct the program. Sometimes the head coach of a given sport has charge of intramurals in that activity with other faculty members serving as assistants. Wherever practical the intramural program should become the responsibility of one person. Coaches of interschool teams rarely give sufficient attention to students of average native ability, or the intramural program is used for the primary purpose of developing material for the school team.

The assignment as intramural director calls for a person with initiative, creative ability, enthusiasm, and a sincere interest in this area. Administration should be as much concerned with the selection of the person to direct intramurals as it is with the choice of a head football coach.

Types of Activity.   Since physical education teaches fundamental skills which have a direct contribution to recreational activities outside of school, numerous seasonal activities in the physical education program are suitable for intramural competition. In fact, the intramural program may well grow out of the instructional program, providing recreation and play experiences beyond those available during the school day. Intramural groups engage in a diversified list of events leading up to such culminating activities as play days and sports days. Activities for any school depend on local interests, time allotment, facilities, staff, and financial support.

Selection of Teams.   Among the numerous methods used to select intramural teams the following appear most frequently: (1) grade in school; (2) homerooms; (3) classification based upon age, height, weight, or a combination of these factors; (4) physical education class section; and (5) voluntary groups. Individual participation usually follows a similar pattern.

Intramural Council.   An intramural council elected by the student body can contribute much to the spirit and development of a good program. This body serves in an advisory capacity to the teacher in charge. The council is concerned with such problems as eligibility, protests, officials, awards, corecreation, and extramural competition.

Intramural Managers.   Two intramural managers should be appointed each sport season, one to be known as the senior manager, the other as the junior manager. The senior manager is responsible for the care of equipment, assisting with the organization of teams, posting schedules, scoring at contest, keeping permanent records, and performing such other duties as the director shall assign to him. The junior manager notifies teams when they are scheduled to play, checks attendance and eligibility of players, posts the score after contests, assists the senior manager with equipment, and performs such other functions as may be assigned to him by the director. In addition, each representative team should have its own manager to perform such duties as may be required.

Eligibility.   Usually no scholastic requirements are enforced unless a student is so far below the average of his class that his spare time is needed for study. Obviously, members of interschool squads are ineligible for intramural competition in any sport in which they compete interscholastically. A student may elect to play on but one seasonal intramural team in the same sport, even though his team has been eliminated in the tournament. Any player may be ruled ineligible to compete in future contests because of unsportsmanlike conduct.

Health Examinations. Health examinations should be required of all participants as a condition of eligibility.

Maximum Participation. A worthy goal in intramural athletics relates to maximum participation. Sound administrative policy encourages a high percentage of students, both boys and girls, to engage in the program either as a team member or individual. However, quality of program should never be sacrificed for quantity. Lack of facilities and a limited staff may restrict participation, and teacher load should take into account intramural responsibilities. Many principals and superintendents recognize the educational significance of intramural athletics, and accept these experiences as an integral part of the school program instead of regarding them as extracurricular.

Use of Facilities. Sound administration recognizes the need for equitable use of facilities among the various types of program activities. Thus a reasonable allocation of facilities, to meet the needs of both boys and girls, must be established for the instructional program, intramural program, and interschool athletics.

DEVELOPING AND MAINTAINING INTEREST IN INTRAMURAL ATHLETICS

To conduct a good intramural athletic program it is important to supplement the basic plan of organization with various technics for developing and maintaining student and faculty interests.

Awards. A unit trophy awarded the team scoring the largest number of points in the intramural program serves the purpose of widening the interests of students in sports. Most authorities agree that individual student awards place false emphasis on the event, unsuited to the principles of democratic education.

Handbook. Many secondary schools present each incoming student with a handbook containing useful information with respect to the curriculum, extramural activities, guidance, student organizations, and similar matters. The handbook affords an excellent opportunity to describe general regulations concerning intramural athletics.

Newspapers. The school newspaper is one of the best sources for disseminating program information to the student body. In many communities intramural directors successfully utilize local newspapers for general publicity purposes. This is an excellent means of interpreting the program to the public.

Assembly Programs. The school assembly offers opportunities for spot announcements and student demonstrations.

Bulletin Boards. Wise use of bulletin boards serves to inform students of policies, regulations, schedules, and general announcements. The material must be attractive and changed frequently.

Bulletins. The daily mimeographed bulletin which many schools circulate to all homerooms serves as a good channel for announcements, schedules, postponements, and game results.

Homeroom Representatives. Many schools follow the plan of having each homeroom designate a student as intramural representative. It is his responsibility to keep his group informed of the intramural policies and procedures.

TYPES OF COMPETITION

There are several types of competition for intramural athletics; among the most common are Round Robin Tournaments and Elimination Tournaments.

In Round Robin Tournaments each team plays every other one, and the final standing is determined by the percentage method.

Table 3 shows the arrangement for four or five teams, although the plan may be amplified to provide for any number of units. Whenever possible an odd number of teams should be avoided because of difficulties encountered in schedule making.*

Table 4 shows the percentage method of scoring Round Robin Tournaments. *The number in the per cent column is determined by dividing the number of games won by the total number of games played.*

The chief advantage of the Round Robin Tournament over the Elimination Tournament is that the former permits a team to continue playing after it has been beaten; whereas in the Elimination Tournament a defeated team is automatically barred from further competition.†

Table 3. *Round Robin Tournament for Four and Five Teams*

FOUR TEAMS

1–2			1st Date: Team 1 Plays Team 2; Team 3 Plays Team 4
1–3	2–3		2nd Date: Team 1 Plays Team 3; Team 2 Plays Team 4
1–4	2–4	3–4	3rd Date: Team 1 Plays Team 4; Team 2 Plays Team 3

FIVE TEAMS

1–2				1st Date: Team 1 Plays Team 2; Team 3 Plays Team 4
1–3	2–3			2nd Date: Team 1 Plays Team 3; Team 4 Plays Team 5
1–4	2–4	3–4		3rd Date: Team 1 Plays Team 4; Team 2 Plays Team 5
1–5	2–5	3–5	4–5	4th Date: Team 1 Plays Team 5; Team 2 Plays Team 3
				5th Date: Team 2 Plays Team 4; Team 3 Plays Team 5

* The number of games necessary to complete a Round Robin Tournament is determined by the formula: $\dfrac{N(N-1)}{2}$. N represents the number of teams entered.

† See footnote for exceptions, p. 189.

Table 4. *Percentage Method of Scoring Round Robin Tournaments*

TEAM	1ST GAME	2ND GAME	3RD GAME	TOTAL PLAYED	TOTAL WON	TOTAL LOST	PER CENT
1	Won	Won	Won	3	3	0	1.000
2	Lost	Won	Won	3	2	1	.666
3	Won	Lost	Lost	3	1	2	.333
4	Lost	Lost	Lost	3	0	3	.000

For various reasons the director may wish to use the Elimination Tournament. The plan is simple when the number of teams competing is a perfect power of 2.° Figure 22 shows such an organization.

Assuming that the number of teams has been determined, the next step is to decide upon the order in which the teams appear. One method is to write consecutive numbers on cards equal to the number of teams enrolled. Each intramural manager or captain selects a card which automatically indicates the relative position of the team he represents.

During the *first round* (Fig. 22) team 1 plays team 2; team 3 plays team 4; team 5 plays team 6; and team 7 plays team 8. Teams 2, 3, 5, and 8 having emerged victorious the tournament proceeds to the *second round* which eliminates teams 3 and 5. In the final or *third round* team 2 is awarded first place, team 8 second place, and team 5 (which now has defeated team 3), third place. A disadvantage of the Elimination Tournament is that a good team may be prevented from further competition early in the series. For example, team 1 was eliminated during the first series, although it is possible that team 1 is better than some of the groups which survived, namely, teams 3, 5, or 8.†

When the number of teams in an Elimination Tournament is not a perfect power of 2 the problem is slightly complicated. Here a system of *byes* must be planned. The tournament should be organized so that *byes* occur during the *first round* of games. No one minds them then,

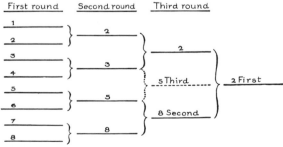

First round Second round Third round

Figure 22. Elimination Tournament when the number of teams is a perfect power of 2.

° The term "perfect power of 2" means that a number may be evenly divided by 2 until the final quotient is 1. For example $8 \div 2 = 4$; $4 \div 2 = 2$; $2 \div 2 = 1$; therefore 8 is a perfect power of 2.

† Sometimes Consolation Tournaments are provided for groups eliminated, or the tournament is seeded by empirically inserting the two best teams in the first and last place, respectively, at the beginning.

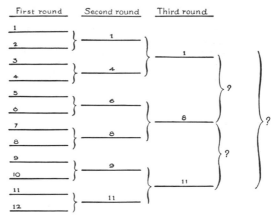

Figure 23. Improper organization of an Elimination Tournament when the number of teams is not a perfect power of 2.

although disputes sometimes result when certain teams are permitted *byes* near the end of the match. A simple illustration may help to explain the difficulty.

Figure 23 shows an Elimination Tournament organization composed of 12 teams. During the *first* and *second round* of games all teams are permitted to play. At the end of the *second round* teams 1, 8, and 11 are still competing for the championship. Now the question arises, which team shall be given a *bye* in the *third round*? By this time interest has become so intense that each group presumably will ask either to play or to draw the *bye*, depending upon whatever advantage is to be obtained thereby. The director now wishes he had planned the tournament so that *byes* had been provided in the *first round*. How could this have been done?

Returning to the original proposition based upon the perfect power of 2 this may be accomplished by referring to Table 5. The rule for such cases follows: *The number of byes in the first series equals the original number of teams (in this case 12) subtracted from the next higher integer which is a perfect power of 2.* By consulting Table 5 it is obvious that this integer is 16. Subtracting to determine the *byes*, one has $16 - 12 = 4$ or the number of *byes* to be drawn in the *first round*.

Proceeding as before, cards are provided equal to the number of

Table 5. *How to Determine the Number of Byes in an Elimination Tournament Based upon the Perfect Power of 2*

$2 \times 2 = 4$ The number of byes in the first series equals the original
$4 \times 2 = 8$ number of teams subtracted from the next higher integer
$8 \times 2 = 16$ which is a perfect power of 2.
$16 \times 2 = 32$
$32 \times 2 = 64$ Example: Assume there are 12 teams. Referring to the
$64 \times 2 = 128$ table one finds that the next higher integer is 16. Now $16 - 12 = 4$ or the number of *byes* to be drawn in the first series.†

† See Figure 24 for the correct representation of these data.

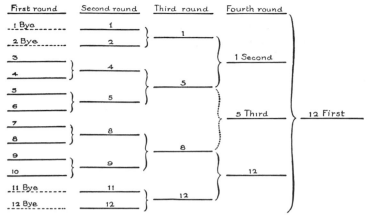

Figure 24. Correct organization of an Elimination Tournament when the number of teams is not a perfect power of 2.

teams entered, and on four of these cards the word "bye" is written. Captains or managers draw cards which indicate the relative position of the various teams. The Elimination Tournament for 12 teams is represented correctly in Figure 24.* In the *first round,* teams 1, 2, 11, and 12, having drawn *byes,* remain idle. In the *second, third,* and *fourth rounds* all teams compete which have not been eliminated. According to Figure 24 team 12 deserves first place, team 1 second place, and team 5 third place.†

Many directors prefer the Round Robin to the Elimination Tournament. Often the Elimination Tournament places an emphasis on quantity rather than quality with reports showing a high percentage of student participation, whereas certain competitors may have participated for only a limited period in a single contest.

FINANCES

Since intramural athletics are a component part of the physical education program, financial support should come from the general school fund.

TIME SCHEDULES

The after-school period immediately following the formal dismissal hour is the most suitable time for intramural athletics. This is the part of the day when students seek recreation and liberation from their pent-up energy.

* With a limited amount of practice the exact number of *byes* is easily determined. For example, if 23 teams are enrolled, 23 is subtracted from 32, leaving 9 byes to be drawn during the first series; 44 teams necessitate 20 byes (64 − 44), and so forth.

† The number of games necessary to complete an Elimination Tournament is one less than the numbers of entries.

Some schools find it necessary to schedule intramurals before school in the morning, during the noon hour, or within an activity period during the latter part of the regular school day. These arrangements usually apply when buses transport pupils to and from school. In these instances it is usually necessary to rush the program to meet rigid time schedules and quantity frequently is given priority over quality.

Use of the physical education class period for intramurals conflicts with sound educational principles which regard class periods as being concerned primarily with instruction.

CORECREATION

Compatible with the objective to develop social competence is the provision for corecreational and coeducational activities. Activities such as dancing, bowling, badminton, volleyball, tennis, and golf offer excellent opportunities for wholesome companionship among young people of both sexes.

PROBLEMS FOR DISCUSSION

1. A junior high school, with an enrollment of 1500 students, operates on a seven period day. During the week each of six physical education teachers is assigned 27 teaching periods and three periods of study hall duty. At the hour of formal dismissal the physical education teachers supervise the building exits and loading of buses. The principal expects them to carry on a broad intramural program daily. What are your reactions to this kind of schedule?
2. A teacher of physical education says, "We conduct intramural games during the physical education periods because we are certain of 100 per cent participation. So many of our students have other interests during after-school hours." Do you agree?
3. During the basketball season in a small secondary school only one gymnasium is available for the following activities: varsity basketball, junior varsity basketball, girls' intramural basketball, and boys' intramural basketball. The director faces a scheduling problem for the intramural program. What are your recommendations?
4. Two different types of school situations pose a problem relative to intramural athletics. One is the school from which pupils are transported to their homes in buses at the hour of formal dismissal; the other is the school with a "double shift" or "extended day" program. What recommendations can you make for organizing an intramural program?
5. Instructors and students may implement the above with problems gained from their own experience and observation.

REFERENCES

American Association for Health, Physical Education, and Recreation: *Current Administrative Problems*. Washington, 1960.
Beaman, H. R. and Humphrey, J. H.: *Intramural Sports, A Text and Study Guide*. W. C. Brown and Company, Dubuque, 1960.

Boyden, E. D. and Burton, R. G.: *Staging Successful Tournaments.* Association Press, New York, 1957.

Educational Policies Commission: *School Athletics.* National Education Association, Washington, 1954.

Means, L. E.: *Intramurals: Their Organization and Administration.* Prentice-Hall, Inc., Englewood Cliffs, 1963.

National Conference for City Directors of Health, Physical Education, and Recreation: (First) *Conference Report.* American Association for Health, Physical Education, and Recreation, Washington, 1956.

National Conference for City Directors of Health, Physical Education, and Recreation: (Second) *Conference Report.* American Association for Health, Physical Education, and Recreation, Washington, 1957.

CHAPTER 14

INTERSCHOOL ATHLETICS

INTERSCHOOL ATHLETICS IN AMERICA

Perhaps more than any other single movement, athletics and sports characterize physical education in America. Gaining nationwide popularity in colleges and universities during the early part of the twentieth century, interscholastic contests spread rapidly into the public school. The influence of formal discipline and faculty psychology, which largely determined the curriculum of that period, found no place for athletics and they emerged without pedagogical sanction, administrative direction, or school control. Indeed, an activity to be called educational must first have been experienced by those who dictated the school policies, and also have achieved the status of appearing in the "social register" of the academic world—the textbooks.

Under the guidance of coaches from outside the school, and without the wise supervision that superintendents and principals might have afforded, athletics gained popular recognition. This approval came not as a tribute to a great educational enterprise but as an intuitive response to a spectacle which appealed to man's fundamental nature.

Contests between schools were planned by students and watched by admiring groups of townspeople. Soon adolescent sponsorship, together with unbridled spectator influence, turned the emphasis from friendly competition to unwholesome rivalry wherein the spirit of winning at all costs assumed major proportions. Occasionally interschool athletics became the pawn of the sporting fraternity. Numerous sharp practices arose during this era, some of which persist, blemishing an otherwise worthwhile educational venture. Thus, the advent of proselyting, commercialism, low eligibility standards, poor sportsmanship, and monetary awards may be attributed largely to this unfortunate beginning.

Slowly school authorities came to realize the necessity of responsible leadership. Early attempts to exercise accountable administrative control arose from the embarrassment of school authorities over unethical procedures, rather than an awakened consciousness by those officials that educational values might be derived from such contests. Gradually superintendents and principals began to accept interschool sports as an essential part of the school program.

ATHLETICS AND PHYSICAL EDUCATION

Within a few short years control of athletics passed from students and spectators to superintendents and principals. Under the guidance of these educational administrators responsible persons were employed to protect and develop the educational values of such activities. Most of this leadership has been assumed by directors and teachers of physical education, the majority of whom are experienced and highly skilled technicians who have received their preparation in one of the numerous professional schools throughout the country. The administrative principle has become established that athletics belong to the school, and that they are an integral part of physical education.

Convincing evidence of this principle is expressed in the Educational Policies Commission* publication, *School Athletics: Problems and Policies.* This publication was prepared in response to widespread expressions of concern over practices in school athletics. Several nationally known leaders in school athletics and physical education participated in the planning and preparation of its content.†

ATHLETICS FOR GIRLS

Widespread differences of opinion exist relative to athletic competition for girls. At one extreme are those who favor an interscholastic program for girls which approximates the type of organization found in the average boys' senior high school. At the other extreme is a group which contends that competition for girls should be restricted to participation in social games with the "desire to win" element largely removed. Between these two points of view are many variations, concerned primarily with such factors as: (1) the extent of competition to be permitted; (2) adequate control over such functions; (3) teams coached by qualified women; (4) games conducted by competent women officials; (5) girls' contests not to be used as added or preliminary attraction for boys' games; (6) provision for the athletic participation needs of the average girl who lacks the skill required for school teams; and (7) other problems of similar nature.

If girls are to be restricted from engaging in interschool competition while boys are encouraged to do so, the reasons for such restriction

* The Educational Policies Commission is jointly sponsored by the National Education Association and the American Association of School Administrators.

† The summary of recommendations of *School Athletics: Problems and Policies* is in the Appendix.

must be found in the kind of social qualities desired in the different sexes, rather than in significant differences in biological needs and interests.

Modern liberalism has brought to women greater freedom in the choice of a vocation and in numerous other matters. Thus, she shares with her brother opportunities to engage in politics, industry, the professions, homemaking, recreation, and, in fact, practically all of the functions of citizenship toward which education is focused. Under such conditions it is difficult to support the view that interschool competition for girls should be abolished, and at the same time subscribe to the policy that there are educational values to be derived from interschool athletics for boys not attainable to the same degree in other forms of public school education. Consistent judgment would appear to recommend similar policies for both girls and boys.

These policies would attempt to improve conditions through education rather than by prohibition. Numerous remedial measures have improved interschool competition for boys relating to such perplexing problems as overemphasis, proselyting, unwise use of gate receipts, unsportsmanlike conduct of contestants, and affairs of similar nature.

The *Division for Girls' and Women's Sports* of the American Association for Health, Physical Education, and Recreation represents a strong organization for the development and control of these activities. This organization establishes procedures and standards aimed to improve the educational values of athletic competition; it supports the view that competitive elements in sports activities may be used constructively for achieving desirable educational and recreational objectives; it recognizes the expressed needs of highly skilled girls, but believes competition through sports is the privilege of all regardless of skill; it holds that a broad physical education program plus intramural and extramural activities take precedence over interscholastic athletics.*

A fair administrative treatment of this topic avoids personal or group biases. It respects the judgments of accepted women leaders, and the pronouncements of organizations founded to perpetuate the worthwhile physical and social values inherent in sport. At the same time such a treatment strives to formulate administrative policies that reconcile the facts of biological and social inheritance with sharp conflicts between nature and nurture that tend to increase as civilization develops. Failure to give due recognition to the seriousness of these conflicts, and to the educational needs of individuals, results in many untenable positions held by persons interested in girls and women.

BIOLOGICAL DIFFERENCES BETWEEN BOYS AND GIRLS

Numerous anatomical and functional differences exist between the sexes. The female pelvis becomes broader after puberty, giving to the

---

* "A Statement of Policies for Competition in Girls' and Women's Sports" is in the Appendix.

femur a marked obliquity which lessens the girl's ability to run or jump. The shoulder girdle of the adolescent boy is wider and stronger than that of the average girl of the same age. Evaluations made of instinctive, emotional, temperamental, and moral traits show no significant differences between the sexes.

Physical strength is a relative matter. Some boys are stronger than others, and marked differences in physical strength should be recognized in scheduling one team with another, especially in those activities involving bodily contact. Where boys lack the physical capacity to engage in a particular type of competition, another sport is recommended for them. Certainly girls should not be expected to attain standards of excellence established for boys in athletic events requiring great strength, although activities suited to the interests and capacities of girls might easily be chosen.

ATHLETIC OVEREMPHASIS

Education seeks to develop in the individual qualities which enable him to serve as a respected member of society. Any athletic program which fosters outcomes in conflict with the best interests of the social group must be regarded with suspicion.

The school provides a series of experiences aimed to inculcate desirable social qualities among youth. Rules and regulations necessary for the successful conduct of these experiences are formulated cooperatively by representatives of the schools concerned. Overemphasis in athletics occurs when established rules and regulations are set aside or ignored to benefit individual participants, the team as a whole, or any other person or persons gaining unwarranted special privilege thereby. Overemphasis takes many forms.

A news item reads:

SCHOOL HEAD NEEDS POLICE PROTECTION

Pursued by dozens of egg-throwing supporters of (Bond) High School, Mr. (Smith), superintendent of schools at (York), was forced to leave town under guard after a football game in which (York) defeated (Bond) 27 to 6.

The ire of (Bond) adherents was aroused by an affidavit presented to the school board by Mr. (Smith), formerly principal of the (Bond) High School, which caused a (Bond) star to be declared ineligible just before the game.

Stones, eggs, and mud were hurled at the car in which the (York) superintendent left town after the game, and cries of 'traitor' started along the street as he passed. A long procession of (Bond) automobiles followed the superintendent's car several miles.*

The account illustrates a kind of overemphasis which leads to unethical social practices opposed to the best interests of public education.

In some schools students are advised to avoid certain difficult subjects to remain eligible for athletics. Overemphasis is present when the time required for practice or competition seriously interferes with the

* The correct names of towns and superintendent are withheld for obvious reasons.

regular school program. A prominent athlete may be in demand during every season of the school year. This is undesirable for the best organic development of the individual as well as for scholastic reasons. Whether or not a schoolboy athlete can be "burned-out" by excessive competition remains a controversial issue, although some physicians and experienced coaches believe this to be true. Perhaps the greatest personal harm to the adolescent boy lies in the distorted relative values which arise out of adulation paid to athletic heroes by fellow students and townspeople. Proselyting, conducting post-season games and all-star games, winning at any cost, and conducting athletics primarily for public entertainment are other examples of an exaggerated premium placed on interschool competition.

The very nature of athletics make a unique appeal to outside influences. The elements of conflict, strife, and rivalry cause certain alumni and others to follow the interschool teams. To prevent overemphasis, active supervision and control by school authorities is imperative.

Principals of schools, superintendents, and boards of education are responsible for the educational values of athletics. These officers are responsible because they determine educational policy, select those who direct athletics, and help to formulate the rules and regulations of state and local athletic associations. Community leaders interested in the welfare of youth are receptive to sound educational guidance and are eager to cooperate in the best interests of youth.

ATHLETIC ASSOCIATIONS

Methods of local and state control are essential to the sound organization and conduct of interschool competition. Fundamentally, the local organization seeks to preserve or insure athletic standards compatible with general school policies; the state association provides standards governing participation between schools; and the National Federation of State High School Athletic Associations regulates interstate competition.

The same association, either local or state, should function in matters pertaining to both boys' and girls' athletics. The local organization may exercise jurisdiction over intramural events as well as interschool contests, although the state association usually limits itself to relationships between municipalities or districts. An administrative problem deserves emphasis at this point. When the *same* association directs the activities of both boys and girls, men representatives often assume the lion's share of control with girls' athletics either patterned after boys' or relegated to an inferior position. Under these circumstances the association should have a girls' or women's committee with a woman chairman that functions as a unit, and is responsible only to the administrative officer of the association.

Local Athletic Associations. In many communities it is customary to maintain a high school athletic association open to all regularly enrolled students. The chief objectives of such an association are: (1) to promote the interests of athletics and (2) to help finance interschool competition through a small membership fee. Unfortunately many of these associations serve primarily to increase the emphasis on interschool competition and to give students, through official representation on the athletic council or committee, unwarranted opportunities to direct the athletic affairs of the school. Athletics should be regarded as an educational enterprise, not as a plaything for adolescent student minds. Interschool athletics bear the same educational relationship to the physical education program that laboratory experiences do to biology, physics, or chemistry. Student responsibility in athletic affairs is justified to the extent accorded pupils in academic subjects. In the final analysis, student fees for membership in such associations represent merely another form of gate receipts.

Depending somewhat upon the size of the community and the number of secondary schools involved, athletics in municipalities are administered by a council or councils and an executive committee or committees. In relatively small cities with one or two high schools, a single council and committee suffices, or perhaps the two may be combined into one unit. Where the educational policies in various schools differ widely, especially in large cities, it is desirable to have an athletic council and an executive committee for all schools. Such a body may be composed of the principals and/or athletic directors of all schools and the director of health education and physical education.

Representation on an individual school council includes the principal or vice principal, two or three faculty members, all head coaches of various sports, and the director of physical education as chairman. It should be the function of the council to adopt regulations governing the organization and control of athletic affairs subject to the approval of the principal or superintendent. The executive committee may comprise the principal or vice principal, the two or three faculty members, and the director of health education and physical education. The executive committee prepares agenda for council meetings, performs duties assigned to it by the council, and deals with procedures that implement administrative policy.

Either the school principal or superintendent (the choice depends upon the local administrative organization) constitutes the final legal authority in all problems pertaining to athletics.

State Athletic Association. Practically all states maintain a strong central organization called the state high school athletic association. Usually the state is divided into districts, with the schools in each district classified according to pupil enrollment as a basis for competition.

The association is governed by a constitution and bylaws, a state board of control or its equivalent, and an executive secretary or commissioner of athletics. Members of the state board of control are elected from the various districts and represent the different school classifications. Its personnel is distributed among superintendents, principals, faculty representatives, directors of health education and physical education, and athletic coaches. Although the number of districts determines to some extent the size of the board of control, an organization composed of nine members represents a satisfactory number, each person holding office for a period of three years, with one-third of the personnel retiring annually.

The State High School Athletic Association and the State Department of Education. Conflicts of opinion arise with respect to the relationship of the state high school athletic association to the state education department. Doubtless numerous political and educational problems enter into the discussion when individual states are considered, although the answer seems relatively obvious when judged by the principles of sound administrative procedure.

For those who believe that athletics are a part of public education, there can be but one answer. Since 1803, when Congress settled the character of the public school system by vesting control of township school lands in the legislatures of the various states, it has been the function of the state to establish standards, to disburse federal and state school funds, and to manage all school affairs not delegated to the local school district. Moreover, in the management of scholastic contests and other matters which involve interrelationships between local districts, it is customary for the state department of education to act as final authority in supervision and control.

From a purely legal point of view, some question may exist relative to the state or local board of education, as a department of government, having the right to redelegate the sponsorship of an educational activity such as interschool athletics to a voluntary organization like the state high school athletic association. Quite certainly this right, if legal, should be voted by the board of education, rather than permit agents of the board (superintendent or principal) to affiliate the local high school with the state high school athletic association without official action. Sometimes the school superintendent or high school principal effects this membership without official approval by the board of education.

Reasons for not obtaining official permission from the board may reside in the belief that interschool athletics represent a sort of quasi-educational activity, outside the usual legal jurisdiction exercised by the board of education. Rather than helping to solve the problem, these reasons present a more serious difficulty. If interschool athletics are not regarded as educational activities as defined by statute, perhaps the board of education has no right to use public funds for the payment of coaches' salaries and other expenses associated with such contests.

As a matter of fact, interschool athletics may not be legal at all without provision being made for them by the state legislature. Unless such contests are made legal, who is responsible in case of accident or injury to players and spectators? Who is responsible if injuries occur during tournaments sponsored by the voluntary state high school athletic association? Obviously steps should be taken, in states where doubt exists with respect to legal status, to have interschool athletics made a part of public education by appropriate state legislation. Such legislation would establish the respective responsibilities of the state high school athletic association, the state education department, and local boards of education. Commendation is due a few states that have provided for interschool athletics by appropriate legislation.

The National Federation of State High School Athletic Associations. This organization is designed to protect and regulate interstate athletic contests and to promote amateur sports among state associations. It was organized in 1920 to deal with many athletic problems resulting from high school contests organized by nonschool organizations and promoters. It has been particularly concerned with preventing exploitation of youth through interschool athletics.

MAJOR AND MINOR SPORTS

Following collegiate tradition numerous high schools classify athletic events as major and minor sports. The custom rests solely upon a collegiate tradition; it is without justification as an educational procedure and many schools and colleges rightfully have abolished the distinction.

ATHLETICS IN ELEMENTARY AND JUNIOR HIGH SCHOOLS

The physical education program in elementary and junior high schools provides an opportunity for developing skills in a large number of activities which may be continued in the senior high school and outside of school. Successful "carry-over" depends largely upon habits, attitudes, and skills developed during this formative period. This philosophy underlies the elementary school and the junior high school movement; it applies to physical education as well as to academic subjects.

Properly organized seasonal activities, intramural athletics, sports days, and occasional invitational contests between schools take the place of season-long scheduled interschool athletics in elementary and junior high schools.

Qualified physical educators bring with them a thorough knowledge of child growth and development. They know that the age from 12 to 14 is regarded as the "awkward age," that during this period the skeletal system normally grows faster than the muscular system, and that the heart increases rapidly in size with the possibility of serious physical strain or permanent injury if the activities are too strenuous. They know, too, that few elementary and junior high schools equip teams properly for events requiring bodily contact, and that although the school does not assume responsibility for injuries received in athletic competition, education must accept the moral responsibility for safeguarding the health of children and young adolescents. In the final analysis, realization of the educational values of competition in these grades depends largely upon the quality of available leadership.

A statement of policy on junior high school athletics approved by the National Association of Secondary School Principals and the American Association for Health, Physical Education, and Recreation recommends a *limited program* of interscholastics for boys with superior athletic ability to develop and utilize this talent.*

THE ATHLETIC COACH

By tradition and title educators often look upon the athletic coach as a person apart from other employees of the school. When athletics become more clearly recognized as *bona fide* curricular activities, tradition may change with acceptance of the coach as a substantial and important member of the staff, and educators may bestow upon him the more appropriate title of *teacher* or *instructor of athletics* comparable to other teachers or instructors in the school. Considerable evidence points in these directions.

The athletic coach or instructor of athletics assumes a responsible position in American education. On the one hand he guides the destinies of youth in life situations of intense interest. On the other hand he instructs boys in the technic of his specialty, and witnesses the results of his teaching in actual and immediate operation. His teachings are openly exposed to public evaluation.

No other teacher enjoys so rich an opportunity for molding the character of adolescent youth, and no other teacher runs so great a risk of having his technical shortcomings exposed. The student of social studies may be brilliant in the classroom and a distressing failure as a citizen, but by this time his instructors are through with him.

Qualifications.   Leadership in any educational activity is essential, but leadership in athletics is of paramount importance. Too often the athletic coach, who might be a potent force in character education, is employed for his ability to produce winning teams. The conditions under which he works may force him to abandon desirable educational outcomes. Winning games is naturally the result of superior performance, but if winning is imperative, other values must take a subordinate position.

Sound character is vital in selecting the athletic coach because the pressures and complexities of the game bring out the true caliber of the man. Years ago an outstanding and successful coach wrote:

It seems to me that there are three fundamental questions that should be asked about a man before he is entrusted with the responsibility of coaching boys. The first

* The basic principles underlying the statement of policy appear in the Appendix.

question to be answered is: *What manner of man is this?* How does he speak and act? Is he sound and clean in mind so that his influence is inspiring and uplifting? Would he set a fine example—not by *posing* but by *being*—the type of man we want each of his boys to be? If these questions cannot be answered favorably, stop then and there. No other qualities can supplant the fundamental qualities of character. The next question is: *Just how well does he know what he wants to teach?* Is he thorough or superficial? Is he progressive or reactionary? Is he original or without imagination? In short, can he bring with him a thorough, solid knowledge, and will he keep that knowledge constantly abreast of changing conditions? And finally: *Can he teach others what he knows?* Can he take knowledge, add expressiveness and impressiveness of speech and action, imbue with enthusiasm and give his students something that will not only be easy to grasp but also *pleasant to master?* Surely the athletic coach of today must measure up to rigid high standards of both education and essential manhood. Any profession so exacting and so demanding is being built upon the bed rock of education and must continue to grow and elevate itself to constantly higher planes.*

In general, then, the qualifications of the coach are essentially no different from those required in any teacher. He must be equipped technically in his specialty and conform in attitudes and appreciations to approved standards of social culture.

Nearly all high school coaches are graduates of an approved college or university. State certification requirements stipulate that athletic coaches must present evidence of preparation equivalent to academic teachers. The athletic coach should be a *bona fide* and full-time member of the high school faculty. And finally, men employed as athletic coaches or teachers of athletics deserve the protection and support of boards of education and administrative authorities, rather than applause or condemnation depending upon the varying success of athletic teams.

Salary.　The entire salary of the athletic coach should be paid by the board of education. His salary never should be augmented by funds from the athletic association or from other sources. Such a plan tends to place athletics on a commercial basis. While it is true that the mental and physical strain of coaching may be greater than in many other teaching positions, the majority of men become coaches because they enjoy the task.

The coach should be paid on the *basis* of the regular teaching load established for a given school. Boards of education often fail to appreciate the number of hours an athletic coach actually works. If his hours exceed the number prescribed for the average teacher he may be reimbursed accordingly, although every informed coach understands that he will give many hours to his work without attempting to affix a "price-tag" to everything he does. Of course here, as in other subject areas, preparation and experience must be considered.

In some school systems athletic coaches, although regular members of the faculty, demand extra compensation for coaching assignments. Several boards of education have met these demands under public pressure; others have raised the question of legally adopted salary schedules, and the moral right of boards of education to grant special privilege.

* F. H. Yost: The Place of Varsity Athletics in a Program of Athletics for All, *Journal of Health and Physical Education,* June, 1931, p. **7.**

Few court decisions have established precedents in this matter, and legislation has failed to indicate the proper course to follow. The problem becomes more complex with increased emphasis placed on inter-school athletics, and the comparatively high salaries paid some coaches in colleges and universities. Surely administrative wisdom, appropriate legislation, and board of education regulations are needed to provide a sound basis for policies adopted by local communities in the solution of this problem, a problem that already has attained huge proportions, and one that deserves serious administrative attention before it grows worse.

As a result of the many requests received by the National Education Association, its Research Division studied the problem of extra pay. Facts available from large urban school districts were analyzed.* One hundred and forty-two school districts with a population of over 100,000 were asked for their most recent salary schedules. The following is the general comment of this study:

> This memorandum shows that a majority of the larger urban school districts make some provision for extra pay for assigned extra duties rendered by classroom teachers in hours beyond the regular teaching day. Only about half the districts, however, pay for any extra duties other than athletics.
>
> Although a few districts pay extra amounts as high as $1500 or more for coaching athletics, the medians of the extra payments are not large. Median amounts of extra pay are shown for 18 different assignments in the athletic program. Ten of the 18 medians are amounts under $300; three are under $200.
>
> For activities other than athletics, relatively few districts pay as much as $400 a year for any extra duties. Median amounts for extra pay for these activities are less than $200 for a majority of the activities reported upon.
>
> When the time spent in performing extra duties is considered, the extra pay appears to be set at modest figures. In most school systems it doubtless would add substantially to the school budget to reduce the class load of teachers so as to recompense them for the extra time given to after-school assignments. Such adjustments would require the school districts to employ additional teachers to cover the class periods vacated by the teachers in charge of activities.
>
> Many school systems have yet to make a careful analysis of the educational, social, and monetary value of the "after-school" activities in the school program. Some have at least set down in words the existing policies on the scheduling of and payments for such activities; others may find it desirable to do so.

As Official or Player.   The extent to which a coach is justified in officiating or playing in games outside of the school organization often presents a problem of considerable magnitude. Sometimes school super-intendents and boards of education seriously oppose such practices, while in other communities no criticism is voiced if the coach obtains extra remuneration in this way.

The matter should be settled with reference to the relation of such activities to his efficiency as a teacher. Similar deleterious effects might result from devoting too much time to the church orchestra, working in one's own garden, or accepting employment in a local business concern.

Both the coach and his superior officer should come to an under-

* Special Memo, Research Division, National Education Association of the United States. Washington, October, 1955.

standing about officiating or playing before employment negotiations are finally completed.

Such an understanding may circumvent administrative difficulties. Occasionally an experienced athlete, and otherwise qualified instructor, becomes a member of the school staff. Because of his competence in athletics and for other reasons, he could make a substantial contribution to the school as an athletic instructor. But as an official or player he can earn more money and avoid the "wear and tear" usually associated with coaching athletic teams. An increasing number of qualified young men reason this way.

HEALTH EXAMINATION OF CONTESTANTS

The demands of interschool athletics are so exacting that no one should participate in them without a thorough medical examination by a reputable physician. When boys or girls are allowed to play in such contests without a competent examination, the risks of injury are too great and the professional reputation of administrators too much in jeopardy.

Most state high school athletic associations require a certificate of physical fitness for every boy or girl who engages in interschool competition. These certificates are placed on file in the office of the nurse, athletic director, or principal. Many state associations provide blanks or forms for this purpose.

PARENTAL PERMISSION

The custom has become almost universal of obtaining parental permission before students are allowed to engage in interschool athletics. Some school systems use a form which is signed by the parent granting permission for the student to engage in specified activities and releasing the school from responsibility in case of injury incurred during practice periods or while playing in scheduled games.

Except in rare instances, court decisions and rulings of attorneys general hold that the school is not responsible in case of physical injuries to contestants. Where an admission fee is charged, the responsibility of the board of education remains in some doubt, and most schools obtain the parent's signature to a statement designed to relieve the school of any obligation in this matter, even though there is serious doubt regarding the legal value of these signatures.

Some years ago many schools attempted to defray the hospital expenses or physician's fees for such injuries, but the difficulties encountered proved of such magnitude that most boards of education abandoned the practice.

The school cannot accept responsibility for injuries received in athletic contests. Accidents inflicting injuries of a similar nature may occur in the science laboratory, auditorium, cafeteria, or other place connected with the school. The board of education is under the moral obligation, however, to provide competent supervision, adequate athletic equipment, sufficient first-aid facilities, and sound insurance.

INSURANCE AGAINST ATHLETIC INJURIES

Payment of medical bills by the school, or expecting parents to assume responsibility for athletic injuries, has been replaced by insurance policies aimed to protect the board of education, athletic coach, parent, and student. Usually the state high school athletic association sponsors its own plan or arranges with an insurance company to provide this service for member schools. At other times the board of education or the parent-teacher association arranges for students to purchase at a small fee an accident policy covering all approved school activities. Usually this does not cover injuries sustained in football. Some schools provide a special policy for this sport and others have their own injury benefit plan.

Good insurance represents a wise investment. Poor insurance often gives little more than a false sense of security. Several reputable companies accept athletic insurance. Due precaution should be taken to determine: (1) the financial resources of the company writing the policy; (2) the legal authority of the company to operate in a given state; and (3) the validity of coverage—that the policy specifically covers what it is supposed to insure.

ELIGIBILITY

When schools first assumed responsibility for the control and supervision of interschool competition, regulations of eligibility were established. Schools now either accept the standards adopted by the state high school athletic association or follow local regulations of their own. Competing schools should exchange certified eligibility lists prior to the contest. In large cities such lists are submitted to the office of the director of health education and physical education.

Because of deep-rooted public interest, and the pressure of outside groups, certain eligibility rules are established and strictly enforced. Usually these rules refer to: (1) age; (2) semesters of competition; (3) maintenance of a passing grade in a given number of subjects; and (4) transfer from one school to another. Most state associations establish 19 years of age as the upper limit of interschool participation. The number of semesters during which an athlete may compete ranges from 8 to 10 in a four-year high school and 6 to 8 in a three-year high school. In nearly all states the contestant must attain a passing grade in three regular subjects. However, some authorities oppose a specific regulation in scholarship and hold that academic standing and deportment satisfactory to the principal are sufficient. The migratory rule stipulates that the student shall attend school in a given community for a specific time before he is eligible for interschool athletics; exceptions provide for families moving from one community to another, if no athletic inducements influence parents in making the change in residence.

PARTICIPATION ON OUTSIDE TEAMS

Few schools permit members of the athletic squad to play on outside teams during the sports season they are members of the school squad. Violation of this rule renders the participant immediately ineligible to represent his school during the remainder of the specific season. In some districts the rule is more drastic, causing the player to lose his athletic eligibility during his public school career. Some schools are more lenient and allow outside participation, provided the athlete obtains written permission from his principal.

PROSELYTING

Most schools have nothing to offer in the form of scholarships because public high schools are free institutions. Proselyting is relatively uncommon because of growing popular disapproval, the vigilance of state high school athletic associations, and the natural deterrent of geographical proximity wherein each school is familiar with the policies of neighboring institutions.

It would be fanciful to conclude, however, that no assistance is given certain high school athletes, or that no attempts are made to encourage outstanding players to transfer from one school to another. Perhaps one of the worst forms of such proselyting involves the practice of moving an entire family to a community and promising the father routine employment merely to get the son for purposes of high school athletics.

Proselyting is a contemptible and unsportsmanlike practice. It should be stamped out through education and by rigid enforcement of state association regulations inflicting severe penalties upon schools which violate these rules. The most serious results of proselyting lie in its effect upon the athlete and his fellow students, engendering in their minds a false sense of relative values and fostering habits of deceit and subterfuge. Proselyting also indicates that the community gives tacit or open approval to athletic overemphasis and gross commercialism.

EXCUSES

Athletic excuses fall into two groups: (1) excuses from regular school work for out-of-town games; and (2) excuses from physical education classes because of membership on an athletic team.

Years ago little attention was paid to the amount of school time lost by teams playing out-of-town games. Finally, absurd schedules took students away from their school work for as many as four or five days during a season. Most school authorities limit the amount of time teams may be excused from regular classes, and athletic schedules are arranged accordingly. Naturally the proximity to other cities or towns is a factor to be considered. Most schools forbid overnight travel except on rare occasions.

Excusing team members from physical education classes poses a different problem. To be physically educated the boy or girl must have developed skill not only in athletic events but also in rhythmic and self-testing activities, and in such individual forms of sport as tennis, volleyball, swimming, and golf, which may be used for leisure pursuits. In brief, the student should not be excused from physical education classes unless he has attained a suitable proficiency in the wide range of activities offered in the total program. Success in one or two athletic events sufficient for membership on a school team is no justification in itself for releasing the athlete from instructional physical education. At best he may be excused during the season in which the event is scheduled.

LENGTH OF SCHEDULES AND PRACTICE PERIODS

The tendency in high school athletics is to work boys too hard and too long. Often practice periods are arranged daily, the schedule of games extends over a period of many weeks, and the number of contests exceeds the educational values obtained therefrom. Herein lies a flagrant source of overemphasis.

The local athletic council should adopt standards and policies governing practice periods and schedule making compatible with the rules of the state association. Since the state association must adapt its standards to meet all sorts of varying conditions throughout the commonwealth, the more enlightened local districts usually plan fewer games and shorter practice periods than the parent organization allows.

Coaches are qualified to supervise the physical condition of team members and to guard against overtraining. No boy should be allowed to represent his school in more than one sport during the same season. Teams should practice and train a sufficient length of time before the schedule opens to develop proper physical condition. Schedules should be arranged with schools of approximately equivalent size and athletic ability.

Besides the undesirable effects of long and numerous practice periods upon the health of the players themselves, school facilities are not available at suitable times for intramural use. In an attempt to formulate a more equitable basis for the development of both intramural and interschool programs, the maximum standards shown in Table 6 are suggested.

Table 6. *Number of Practice Periods Per Week and Length of Session*

ACTIVITY	NUMBER OF PRACTICE PERIODS PER WEEK	LENGTH OF PERIOD PER SESSION IN MINUTES
Football	4	120
Basketball	4	90
Baseball	4	120
Track	3–4	60 to 90
Tennis	4	60 to 90
Golf	4	120
Swimming	4	60 to 90
Soccer	4	90
Ice Hockey	4	90
Speedball	4	90
Lacrosse	3	90
Wrestling	3	90

CONTRACTS

Proceeding in a business-like manner, contracts should be signed by the proper representatives of opposing schools for each interschool contest. State high school athletic associations require the use of contracts among member schools, providing forms for this purpose. Verbal agreements often lead to misunderstanding, distrust, and open controversy detrimental to athletic sport. Where schedules are made by an athletic league for contests within the league itself, contracts may not be necessary. Rules and regulations of the league are sufficient.

OFFICIALS

Competent officials are as essential to the success of an athletic program as qualified coaches. During the actual contest the official enjoys a most strategic position for instilling sound principles of social education of value to participants and spectators. No person is qualified to officiate at interschool contests who lacks ideals of good sportsmanship, who is not familiar with the rules of the game, or who is hesitant about calling the plays as he honestly sees them.

The state high school athletic association provides a list of properly certified officials, and insists that schools belonging to the association use these men or women for interschool games. Athletic officials should be required to pass examinations covering the rules of the sport and in actual officiating. The eligibility of officials should be as carefully guarded as the eligibility of coaches or players.

Few restrictions govern the remuneration received by officials, although some state and local associations attempt to standardize this procedure. Standards for eligibility and remuneration of officials go hand in hand, and should receive equal consideration.

Usually the contract for athletic contests states that officials shall be mutually agreed upon several days before the game. Unless otherwise specified, the home team makes the final selection of officials, subject to the approval of opponents, and defrays the expense involved.

When a person is engaged to officiate an athletic contest, it has been customary to pay him a certain fee, plus traveling expenses. Sharp practices in "padding" expense accounts have been responsible for the development of an administrative policy whereby the official receives a stipulated sum covering both the officiating fee and traveling expenses. This plan has much to commend it because the official knows exactly how much money he is to receive, and the school the precise amount it is to pay.

Since officials are engaged weeks or months prior to the actual contest they should be reminded of the contract, in writing, approximately one week before the date of the game. The form letter used for this purpose usually contains such information as the: (1) date, hour, and place of the game; (2) names of the opposing teams; (3) fee to be paid; and (4) request that the official be on hand at least 30 minutes before the game begins.

FINANCING ATHLETICS

If athletics are to be regarded as desirable educational experiences, and as an integral part of the school program, the board of education should provide funds for these activities in precisely the same way that finances are made available for other forms of education. Such a procedure helps to remove the overemphasis and outside domination which frequently characterize various athletic events.

Most boards of education rely on admission fees to defray the cost of interschool programs, and even to provide funds for the partial support of intramural contests, athletic fields, and other school projects. Admission charges, pupil fees, and appeals to the public for special donations usually tend to demoralize an educational activity, and to focus public attention on the spectacular or commercial aspects of the enterprise.

In school systems where customary practice favors reliance upon gate receipts, the transfer to board of education support represents a gradual administrative process.

The sale of athletic tickets requires an efficient accounting system established by the athletic council or board of education. Unless careful supervision is maintained, the number of tickets given to student salesmen often fails to check with the amount of money turned in and tickets returned. Each student salesman signs a statement signifying that he has received a certain number of tickets and will be responsible for them. Probably the best plan is to restrict the sale of tickets to responsible adults. All athletic financial accounts should be audited periodically.

Complimentary tickets create a problem. Members of the press are admitted upon presentation of their professional card, and the police-man's uniform allows him to pass. The practice of giving complimentary tickets to members of the squad, teachers, school officials, and others leads to controversy and petty manipulation. If admission fees are charged, all who attend as spectators should pay the prescribed amount. Those who have a direct responsibility to perform in connection with the contest, and who attend wholly in an official capacity, should be admitted free.

KEEPING ACCURATE RECORDS

Well organized departments employ accurate methods of book-keeping. Athletics require: (1) permanent records of the various sports, (2) individual participation records, (3) seasonal statistical summaries, (4) annual statistical summaries, and (5) accurate inventory of supplies and equipment.

TOURNAMENTS

State championships and the selection of all-star teams represent the products of a professional rather than an educational point of view. In some states district and sectional tournaments select teams for the final games played to determine the winner in various sports.

Perhaps state tournaments suggest the neglect of educational guidance directed toward the proper organization and conduct of athletic activities. At best these tournaments serve to finance state high school athletic associations, stimulate alumni and community interest, publicize coaches, and provide newspaper copy. On the debit side these contests add little in the form of wholesome experiences for participants not available in regularly scheduled season games, often produce an un-wholesome physical effect on players, and foster opportunities for gambling difficult to control.

AWARDS

Among school and college authorities the almost universal custom prevails of awarding insignia or letters to athletic teams. There is some question concerning the educational soundness of this procedure. On the one hand are persons who would abolish awards entirely; on the other hand are persons who contend that the practice of granting insignia is justifiable when it is not overdone.

Those who favor abolition of all awards believe that boys and girls should compete in athletic activities for the love of playing and for the benefit—physical, mental, moral, and social—derived from such competition. It is their belief that awards are harmful, in that they turn the thoughts of participants to awards rather than to the activities and the values inherent in them. The practice of granting awards, they say, has developed in some athletes the attitude that the school owes them something. This feeling may lead some students to justify their acts in stealing certain articles of athletic equipment for their personal use. It is further believed that when the award ceases to be a symbol of achievement, and becomes a prize of monetary value, the professional spirit replaces the amateur, and school boys begin to compete for gain and personal glorification rather than for love of the sport and the benefits derived from competition. This group points to the fact that when Greek laurel wreaths were replaced by valuable prizes, the result was professionalization and final disappearance of amateur sport in Athens.

Those who believe in awards contend that man has always competed for prizes. From the time when the ancient Greeks who crowned the Olympic victors with laurel wreaths—the first great awards for which athletes competed—down to the present, people in all walks of life (art, science, literature, education) have striven for honors which attract the interest and approval of their fellow men. This group believes that the evils are not so much in the awards themselves as in the use made of them. Although reasoning by analogy is sometimes fallacious, they believe it pertinent to say that since athletics are not abolished because of certain evils that have appeared from time to time, so the granting of awards should not be abolished, merely because the practice is sometimes overdone.

There is middle ground between these two extreme points of view. Because of the long tradition of granting awards in the older schools and colleges, and because of the prevalence of this practice in other activities of life, simple awards—mere symbols of achievement with little or no monetary value—appear justifiable.

The actual standards for giving awards should be established by the local athletic council, in keeping with regulations adopted by the state association.

PURCHASE AND CARE OF ATHLETIC EQUIPMENT

The trend is toward the purchase of athletic equipment by boards of education, even though present administrative practice frequently delegates this responsibility to the athletic association. Under recommended conditions athletic supplies and equipment are secured from general school funds. It is common practice for schools to provide books, pencils, paper, industrial arts supplies, and home economics utensils without cost to children. Probably the chief reason why this service is not often extended to the purchase of athletic equipment lies in the fact that athletics often are regarded as extracurricular activities, as something apart from the regular function of the school.

In the minds of informed educators there is almost unanimous agreement that the athletic program is a component part of the school curriculum. Recognition of this principle has been slow to materialize, owing to the unsavory reputation of athletics in its early days, and to the continued gate receipts which give the appearance of commercialism rather than of education.

Spontaneous public interest in numerous localities, exemplified in elaborate stadia to accommodate large crowds, caused interscholastic athletics to get into the class of *big business.* In many places money poured into the athletic fund and equipment budgets grew higher and higher. Commercial concerns dealing in athletic supplies, and sensitive to the growing demand for better and more expensive materials, rushed forward with elaborate displays aimed to attract the attention of schools with money to spend. Poorly equipped teams competing with those from institutions more generously supplied aroused alumni and supporters to demand improvements.

The situation was intensified by practices in colleges and universities. It is common knowledge that the secondary school often follows a pattern set by the college. Many high school coaches, influenced by the false favors shown them as college athletes, have unwittingly transferred college standards to the secondary school. As students they had little knowledge of, nor were they concerned with, the financial organization which furnished lavish equipment. Transferred to the scene of high school coaching, and confronted with the problem of ordering and paying for equipment as well as using it, they sometimes make mistakes.

Interschool teams should be provided with adequate and safe equipment. Unwarranted expenditures are both financially and educationally unsound. Adolescent boys frequently develop a false sense of financial values when extravagant expenditures are made to outfit teams. Careless use of athletic clothing and playing equipment often results. Slightly used equipment is thrown aside and replaced by new, instead of being repaired and returned to active service. Many coaches or faculty representatives, unaccustomed to purchasing athletic materials in quantities, contract deficits which not only embarrass the administration but also teach boys extravagance and waste.

There seems to be only one way out of the difficulty. Expenditures for interschool athletic equipment should be placed in the hands of the board of education.

The proposal that athletic supplies be purchased by boards of education is supported by reasons of economy. Boards of education employ purchasing agents who are familiar with problems of finance. While athletic departments should *recommend* the type of equipment needed, the actual *purchases* should be made by the person qualified to perform this function.

Irrespective of the source from which funds are obtained for the purchase of athletic equipment, the physical education department is concerned with its proper use. A bookkeeping system should be installed which accounts for each article from the time it is purchased until it ceases to be of service. Students loaned athletic clothing or equipment belonging to the school should have an individual record card which contains a list of the articles received, the date of issue, and condition of the material. The card is signed by the student in the presence of the faculty representative. The account is canceled when such equipment is returned in good condition showing only reasonable wear. The individual card system prevents theft, unaccountable loss, or misuse.

At the end of the sport season all equipment is collected, cleaned, repaired, and stored for future use. This is an important administrative item that, properly organized, greatly reduces the cost of athletics.

PROBLEMS FOR DISCUSSION

1. A number of high schools comprise an interschool athletic league for girls and conduct their activities similarly to the boys' program. Some of the women teachers oppose the continuance of a program on this basis and suggest a plan which calls for a broad intramural program with culminating interschool competition through sports days. Other teachers maintain that such a plan will destroy the competitive spirit of youth and school spirit of the student body. Furthermore they argue that the public will not stand for deemphasis of girls' athletics. What is your opinion?
2. A high school football team is invited to play a post-season bowl game for charity in a city 1000 miles away. The invitation is extended by a service club of that city to the mayor of the home city. The mayor refers the invitation to the chairman of the school board and the superintendent of schools who agree that the school board should decide the matter because there is a school board regulation prohibiting post-season games. Considerable pressure for the game is received from some citizens and the local press. After prolonged discussion the school board votes to waive the regulation on the basis that such a game will provide a unique opportunity for high school boys to see another part of the country and will develop good public relations. What is your reaction to this decision?
3. A county coaches' association launches a strong campaign with all boards of education concerned to establish a uniform extra-pay scale for athletic coaches. The county health, physical education, and recreation association opposes the practice of extra pay for coaches. However, the latter association is willing to support the coaches' extra pay if a similar scale is approved for all physical education teachers assigned to after-school intramural athletic activities. What position would you take in this situation?
4. Instructors and students may supplement the above with problems gained from their own experience and observation.

REFERENCES

American Association for Health, Physical Education, and Recreation: *Athletic Directors National Conference Report* (1959), *Interscholastic Athletics in Junior High School* (1958), *Coaches Handbook* (1959), The Association, Washington.
American Association for Health, Physical Education, and Recreation: *Current Administrative Problems.* Washington, 1960.

American Association for Health, Physical Education, and Recreation: *Standards for Junior High School Athletics.* Washington, 1963.

Educational Policies Commission: *School Athletics: Problems and Policies.* National Education Association, Washington, 1954.

Forsythe, C. E.: *The Athletic Director's Handbook.* Prentice-Hall, Inc., Englewood Cliffs, 1956.

Forsythe, C. E.: *The Administration of High School Athletics.* ed. 4. Prentice-Hall, Inc., Englewood Cliffs, 1962.

National Conference for City Directors of Health, Physical Education, and Recreation: *First Conference Report* (1956), *Second Conference Report* (1957), *Third Conference Report* (1960). American Association for Health, Physical Education, and Recreation, Washington.

National Education Association: Research Memo, *Extra Pay for Extra Duties.* Washington, 1963.

PART III

FACILITIES

Because the functional design of the school plant is based on its use as a community-school recreation center, it is essential that all agencies and specialists concerned pool their resources in planning. This results in increased efficiency with less cost. In some instances, school, recreation, and park officials find it desirable to enter into joint financing as well as joint planning. In large urban areas housing authorities also are involved.

CHAPTER 15

INDOOR FACILITIES

IMPORTANCE OF INDOOR FACILITIES

Providing adequate indoor facilities represents a tremendous problem for the administrator and his staff. Most essential is the interrelationship of administration, supervision, and instruction with emphasis on the need for mutual understanding and respect between these professional groups to insure tools with which to work.

Construction of these facilities challenges the attention of both architects and educational experts. The architect has the answers to the technical problems of building construction, but the administrator and his staff know the types of facilities and equipment best suited to the program.

The modern concept of joint community-school use of public school facilities calls for careful planning which provides for community recreational needs as well as for the school program. In communities where the administrative control of community recreation resides in a municipal department other than the board of education, joint planning of facilities is essential. Further, it has been found increasingly desirable to utilize funds from the community recreation budget to establish, in or adjacent to school buildings, certain facilities for use in both school and recreation programs.

TEACHING STATIONS

The term *teaching station* is widely used in referring to a specific area or room to accommodate a class group for instruction in physical education.

The *main gymnasium* is the most prevalent type of teaching station area. Depending on its size, movable partitions, and pupil enrollment, it may serve as two or more stations.

In addition to the main gymnasium, smaller units for special purposes may be necessary. These should be a minimum of 35 by 50 feet in size and equipped for the special needs served. One type of smaller teaching station is for *adapted activities* and the special apparatus suitable to this program. Another is a *dance center* or *studio* equipped and decorated to create the atmosphere desired by the dance teacher. A third type, often called the *lounge*, is equipped with tables, chairs, and recreational game equipment. This station serves as a recreational and instructional center for students, as well as for evening community groups.

In some schools it is more practical to design a larger auxiliary unit for multiple use. In these instances installation of an insulated, power-driven folding partition is essential. An area of this type may be used for such activities as gymnastics, dancing, wrestling, and fencing.

THE FIELD HOUSE

A comparatively new venture in indoor facilities is the dome field house. Regarded as an extravagance at first, many school architects now recommend this structure for reasons of economy. The area, unmarked by structural supports, serves a multiple purpose: as a gymnasium it provides adequate space for a variety of physical education activities including athletics; as a meeting place it accommodates large groups assembled at commencements and other public functions—functions too large for the school auditorium. It is suggested that architects be consulted about this type of dome facility in planning new buildings.*

AUDITORIUM-GYMNASIUM

A combination auditorium-gymnasium attempts to conserve space and reduce construction cost. A few school systems have gone a step further and constructed a combination auditorium-gymnasium-cafeteria. This arrangement is in fact expensive since it affords most unsatisfactory conditions, restricting all programs, and preventing simultaneous schedules in different programs. It is not recommended.

LOCATION OF GYMNASIUM FACILITIES

Adaptability to purpose favors locating the gymnasium facilities adjacent to playing fields, and on the ground floor. Location of these facilities in a wing of the building helps to eliminate the possibility of

* Further information on the subject may be obtained from the publication, *"Conventional Gymnasium vs. Geodesic Field House,"* Educational Facilities Laboratories, Inc., 477 Madison Avenue, New York 27, New York.

objectionable noise in academic classrooms. With this arrangement corridor gates and a separate entrance may be installed to separate this area from other parts of the school building, thereby aiding the traffic control of community groups.

PHYSICAL FEATURES

These features refer to such items as size, floor construction, obstructions, and walls. The sections which follow describe essentials related to each item.

Size. The intended use of a gymnasium determines its size. Factors to consider are: school grade levels to be served, number of teaching stations required, official sizes of playing courts, community use, and spectator space. The diagrammatic scheme in Figure 25 represents a guide for determining the size of a gymnasium. Table 7 gives suggestions for gymnasium sizes and types.

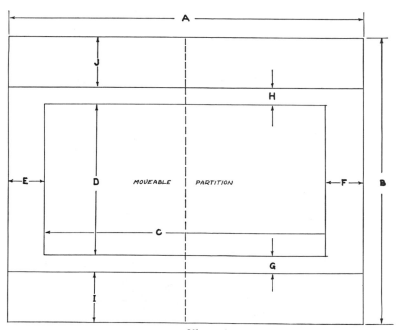

KEY TO FIGURE 25 DIMENSIONS:

A and B: Overall size of Gymnasium, inside measurements.
C and D: Basketball court size: 74' x 42'—junior and elementary schools
            84' x 50'—high school boys and girls.
E and F: End safety zones 6' minimum, 8' preferred for added safety.
G and H: Side court safety clearance areas 6' minimum, 8' preferred for added safety.
I and J: Space devoted to folding bleachers set on the main floor. The amount of space will vary according to needed seating.

Figure 25. Recommended gymnasium floor space with choice as to size of teaching station and amounts of seating. (Courtesy of Second National Facilities Conference. *Planning Facilities for Health, Physical Education, and Recreation.* The Athletic Institute, Inc., Chicago.)

Table 7. Suggested Gymnasium Sizes and Types

RECOMMENDED TYPE OF SCHOOL	TYPE	DIMENSIONS AS RELATED TO FIGURE 24										CEILING HEIGHT	NO. & SIZE OF TEACHING STATIONS PROVIDED IF MOVABLE PARTITIONS ARE USED	APPROX.‡ SEATING WITH FOLDING BLEACHERS SEATING	NUMBER TIERS OF SEATING
		A	B	C	D	E	F	G	H	I	J				
Elem.	I	86'	54'	74'	42'	6'	6'	6'	6'	0'	0'	20'	2–43' x 54'	0	0
Jr. H.S.	II	86'	65'	74'	42'	6'	6'	6'	6'	11'	0'	22'	2–43' x 65'	350	6†
*Jr. H.S.	III	96'	72'	84'	50'	6'	6'	6'	6'	11'	0'	22'	2–48' x 72'	385	6†
Community Use															
H.S. Girls	IV	96'	70'	84'	50'	6'	6'	6'	6'	8'3"	0'	22'	2–48' x 70'	320	5†
H.S. Boys	V	96'	78'6"	84'	50'	6'	6'	6'	6'	8'3"	8'3"	24'	2–48' x 78'6"	640	5
H.S. Boys	VI	100'	93'5"	84'	50'	8'	8'	8'	8'	13'8"	13'8"	24'	2–50' x 93'5"	1070	8
H.S. Boys	VII	100'	104'5"	84'	50'	8'	8'	8'	8'	19'3"	19'3"	24'	2–50' x104'5"	1500	11

*Larger basketball court where adult community use is anticipated.

† Bleachers on one side only.

‡ Figures in this column assume that seating on side walls is continuous. If there are breaks in continuous seating, higher seating must be provided to maintain these seating capacities. For each added tier of folding bleachers, add 22" to dimensions B, I, and J, Figure 25.

(Courtesy of Second National Facilities Conference. Planning Facilities for Health, Physical Education, and Recreation. The Athletic Institute, Inc., Chicago.)

Floor. Years of experimentation reveal several different types of suitable flooring with staunch advocates for each of them. Many experts recommend hard maple boards for top flooring, although some prefer birch or beech. Standards for all board floors include the following items: (1) boards free from knots and relatively straight-grained; (2) boards 1¼ inches in width and ¾ inch in thickness; (3) boards tongued and grooved and fastened to a sub-floor laid diagonally; and (4) the sub-floor laid on joists supported by girders resting on concrete piers (Fig. 26).

Floors should be sanded to a smooth surface, cleaned with water, and properly sealed. Numerous commercial concerns recommend satisfactory products as preservatives. These are applied according to the manufacturer's specifications.

Floor markings for various games are painted on *after* the sealer coat and *before* the finish coats are applied. Lines are painted in varying widths and colors.

Obstructions. Avoid such obstructions as posts, stairs, radiators, pipes, ducts, or other objects which interfere with the practical use of the playing area. Although tolerating such obstructions may lower the initial cost of construction, they continue as safety hazards. Recess lights, bell systems, and clocks into the walls, or protect them by a strong wire screen.

Walls. Durable and smooth walls up to a height of 10 to 12 feet from the floor help to prevent injuries. Corners below door height should be rounded and all possible projections should be avoided.

Glazed brick provides an excellent material for walls, although some architects recommend glazed terra cotta or wood. Above the 10 or 12 foot level, a material should be selected which decreases noise and sound reverberation. Unglazed cream-colored tile or cinder block, which reflects light without glare, serves admirably for this purpose. Original construction may include wall space for instruction in such games as tennis or handball. Where the walls and floor meet, rounded corners facilitate cleaning. A 3 by 4 inch angle-iron screwed to the floor serves the purpose.

Ceiling. State or local building codes govern ceiling construction in various geographical areas. Acoustically treated ceilings are essential for reducing noise. Original plans should make provision for the support of apparatus.

Spectator Accommodations. Such provisions refer to: (1) seating facilities; (2) entrances and exits; (3) toilets and washrooms; (4) ticket booths; and (5) check rooms.

Where the gymnasium is used extensively as a community center, many architects recommend some kind of permanent bleachers. Three common types are: (1) those constructed permanently along the sides of the gymnasium; (2) those fastened to wheels, and moved out of the way when not in use; and (3) those attached to and telescoped against

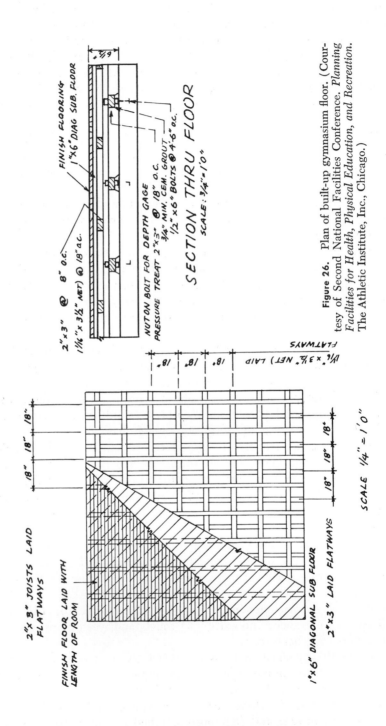

NUT ON BOLT FOR DEPTH GAGE
PRESSURE TREAT 2"x3" @ 18" O.C.
3/4" MIN. CEM. GROUT
1/2"x6" BOLTS @ 4'-6" O.C.

FINISH FLOORING
1"x6" DIAG SUB. FLOOR

2"x 3" @ 8" O.C.
1 1/16"x 3 1/2" NET) @ 18" O.C.

SECTION THRU FLOOR
SCALE: 3/4"=1'0"

2"x 3" JOISTS LAID
FLATWAYS

FINISH FLOOR LAID WITH
LENGTH OF ROOM

1"x 6" DIAGONAL SUB FLOOR
2"x 3" LAID FLATWAYS

1 1/16"x 3 1/2" NET) LAID
FLATWAYS

18" 18" 18"

18" 18" 18"

SCALE 1/4" = 1'0"

Figure 26. Plan of built-up gymnasium floor. (Courtesy of Second National Facilities Conference. *Planning Facilities for Health, Physical Education, and Recreation.* The Athletic Institute, Inc., Chicago.)

the wall except when used for seating purposes. Many authorities favor the third type. Built-in bleachers usually occupy space needed for regular physical education classes. This difficulty may be circumvented to a degree by utilizing the area under the bleachers for equipment storerooms, shower rooms, locker rooms, and offices.

Folding Partitions. Two or more teaching stations are provided by the installation of folding partitions. The partitions extend from floor to ceiling and are recessed when folded. They should be motor-driven and properly insulated against sound transmission. Floor tracks are safety hazards and should not be installed.

Doors. Doors should be in sufficient number and size to permit efficient and safe movement of pupils and spectators. Fire ordinances and building codes in most communities govern the minimum size, type, and number of exits. Appropriate exit signs appear above all doors leading to the outside. Doors to storage rooms, used for heavy apparatus mounted on casters, should not have saddles.

Lighting. Modern techniques of artificial lighting, with improved fixtures, provide a quality of intensity of light for gymnasiums that is superior to natural light. Artificial lighting, coupled with modern methods of heating and ventilation, result in a minimum use of windows, thus eliminating the problem of glare from natural lighting.

Artificial lighting depends upon the number of footcandles required. A footcandle is a measurement of illumination equivalent to that produced by a standard candle at a distance of 1 foot. Artificial lighting should provide 20 to 30 footcandles of light at floor level without irregular shadows. Select artificial lighting fixtures of semi-indirect or indirect type, with reflectors made of plastic or white enamel. Recess fixtures into the ceiling and protect them with a nonbreakable and translucent covering, or suspend them from the ceiling, level with the lower chord of trusses, and inclosed in a strong wire basket hinged to the main support.

If natural lighting is preferred, locate windows 10 to 14 feet above the floor on the two long sides of the gymnasium. The ratio of window space to floor area approved for classrooms (one-fourth to one-fifth) represents an adequate standard for gymnasiums. Wire screens covering the windows and inserted flush with the wall prevent breakage. Such guards should not interfere with the opening and closing of windows. A band of directional glass blocks may be more desirable than regular wall windows. This arrangement, as well as tinted glass, helps to prevent glare. Avoid skylights unless they are absolutely necessary.

Electrical Installations. Wire the gymnasium for public address system, bell system, audio-visual equipment, scoreboards, transcription players, television, and cleaning apparatus. Extra outlets spaced approximately 20 feet apart around the gymnasium provide illumination for dances and various social recreational activities.

Heating and Ventilation. A satisfactory temperature for the gymnasium is 65° to 70°F., provided the humidity varies from 40 to 60 per cent. Some architects recommend radiators or combination unit ventilator-heaters recessed in the wall behind wire guards. Others prefer hot-air blast systems with provisions for washing and recirculating air. Install radiators underneath the balcony or along the wall at a height of 10 to 12 feet. Regulate gymnasium temperature by thermostatic control.

Proper ventilation suggests either the open window method or a mechanical fan system with exhausts. As a general rule, forced ventilation takes precedence over the open window method, although large gymnasiums may require both types. The mechanical system should provide enough fresh air to eliminate odors during the periods of greatest gymnasium load. Air movement in gymnasiums should be far greater than in classrooms, therefore larger fans are used. Ventilators located above the floor insure less interference with the activity program. Mechanically operated windows of the swinging and louvre types have supplanted the ordinary casement sash.

Drinking Fountains. Some authorities recommend locating drinking fountains in a convenient corner or along the side of the gymnasium, recessing them into the walls. Plan for recessed cuspidors with each drinking fountain of this type. Other authorities recommend placing drinking fountains in the dressing room or in the corridor just outside the gymnasium.

Storage Rooms. Provide adequate storage rooms for supplies and equipment adjacent to the gymnasium and on the same floor level. The recommended area is 250 to 300 square feet for each teaching station. Doors at least 6 feet in width, with a flush threshold, connect the gymnasium and the storage room.

Adequate shelving and cupboards (with locks) are essential in the rooms used for storing supplies. Separate storage facilities are preferable for community recreation groups.

CLEANING

Sweep or vacuum gymnasium floors daily. More frequent cleaning with a large chemically treated floor mop may be necessary. Remove dust which may collect on apparatus, beams, and other projections.

Corn-meal wax scattered on the floor prior to dancing gives good protection. This preparation may be applied to any floor finished with a standard quality of gymnasium floor seal. If swept up after dances it leaves the floor in good condition. This wax may be prepared by mixing 1 quart of oil of paraffin to 100 pounds of corn meal.

CLASSROOMS

New secondary school buildings should contain classrooms as a part of the gymnasium unit. Classrooms facilitate special instruction in play, exhibitions, posture, game rules and strategy, and numerous other items associated with the program. Include adequate storage space for supplies and equipment.

STAFF FACILITIES

Adequate facilities for teachers are essential to effective performance of their duties. These include offices (Chapter 5), dressing rooms, showers, lavatories, toilets, and storage space. Locate these facilities adjacent to the office. Some schools with large staffs prefer a faculty dressing unit off the main dressing room.

FURTHER SOURCES FOR PLANNING FACILITIES

Over the years remarkable progress has been made in gymnasium construction and equipment. Exemplary of this is the publication, *Planning Facilities for Health, Physical Education, and Recreation* (revised edition) published by The Athletic Institute, Inc. This report represents the sound judgment of the professions concerned with health education, physical education, recreation, athletics, and resident camps.

PROBLEMS FOR DISCUSSION

1. The director of health education and physical education discusses with the school plant planning committee the advantages of a separate gymnasium as compared with the disadvantages of the combination auditorium-gymnasium. At the conclusion of the director's discussion, the committee agrees to provide each large elementary school (22–24 classrooms) with a standard gymnasium and each small elementary school (12–14 classrooms) with a combination auditorium-gymnasium. Can this be justified on the basis of sound principles of a physical education program?
2. A community plans a new high school building for 1500 students, and as director of health education and physical education you recommend the following facilities:

One main gymnasium with a motor-driven dividing partition, 100 feet by 135 feet
Two auxiliary gymnasiums, 40 feet by 60 feet
One dance studio, 40 feet by 25 feet
Adequate locker and shower facilities to accommodate the anticipated enrollment plus 10 per cent
Three team rooms, complete with locker and shower facilities
One swimming pool, 75 feet by 35 feet
One lounge or game room, 25 feet by 25 feet
Adequate storage and service rooms
Separate storage room and office for community recreation director
One each instructor's office for men and women, 25 feet by 20 feet
One conference room, 25 feet by 15 feet.

It becomes necessary to take a 15 per cent reduction in cost. What adjustments do you recommend?

3. You are the department head in a school located in a community which lacks physical recreation facilities outside the school. You receive frequent requests from out-of-school groups who wish to use school facilities. These groups include Boy Scouts, church organizations, dance clubs, town basketball teams, and others. Many of these organizations have competent and responsible direction, others have dubious leadership. How can you, as an administrator, formulate a policy on this matter which will give appropriate consideration to all groups, and at the same time protect the school and your department against financial loss due to carelessness in the use of facilities?

4. Instructors and students may implement the above with problems gained from their own experience and observation.

REFERENCES

American Association for Health, Physical Education, and Recreation: *Current Administrative Problems*. Washington, 1960.

Butler, G. D.: *Recreation Areas, Their Design and Equipment*. ed. 2. The Ronald Press, New York, 1958.

Conventional Gymnasium vs. Geodesic Field House (Report). Educational Laboratories, Inc., 477 Madison Avenue, New York.

High Schools 1962 (Report). Educational Facilities Laboratories, Inc., 477 Madison Avenue, New York.

New York University, School of Education: *The School's Role in Coming of Age in a Big City* (Report). New York, 1962.

Planning Space for Physical Activity, *Journal of Health–Physical Education–Recreation*. American Association for Health, Physical Education, and Recreation, Washington, April, 1962.

Scott, H. A. and Westkamper, R. B.: *From Programs to Facilities in Physical Education*. Harper & Row, Publishers, New York, 1958.

Second National Facilities Conference: *Planning Facilities for Health, Physical Education, and Recreation*. The Athletic Institute, Inc., Chicago, 1956.

U. S. Department of Health, Education and Welfare: *Environmental Engineering for the School, A Manual of Recommended Practice*. Superintendent of Documents, U. S. Government Printing Office, Washington.

Vannier, M. and Foster, M.: *Teaching Physical Education in Elementary Schools*. ed. 3. W. B. Saunders Company, Philadelphia, 1963.

CHAPTER 16

SWIMMING POOLS

THE IMPORTANCE OF SWIMMING

An increasing number of elementary and secondary schools contain swimming pools where students develop aquatic recreational skills and learn water safety. Perhaps more than any other, swimming represents the ideal physical activity. From a physiological point of view, swimming allows for maximum functioning of large muscle groups without danger of strain. The value of hydrotherapy is recorded in medical history, and numerous modern hospitals give aquatic treatment for patients suffering from certain nervous and muscular disorders. The growing popularity of swimming as a recreational activity finds great numbers of persons of all ages enjoying the year-round advantages of pools and beaches. This interest places a responsibility on the schools to teach various aquatic technics which lead to real enjoyment and safety.

Years ago the fear of contamination kept persons away from public bathing beaches and swimming pools. Certain educators and health officials voiced the opinion that pools in school buildings might be responsible for the spread of epidemics and other disasters. This opinion has been dissipated. Modern means of sterilization and supervision have changed public opinion until most educators and health officials readily accept swimming as an important activity in the maintenance of good health and as a means of wholesome recreation.

POOL LOCATION

Location of pools in the basement prevents adequate ventilation and natural lighting. Pools built on the ground floor facilitate these needed elements.

229

Proper location with respect to dressing rooms, showers, and toilets favors the routing of swimmers. Students leave the locker room, pass the toilets and take showers before arriving at the pool entrance. Clearly marked and separate entrances and exits to and from the shallow end of the pool contribute to safety. At the close of the period, students take showers and return to the dressing room. Pools used for both sexes have separate entrances and exits.

POOL CONSTRUCTION

As a result of continuous and cooperative efforts of swimming experts, sanitarians, architects, and administrators, numerous standards are available for the construction of safe and sanitary pools.

Size and Shape. The design of pools depends upon the use made of them. Competitive swimming requires a pool length of 60 to 75 feet, in conformity with official rules. Approved dimensions are 75 feet 1 inch long and 28 or 35 feet across to provide standard lanes 7 feet wide.

Joint school-community use of the facilities should be considered when establishing water depth. The shallow end approximates 3 or 4 feet and the deep end is governed by safe diving requirements. Most swimming authorities recommend a minimum of 10 feet where a 1-meter diving board is installed. The pool bottom should have a slope of 1 foot in 15 feet in the sallow area and 1 foot for each 3 feet in the deeper water (Fig. 27).

Vertical walls free from protruding obstructions help to prevent accidents and to maintain sanitary standards.

For practical purposes the size of the pool depends on the number of persons to be accommodated at peak load. The standard is 27 square feet of water surface per swimmer for recreational purposes, and 45 square feet for instruction.

Materials. Although any material which provides a water-tight tank with smooth walls will suffice, experience proves that white or light-colored tile or glazed brick are best. The bottom and sides of the pool should be smooth without cracks or open joints. Rounded corners facilitate cleaning. Painting the inside of the pool decreases its attractiveness and increases the cost of sanitary maintenance.

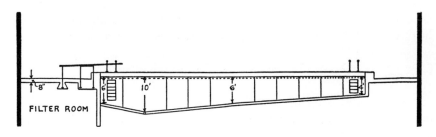

Figure 27. Section of swimming pool.

MARKINGS

Competitive water sports require lanes 7 feet wide. These are marked on the surface of the water with removable steel cables entirely covered with cork or wooden floats.

The bottom of the pool is marked with guide lines in the *center* of each lane, of the same material as the pool lining, but of contrasting color. These lines are 10 inches wide and continue the length of the pool, except for 4 feet at either end. Crossbars of the same width and 2 feet long are placed 3 feet from either end of each guide line. Guide lines extend up the walls of the pool from the bottom to the surface of the water.

The *depth* of water is indicated on the walls and near the top at the shallow end, deep end, and at the 5-foot depth. The *distance* from the end of the pool is marked at 5-foot intervals to facilitate teaching and testing.

Inlets and Outlets. Water inlet and outlet arrangements should provide the best combination of water circulation, disinfection, chemical mixing, and skimming. Small pools may require but a single inlet and outlet, provided stagnate areas are eliminated. The outlet is located at the deepest portion and on the floor of the pool. Adequate outlets completely drain the water within 4 hours. Both inlets and outlets are covered with a noncorrosive metal grating. An orifice at least four times the area of the discharge pipe prevents suction currents.

Satisfactory pipe connections permit passage of used water to the sewer as well as to the recirculation system. Adequate removal of surface contamination should be insured to prevent the possibility of scum that enters an outlet from drifting back into the pool.

Steps, Step-holes, and Hand-holds. Proper construction of ladders, by recessing them into the side walls of the pool near both ends, minimizes the possibility of accidents. Hand-holds in the runway, or hand-rails at the top on either side projecting over the runway, insure safety. A step surface of nonslip material, and drains leading into the pool, facilitate cleaning and prevent the accumulation of waste. Without overflow gutters at the ends of the pool, hand-holds assist in teaching the back-stroke; two of these are located in each lane, 12 to 16 inches above the water line, and 18 to 20 inches apart.

Overflow Gutters. Shall overflow gutters extend completely around the pool or only along the sides? Numerous swimming coaches believe that depressions in the wall at the ends of the pool interfere with the free action of swimmers while making turns. On the other hand, some authorities recommend placing overflow gutters on all four walls. The gutters should be: (1) deep enough to keep waste material from washing back into the pool and to serve as a hand-hold for nonswimmers; (2) provided with a curved outer surface for cleaning, and to prevent back-wash; (3) equipped with sufficient openings leading directly to sewers (at least one in every 10 feet) to permit rapid drainage; and (4) recessed into the wall, but projecting slightly into the pool (not over 2 inches).

Diving Boards. Regulation diving boards are 1 meter and 3 meters in height, depending on ceiling height and pool depth. A minimum depth of 10 feet is required for the 1-meter board and 12 feet for a 3-meter board. Not less than 12 feet of unobstructed space is needed above the board.

Boards of wood with cocoa-mat tread, aluminum or stainless steel, and wood covered with fiberglas are recommended.

From 8 to 10 feet of pool space from the extremity of the board is reserved for divers. Not more than two or three persons are allowed in this area at one time, although three times this number may be on the deck awaiting their turn to dive.

Decks. An area approximately 10 feet wide on the sides and 20 feet at the ends is reserved for decks. To prevent accidents the deck surface is of nonslip construction with a gentle slope, ¼ inch to the foot, to carry away excess water. Architects design decks to slope away from the pool with outlets leading directly to the sewer system.

It is less expensive to construct the deck with a slight slope toward the pool with outlets connected with the overflow gutter drainage system. Water from the deck is deflected from the pool and into the drains by a slightly raised coping around the perimeter of the pool basin.

Walls and Ceiling. Selection of materials for walls and ceiling presents two problems: (1) to avoid moisture condensation; and (2) to prevent sound reverberation. Cork, gypsum, sound-proof plaster, or similar materals are recommended for walls. Celotex, cork, or some cloth material may be used for the ceiling.

Heating. Desirable pool temperatures vary with outdoor temperatures, and with the activity of swimmers. In cooler weather the water is kept at approximately 78° F. For teaching beginners the temperature ranges from 75° to 80° F.; for recreation, 74° to 76° F.; and for competitive swimming, 70° to 72° F. Higher temperatures require a greater amount of residual disinfectant but this cost often is justified by the increased use of the pool. The temperature of the room exceeds the temperature of the pool by not more than 5° F.

Lighting. Natural lighting, when carefully planned, is desirable. Windows should be of glass block or tinted fiberglas. Excessive natural light causes too much glare and encourages the growth of algae. It is recommended that windows be installed only on the north side of the pool. Many authorities on swimming pool design favor complete artificial illumination which permits uniform lighting under all conditions. They also favor under-water lighting for pool attractiveness, promotion of safety, and facilitation of cleaning.

Ventilation. Mechanical ventilation is essential in all pools accommodating more than 25 students, unless unusual window lighting is available and outside prevailing temperatures are moderate. The ventilating system should be of a type which can be regulated to eliminate drafts and too rapid evaporation of water from the swimmer's skin.

Spectators. The visitors' gallery should be separate from the pool without direct passage between swimmers and spectators. To improve the view of spectators, and for sanitary reasons, no part of the gallery should extend over the water.

Nonabsorbent construction materials are best, with floor drains connected with the sewer. Thus, the gallery may be cleaned after use, without the danger of foreign particles entering the pool.

Even though public demonstrations are not planned, the spectators' gallery is a useful part of the pool, since students temporarily excluded from swimming may profit by observing the class.

SANITATION AND DISINFECTION

To safeguard the health of swimmers, complete circulation of water throughout all parts of the pool is necessary during the swimming period. Moreover, some method of destroying harmful bacteria is essential. Faulty technics of caring for the pool have been largely responsible for the criticism leveled at this important part of the physical education program. That the swimming pool need not constitute a health hazard is a fact known to every well informed administrator of health education and physical education.

Types of Possible Infection. The most common types of health disorders transmitted by the pool are common colds and infection of the sinuses, ears, and eyes. Proper health education, together with constant supervision of swimmers, helps to prevent the spread of colds since persons showing evidence of this condition should not enter the pool. Individuals with a history of sinus infection should refrain from diving, and should not force water into the nose under pressure. Pupils susceptible to sinus infection frequently use mechanical clips to prevent the passage of water into the nostrils. Several kinds of ear stopples are available, or oiled wool is sometimes used, for persons with sensitive ear canals.

Athlete's foot (epidermophytosis) is the most common of superficial fungus infections. There is still some dispute among medical authorities about the spread of this disease through contact with floors of dressing rooms, shower rooms, pool entrances, exits, and decks. Some research reveals that exogenous exposure of the feet apparently plays only a minor role—if any in the acute attacks of fungus disease.

Prevention is the best means of control; therefore, hygienic measures are important. The feet of all bathers should be inspected regularly and persons showing infection should be excluded. All participants should be advised concerning sound personal hygienic measures.

Although it is held that personal hygiene and local skin resistance are more important than sterilizing the environment, it is wise to follow sound hygienic measures. The advice of local or state health departments should be followed.

Disinfection. Disinfection may be administered by circulation, filtration, chemical treatment, or a combination of filtration and chemicals. The constant circulation of water through the pool from city mains to the sewer is unsatisfactory, except where the supply of pure water is inexhaustible and inexpensive.

Pools of the recirculation type require ample space. Pipes, inlet and outlet valves, pump, hair catcher, filter, water heater, and chlorinator must be readily accessible. Again, the entire system should be designed to provide an adequate volume of recirculated water based upon the swimming load limit.

Filtration removes foreign particles such as skin scales, lint from suits, and a large percentage of bacteria. While slow sand filters and rapid gravity filters are sometimes used, pressure filters are more common. All filters are cleaned daily by reversing the valves and pumping water through the sand in the opposite direction. This process washes the alum coagulant from the sand particles. If the water is passed through the filters regularly and if the filters are properly cleaned, the water in the pool may not need to be changed oftener than once every three months. The addition of alum clumps the bacteria together around the sand particles, thus increasing the effectiveness of filtration. A safe standard is maintained by passing the water through the filter every 8 to 12 hours when the pool is in constant use. Water is forced through the filtration system, preferably by an electrically driven centrifugal pump, although plunger pumps are sometimes employed. Another filter medium used in the filtration of swimming pool water is diatomaceous earth commonly called "diatomite." This type of filter requires less space. It is economical to operate and uses less water in the backwashing process.

Hair catchers are essential in the recirculation system to prevent hair, lint, and other foreign particles from entering the filters. Slotted strainers of nonrust material containing openings not more than $\frac{1}{32}$ of an inch across are better than the conventional strainer with perforated surface. Simplicity of design and ease of cleaning are essential factors.

A water heater is indispensable in a northern climate. Admitting steam directly into the water, or placing heating coils in the pool, are unsatisfactory because of the danger to swimmers and the lack of uniformity in temperature. The water heater should be thermostatically controlled.

Sanitarians generally agree that chlorine is the most satisfactory chemical for bacteria and algae control of pool water. This is available in several different forms: sodium hypochlorite; calcium hypochlorite; chlorinated cyanurates; and chlorine gas. When attached to the recirculation system, chlorine is expected to disinfect the entire flow of water returning to the pool, and the residual amount of disinfectant remaining in the water should immediately destroy any pollution disseminated by swimmers.

Chlorine gas is less expensive than liquid, but is extremely dangerous if handled incorrectly or if a leak develops. For this reason sodium hypochlorite, a liquid chlorine, is preferable. It can be used either by hand treatment or fed into the effluent of the filter with a mechanical feeder. Inexpensive chlorine bricks are available which may be thrown into the pool. This method is advised only in case of emergency.

Another method of keeping the pool free from harmful bacteria involves exposing the water in thin films to ultraviolet rays. The advantage of this plan over chlorine is that no chemical is used, hence the avoidance of undesirable odor or taste which sometimes offends swimmers. Disadvantages of ultraviolet ray treatment include the purchase of expensive and sensitive apparatus and the ineffectiveness of the system if the water is slightly colored. Under carefully controlled conditions the ultraviolet ray process may prove satisfactory.

Standards for Sanitation.   Proper administration of the pool is dependent upon the use of certain tests conducted at regular intervals by competent personnel.

Bacterial Content.   There are numerous kinds of bacteria. Some (pathogenic bacteria) cause disease in man; others are harmless. In the determination of bacteria present in pool water, differential diagnosis is only partial and usually seeks to determine the presence of the colon bacillus. The count may be very high with no pathologic bacteria present, but a high count is an index of contamination. Therefore, a count over 1000 per cc. of water is usually taken as an indication of pollution, regardless of the fact that a differential diagnosis is not made. Local boards of health generally set standards governing the bacterial content of swimming pools; these standards vary. In one school district 300 bacteria per cc. may be permitted, whereas in another section of the country the range may approximate 1000 bacteria per cc. of water. It is important that the administrator become familiar with the board of health regulations governing the bacterial control of swimming pools in his district and that he follow these rules. If proper attention is given to filters and disinfection, it is not uncommon to obtain a zero bacterial count.

Chlorine Content.   Supervisors of the pool should be supplied with the proper instrument for making the orthotoluidine test when chlorine, hypochlorite of lime, or other chlorine compounds are used. This test should be made daily when the pool is in use. The amount of available chlorine should not be less than 0.2 ppm. (parts per million), nor more than 0.5 ppm.

Acidity and Alkalinity.   The test for pH of water is made daily, just as the chlorine content is tested.* This simple test can be made by the pool supervisor with appropriate equipment. The pH should approximate 7.2.

Clearness.   When in use, the water shall be sufficiently clear so that a 6-inch black disk is visible if placed on the bottom of the pool at its deepest point and observed at a distance of 10 yards.

* pH is the symbol for hydrogen ion concentration.

CLEANING

The sides and floor of the pool should be cleaned of all sediment, floc from suits, hair, or dirt. For this purpose a long brush may be used, sweeping the foreign material toward the pool outlet. A better method is to use a suction cleaner propelled by the pump attached to the recirculating system. The pool should be flooded each morning to remove dust which has settled on the water. Under normal conditions it will be necessary to add approximately $\frac{1}{25}$ of the total volume of water to replace that which has been washed away during the preceding day's use.

Algae may be removed by adding 1 part copper sulfate to 1,000,000 parts of water; after using copper sulfate the pool should be drained and scrubbed.

EMERGENCY EQUIPMENT

As a further means of protecting the health and safety of swimmers, emergency equipment should be available at all times, under the immediate supervision of an instructor or attendant who understands thoroughly the use of these implements. The necessary life-saving apparatus includes: pool hooks, ropes, and buoys. Some administrators recommend an inhalator as emergency equipment. A first-aid cabinet is indispensable.

Obviously the person in charge of the pool must be thoroughly familiar with life-saving methods as taught by the American Red Cross.

STORAGE

A room of sufficient size and directly accessible to the pool deck is essential for storing supplies and equipment used in the pool area.

SUITS, CAPS, AND TOWELS

Nude bathing for boys is practiced universally. When suits are worn, those of simplest design and made of cotton or nylon materials are preferred. Cotton is inexpensive and easy to launder. Thin rubber caps protect girls' hair, and if proper attention is given to keeping them off the floor or away from places where dirt may accumulate, there is no need for caps to be regarded as unsanitary.

All suits and towels must be washed with soap and boiling water, rinsed and dried thoroughly each time they are used.

SUPERVISION

A swimming instructor or capable attendant having a valid American Red Cross Instructor's certificate must be present whenever the pool is in use. Several supervisors may be needed; the number depends upon the number of swimmers using the pool at any one time. Such persons should have full authority to enforce all rules of safety and sanitation.

Before entering the pool all persons are required to take a cleansing shower bath in the nude, using warm water and soap. The body is thoroughly rinsed and all soap suds removed before entering the pool enclosure.

Each person is inspected for skin diseases, sore or inflamed eyes, nasal or ear discharge, or communicable disease, and excluded from the pool is any of the above conditions exists. Moreover, students with exposed subepidermal tissue caused by open blisters, cuts, or abrasions are warned that use of the pool may cause infection to themselves or others.

Whenever the water is withdrawn, all doors leading to the entrances and exits are locked, and no person is allowed to enter the enclosure except those responsible for the upkeep or sanitation of the pool.

Persons in charge of the pool are supplied with a notebook or proper form to record daily the number of persons using the pool, the volume of new water added, the temperature of the air, and the temperature, chlorine content, and pH of the water. Semiweekly or weekly reports of the bacterial count and the presence of *B. coli* are recorded.

For the purpose of maintaining proper hygiene and sanitation, suitable placards embodying the rules governing the use of the pool are posted conspicuously in the dressing rooms or pool enclosure. As a part of the health instruction program, students should familiarize themselves with these regulations and with the hygienic principles underlying them. Since local conditions vary, each school should establish its own rules in accordance with school and public health requirements. A suggestive list follows pertaining to summarized responsibilities of swimmers, instructors, and attendants or engineers. The list is organized upon the basis of functions; each administrator of a school or city system may allocate these functions in accordance with local policies:

1. All persons must have a thorough health examination, with especial emphasis on heart irregularities.
2. A cleansing shower bath (without suit) including warm water and soap is required. The body must be carefully rinsed to remove soap.
3. Before taking the shower bath, students needing to use the toilet should do so, since those leaving the pool to use the toilet are required to bathe again before reentering the pool.
4. The instructor supervises the shower baths.
5. Inspectors inspect each swimmer after the shower bath and exclude those showing evidence of skin disease, open lesions, bandaged wounds, boils, inflamed eyes, discharging nasal or ear passages, colds, or communicable disease. Those with unclean bodies must return to the shower room for a more complete bath.
6. Sterilized suits of either cotton or nylon and bathing caps may be worn by girls. Nude swimming for boys is required.

7. Before entering the pool all swimmers pass through the foot bath (provided the board of health recommends this facility).

8. The total number of swimmers using the pool during any period shall not exceed 20 for each 1000 gallons of clean or refiltered water.

9. Spitting, spouting water, or blowing the nose in the pool is prohibited. Overflow gutters are provided to receive waste.

10. Boisterous or rough play, such as running around the pool or pushing others into the pool or off the diving board, is forbidden.

11. Divers are advised to wear rubber caps or use greased cotton or wool to close ear passages. Infection of the ear drum or canal may result from forcing water into these areas.

12. Solo bathing, i.e., swimming alone, is not permitted.

13. Temperature of the water is maintained at 75° to 80° F.; air temperature approximately 5° F. warmer.

14. An instructor or other duly qualified person is on duty at all times when the pool is in use.

15. The instructor is suitably dressed to enter the water quickly in case of an emergency.

16. Pool hooks, ropes, buoys, and first-aid equipment are available and in condition for immediate use.

17. Doors leading to the pool are locked when the pool is not in operation.

18. Visitors are separated from the pool or runways.

19. All dirt, lint, hair, and water discoloration are removed daily. After use the overflow gutters are flushed to remove pollution.

20. The entire pool is cleaned at regular and frequent intervals.

21. Daily and weekly reports are made, recording the number of persons using the pool, volume of new water added, and temperature of the air and water.

22. Water samples are tested daily for bacterial content, insufficient or excess chlorine, and pH. These reports are posted in a conspicuous place.

23. Any unsatisfactory condition is reported immediately to the proper **authority.**

PROBLEMS FOR DISCUSSION

1. A county director of physical education recommends the construction of a swimming pool for every new secondary school in a rapidly growing suburban area. Several school board members oppose the recommendation on grounds that building of classrooms to meet increased enrollment is more important than pools. Furthermore, the board chairman points out that nearby lakes furnish unlimited opportunities for swimming; therefore, taxpayers could be spared the burden of expensive swimming pools. How would you handle the problem?

2. There is an outbreak of athlete's foot among the student body of a local high

school. The president of the P.T.A. reports that parents are certain their children have contracted the disease at the swimming pool. They demand that footbaths be reinstalled and the pool entrance, exits, and deck be cleaned daily with a strong disinfectant. What should be done?

3. Select a given situation and prepare a list of directions for use of the pool to be followed by swimmers, instructors, attendants, and engineers.

4. Instructors and students may implement the above with problems gained from their own experience and observation.

REFERENCES

American Public Health Association: *Recommended Practice for Design, Equipment, and Operation of Swimming Pools and Other Public Bathing Places.* New York, 1957.

Means, L. E. and Gibson, C. D.: *Planning School-Community Swimming Pools.* California State Department of Education, Sacramento.

Planning Space for Physical Activity, *Journal of Health–Physical Education–Recreation.* American Association for Health, Physical Education, and Recreation, Washington, April, 1962.

School of Education, Stanford University, Educational Administration Monograph No. 3: *Swimming Pools for Schools.* Palo Alto.

Scott, H. A. and Westkamper, R. B.: *From Programs to Facilities in Physical Education.* Harper & Row, Publishers, New York, 1958.

Second National Facilities Conference: *Planning Facilities for Health Education, Physical Education, and Recreation.* The Athletic Institute, Inc., Chicago, 1956.

Swimming Pool Data and Reference Annual. Hoffman-Harris, Inc., 425 Park Avenue, South, New York, 1962.

U.S. Department of Health, Education and Welfare: *Environmental Engineering for the School, A Manual of Recommended Practice.* Superintendent of Documents, U. S. Government Printing Office, Washington.

CHAPTER 17

DRESSING AND LOCKER ROOMS

Modern programs of health education and physical education emphasize the importance of sanitary and well equipped dressing facilities. The broad program of physical education involves big-muscle activities which call for a complete change of clothing and a shower following each period of instruction. To facilitate freedom of body movement, and the application of sound personal hygiene, these facilities are essential.

MAIN DRESSING ROOM

In secondary schools dressing rooms are needed which provide storage lockers for all pupils and dressing lockers for the peak physical education class load. Additional dressing rooms are desirable to accommodate interschool sports squads and community groups.

In elementary schools the arrangement may be modified according to the type of program conducted by the school and the community recreation needs.

TEAM AND COMMUNITY ROOMS

It is desirable to construct a separate home team dressing room in those high schools which conduct a broad interschool athletic program. Multiple use of the main dressing room for such purposes usually is unsatisfactory. The separate room provides for better supervision, and the installation of large lockers furnishes adequate space for bulky equipment.

For visiting teams and community groups one or more rooms of sufficient size to take care of peak loads are recommended. This arrangement allows for privacy desired by visiting teams, and meets the needs of community recreation groups.

Because of the nature of their sports program a separate home team dressing room is unnecessary for girls. Visiting school groups may be assigned to the women's community dressing room.

GIRLS' DRESSING ROOMS

Ideas have changed with respect to approved dressing room arrangements for girls. Previously, it was considered necessary to provide a unit of 4 full-length lockers around a shower stall, or to use individual permanent lockers with a sufficient number of private dressing booths to serve the peak class load. Although the second plan is still favored in some communities, the first plan has become obsolete.

Increased freedom for the American girl in matters of dress and social customs points the way toward changes in dressing room arrangements. Many authorities believe that girls' dressing room facilities, with few exceptions, should be similar to facilities provided for boys. Economy of construction, improved sanitation, and facility of supervision favor this arangement.

LOCATION

Dressing rooms should be located on the gymnasium floor level in proximity to the activity areas. Particular attention should be given to locating the main dressing rooms so as to serve functionally the indoor and outdoor teaching areas. Team and community dressing rooms should be easily accessible to activity areas, showers, and toilets. It is essential that arrangements be made to separate the main dressing room from team and community room by locked doors or corridor gates. Caution should be taken to design the dressing room areas so that persons outside cannot see into them. Access to the activity areas never should be through public corridors.

PHYSICAL FEATURES

Size and Shape. The size and shape of dressing rooms depend largely upon the number of persons to be accommodated and the types of lockers installed. Other influencing factors are space required for benches and the proximity to shower and toilet rooms.

Floors. Tile flooring of impervious materials such as quarry tile, with a nonslip surface, have advantages in terms of appearance and sanitation. For reasons of economy, concrete floors are commonly used. This type of flooring should be treated with a floor seal to prevent penetration of moisture and to facilitate custodial care. Installation of hose bibs, floor drains, and coved locker bases permits frequent cleansing with a hose. A slight floor pitch toward the drains is essential.

Walls. Smooth-faced brick or painted cinder block is best for all walls not covered by lockers. Unexposed walls may be constructed of common brick or cinder block. Since dark floors decrease the appearance of stains, walls need to be painted in light color to brighten the room. Covering radiator pipes and electrical switch cabinets insures safety and prevents collection of dust on these exposed surfaces.

HEATING, LIGHTING, AND VENTILATION

Approximately 75° F. is a comfortable temperature for dressing rooms.

Both natural and artificial light are desirable. Operable windows, glazed with obscure glass, insure privacy. Appropriate construction standards recommend a sufficient number of windows to permit sunlight to reach the most remote corner of the room. Artificial lights, inserted flush with the ceiling above the aisles, provide best illumination. Exposed light bulbs are protected against breakage by strong non-corrosive wire guards. All artificial lights are operated by a two-way switch; one located in the instructor's office, the other (a key switch) in the dressing room. Wall electrical outlets are placed a minimum of 3 feet above the floor.

Except for small units, a mechanical ventilation system is needed to remove unpleasant odors.

LOCKERS

Two types of lockers are recommended for the main dressing room. *Storage* lockers are used for physical education costumes, and *dressing* lockers are used for street clothing. The following sizes are most satisfactory.

Storage lockers:	Dressing lockers:
9″ x 12″ x 24″	12″ x 12″ x 72″
9″ x 12″ x 20″	12″ x 12″ x 60″
12″ x 12″ x 12″	12″ x 12″ x 48″
	12″ x 12″ x 36″

For team and community rooms only individual dressing lockers are recommended. The most satisfactory sizes are: 12″ x 18″ x 72″ and 18″ x 18″ x 72″.

For the main dressing room the combined storage-dressing locker arrangement is favored by most authorities. This provides a uniform height and conserves locker-room space. Figure 28 shows these arrangements.

ADAPTATION	SIZE OF LOCKERS AND BATTERY ARRANGEMENT	ARRANGEMENT OF LOCKERS ONE PUPIL EACH PERIOD	OVER-ALL HEIGHT WITH 8" BASE	NUMBER STUDENTS PER DAY	AREA REQUIRED INCLUDES 4" FOR VENTILATION
6-PERIOD DAY	A [6 STORAGE 9" x 12" x 24" / 1 DRESSING 12" x 12" x 48"] B [6 STORAGE 9" x 12" x 24" / 1 DRESSING 12" x 12" x 72"]	A. B.	A. 56" B. 80"	240	A [152 SQ. FT.] B [115 SQ. FT.]
6-PERIOD DAY	6 STORAGE 9" x 12" x 20" 1 DRESSING 12" x 12" x 60"		68"	240	115 SQ. FT.
6-PERIOD DAY	6 STORAGE 12" x 12" x 12" 1 DRESSING 12" x 12" x 48"		56"	240	93 SQ. FT.
6-PERIOD DAY	12 STORAGE 12" x 12" x 12" 2 DRESSING 12" x 12" x 36"		80"	240	133 SQ. FT.
8-PERIOD DAY	8 STORAGE 9" x 12" x 24" 1 DRESSING 12" x 12" x 48"		56"	320	187 SQ. FT.
8-PERIOD DAY	8 STORAGE 12" x 12" x 12" 1 DRESSING 12" x 12" x 48"		56"	320	133 SQ. FT.

Figure 28. Combined storage-dressing locker arrangements and locker area required for different types of storage-dressing units. (Courtesy of Second National Facilities Conference. *Planning Facilities for Health, Physical Education, and Recreation.* The Athletic Institute, Inc., Chicago.)

Lockers are installed on a coved concrete base 6 inches above the floor. Provision should be made for a 4-inch ventilation space between lockers when arranged back to back. Louvred doors, perforated backs, and slanting tops are recommended (Fig. 29).

Locks. Lockers equipped with permanent door locks are not recommended. Forgotten, mislaid, and duplicate keys result in continuous trouble for the instructor or locker room attendant. Similar difficulties arise when padlocks equipped with keys are used. The best method is to furnish each student with a combination padlock. Two master sheets of all combinations should be prepared, one kept in the instructor's file

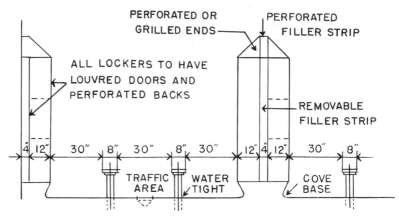

Figure 29. Detail of locker and bench installation. Note that locker heights and widths are variable. (Courtesy of Second National Facilities Conference. *Planning Facilities for Health, Physical Education, and Recreation.* The Athletic Institute, Inc., Chicago.)

cabinet equipped with a lock, the other in the fireproof safe of the principal's office.

Combination locks with a master key attachment, although more expensive to install, provide the most satisfactory system. The student uses the combination, but the instructor or locker attendant has the master key. In case the student forgets the combination, or the locker must be opened for other reasons, the master key readily accomplishes the purpose.

A definite system should be established for distribution of locks and assigning lockers. The use of card files for records is recommended. It is desirable for each student to fill out a card in triplicate registering his locker number and lock combination. One card may be for the alphabetical file; the second for a numerical file; and the third for the use of instructors. The first and second cards should be filed in a secure place such as the safe in the principal's office. Similar systems may be developed to meet the needs of individual situations.

Benches. Benches 8 inches wide, with rounded corners, are permanently fixed to the floor. Satisfactory height ranges from 14 to 16 inches above the floor. Aisles are approximately 9 feet from locker to locker with a 30-inch passage between inches.

Mirrors. Dressing rooms should be equipped with 12 by 18 inch mirors at the end of each alternate row of lockers, or at other points for advantageous use. Mirrors at the end of each row of lockers are recommended for girls. All mirors should be encased in noncorrosive metal frames and fastened securely to walls or locker ends. They are placed at medium height with shelves installed below as an essential convenience.

Hair Dryers. If swimming is included in the program the installation of electric hair dryers in the girls' dressing room is essential. The number of dryers equals the peak load divided by 3.

Bulletin Boards, Chalkboards, and Drinking Fountains. These items should be installed at convenient locations.

PHYSICAL EDUCATION COSTUMES

Where students dress for instruction in physical education, some type of uniform gymnasium costume is desirable. Standard equipment for boys includes a T-shirt, short trunks, cotton or wool socks, and tennis or basketball shoes. Sometimes a supporter and sweat shirt are added as regular equipment. The sweat shirt is used for outdoor activity during cold weather. Costumes of uniform design and color add to the appearance of the class. Where junior and senior high schools are housed in separate buildings, care should be exercised to select the same type of garments for use in both schools.

The suit of one-piece construction and of wash-and-wear material is recommended for girls. One-piece garments fall into several distinct styles designed by leading garment manufacturers. These costumes emphasize adaptability, attractiveness, economy, and freedom of movement.

When students purchase suits from commercial vendors, each vendor should be provided with exact specifications and sources of procurement. Special caution should be taken that specifications and procurement comply with local school board regulations.

Free textbooks and supplies are furnished by most boards of education and some have extended this principle to the purchase of gymnasium costumes. Ideally such equipment should be provided at public expense. This procedure facilitates laundering and insures a clean uniform when needed. In several public schools the board of education purchases costumes in large quantities, selling them to the students at cost.

LAUNDERING

School authorities solve the problem of clean uniforms and towels in one of three ways:
1. Delegating the responsibility to the student and his family
2. Arranging with a commercial laundry to provide clean equipment at nominal cost paid by the school or student
3. Maintaining school laundries.

Delegating this responsibility to the student and his family seldom proves satisfactory. Some adolescent youths follow the course of least resistance and neglect to bring clean equipment. The result is obvious; soiled uniforms are used over and over again, while towels could easily be mistaken for the janitor's dust cloth except that the latter presents a less offensive odor. Principles of good personal hygiene demand clean uniforms.

In many school systems towels are furnished and kept clean by a local commercial laundry at nominal cost. The laundry collects soiled towels daily and supplies clean ones. The board of education assumes the financial responsibility for laundry service, or students themselves pay a small fee for the use of clean towels. Boards of education should finance this service.

Many large city schools operate laundries to wash towels and uniforms used in the gymnasium and cafeteria. Frequently a laundry in a centrally located school serves the entire school system. Others install automatic washers and dryers which are operated by dressing room attendants.

All things considered, the type of laundry system depends upon the size of the community and the use made of departmental facilities. Disregarding the plan of bringing towels from home which seldom proves satisfactory, smaller school districts probably decide to contract with a local commercial laundry to furnish clean towels at a stipulated cost. In larger municipalities where the gymnasium, athletic field, or swimming pool are in almost constant use by students and community, the trend favors school laundries.

SUPERVISION

An administrative responsibility frequently overlooked is adequate supervision of the dressing rooms. No program of physical education is satisfactory without this service. Desirable types of supervision are: (1) the paid attendant—one of the custodial staff; (2) an assigned teacher; or (3) a dressing room attendant.

TIME FOR DRESSING

The amount of time allowed students to put on gymnasium costumes and to dress after activities varies in different communities. Perhaps the average is from 7 to 10 minutes to prepare for the instruction period, and from 12 to 15 minutes for the shower bath and to dress in street clothes. The proximity of locker-shower facilities to teaching stations, and the size of classes, are factors that affect time for dressing.

One of the principal reasons why some students dislike physical education is the highly organized routine which forces them to hurry at the beginning of the period to appear at class on time, and the restricted number of minutes at the close of the period for shower baths and dressing. When regular class periods are 45 to 50 minutes in length, the time spent in dressing rooms and shower baths greatly reduces the effectiveness of the physical education instruction period. Under these conditions some instructors prefer to rush children through the shower bath and locker room, accepting the risk of incurring a dislike for physical activity. Other instructors dispense with the bathing requirement, even though facilities are available.

This administrative problem is real. On the one hand, adequate time in the shower and dressing room is necessary if students are to enjoy the experience. On the other hand, a single class period is too short for all the activities that must be crowded into it.

Probably the best method of solving the problem is to schedule a double period for physical education. Certainly students should wear appropriate dress for physical activity, the shower bath after exercise is essential for esthetic reasons, and most students dislike returning to classrooms perspiring and disheveled.

PROBLEMS FOR DISCUSSION

1. Visit at least two school buildings and describe the locker system. Do the facilities meet desired standards? Could the facilities be improved? Consult a local architect and determine the cost of recommended changes. Would the cost have been greater or less if the locker room had been properly planned when the building was constructed?
2. Some authorities disapprove of the separate dressing room for interschool athletic teams. They maintain that mingling in a single dressing room promotes in participants an understanding and companionship conducive to sound educational practice. Most athletic coaches favor the seperate dressing room because it allows privacy desired for preparing teams for a contest. The school principal agrees in theory with those who disapprove of separate team rooms, but is greatly concerned with such problems as: (1) the lack of adequate locker and storage space for team equipment, (2) the extra wear and tear on the main dressing room, and (3) the frequent pilfering and breakage of student lockers. What arrangement do you believe is most practical?
3. Discuss the problem of providing adequate time for dressing and undressing. What factors deserve consideration? Describe a practical situation and propose a policy, procedures, and a one-three-five-year program designed to correct the conditions found.
4. Instructors and students may implement the above with problems gained from their own experience and observation.

REFERENCES

Conventional Gymnasium vs. Geodesic Field House (Report). Educational Facilities Laboratories, Inc., 477 Madison Avenue, New York.

High Schools 1962 (Report). Educational Facilities Laboratories, Inc., 477 Madison Avenue, New York.

Planning Space for Physical Activity, *Journal of Health–Physical Education–Recreation.* American Association for Health, Physical Education, and Recreation, Washington, April, 1962.

Scott, H. A. and Westkamper, R. P.: *From Programs to Facilities in Physical Education.* Harper & Row, Publishers, New York, 1958.

Second National Facilities Conference: *Planning Facilities for Health Education, Physical Education, and Recreation.* The Athletic Institute, Inc., Chicago, 1956.

CHAPTER 18

SHOWER ROOMS

SHOWERS AND EDUCATION

Recognized as an important factor in well organized programs of physical education, the shower room represents one of the numerous examples of the close association between health education and physical education. Properly constructed and wisely administered shower rooms provide one of the best laboratories for inculcating certain health practices of personal cleanliness while youth enjoys the cleansing and invigorating properties of the bath. By unanimous agreement the shower bath after exercise constitutes an integral part of the physical education period.

LOCATION AND TYPE

Preferably the dressing room and shower room are separate but adjacent units (Fig. 30). Because of the undesirable features of wet floors and moisture-laden air, locating shower rooms and dressing rooms in the same area has been abandoned.

In accordance with specifications described for the location of lockers, it is recommended that the shower room be placed on the ground floor rather than in the basement. In this preferred location the shower room receives natural light and ventilation, and easy access is given to dressing rooms, lavatories, gymnasiums, and swimming pools. Such an arrangement facilitates supervision and community use.

Showers may be centrally or individually controlled. For the former, showers are arranged in two lines, each with three shower heads set for warm water; the fourth for water of medium temperature; and the fifth for cool or cold water. This plan accommodates a continuous line of

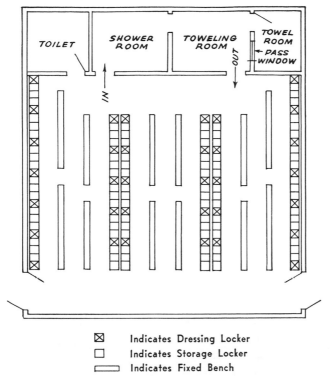

Figure 30. An illustrative arrangement for boys' dressing room. (Courtesy of Second National Facilities Conference. *Planning Facilities for Health, Physical Education, and Recreation.* The Athletic Institute, Inc., Chicago.)

pupils without delay of waiting for squads or relays to complete the bath. The gang-type shower saves water and time and assures a bath of regulated temperature and duration. A sufficient number of individually controlled shower heads is essential for after-school and recreational groups, and for athletic teams.

The individually controlled shower affords an opportunity to teach young people how to use a shower, and with proper supervision helps them practice what they have learned.

Years ago the approved plan for girls consisted of a unit which included a single shower head, drying rooms, and dressing rooms with lockers and hair drying machines (Figs. 31, 32). One or two girls from each class were assigned to the unit, with enough lockers available to accommodate all persons expected to use the unit from the various classes. This plan insured privacy, although the cost of constructing and maintaining the large areas, and the questionable educational values derived therefrom, led to desired changes.

Most new secondary schools are equipped with gang showers for girls, similar to those recommended for boys. Transition from the old to the new requires a carefully planned educational program for some girls and their parents who perpetuate a rather prudish sort of privacy

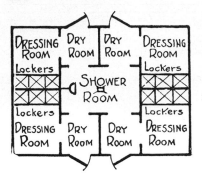

Figure 31. Girls' locker, shower, and drying room cloistered around a single shower head.

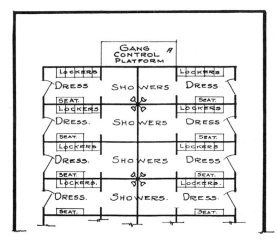

Figure 32. Semiprivate shower booths for girls. Girls enter the shower compartment from the dressing booths. Partitions between the showers are 5 feet high, which facilitates supervision by the instructor or attendant standing on raised platform at A.

in such matters. Generally, women teachers and supervisors of physical education approve gang showers for girls with approximately 2 to 5 individual showers and dressing cubicles to meet certain individual needs. Tradition alone represents an untenable excuse for continuing with individual dressing booths when economy, sociability, sanitation, and the principles of social and mental hygiene favor gang showers.

PHYSICAL FEATURES

Size and Shape. Gang-type showers require approximately 12 to 14 square feet of space for each shower head. Individual showers require a larger area, the proportion being 1 shower head for each squad of 4 boys or girls, using the largest class as the scheduling basis. The room should be at least 8 feet high.

Ordinarily the rectangular shower room is more economical than a square area, although the latter is satisfactory if shower heads are placed on four walls and a separate drying room is adjacent.

Plumbing. Concealed plumbing adds to the attractiveness of the room, but also increases the cost of installation and repair. In either event easy access should be maintained in case of an emergency. The size of supply and outlet pipes depends upon the amount of water needed and should be determined upon the basis of maximum load.

Water Supply.   Provision must be made for an adequate supply of water, both hot and cold, when the facilities are in use. Thermostatic control is necessary to keep water from exceeding 120° F.

Construction Materials.   For the floor of the shower room, tile (mosaic, gramolith, terrazzo) is superior to concrete. Obviously a slippery surface is to be avoided. Some authorities recommend sloping the floor toward the center of the room and the drain, with gutters along the sides attached to small drains in each corner. Most authorities favor sloping the floor toward the walls with appropriate outlets. In either plan, drainage capacity must exceed the maximum flow of water.

Light-colored glaze tile provides satisfactory walls and ceiling. A vaulted ceiling surface sheds moisture against the walls. Unless thoroughly waterproofed, plaster never gives a suitable covering for walls and ceilings.

All doors and window sash require a copper covering to prevent rust or swelling. Since doors and windows must be opened frequently, the cost of this covering is a justifiable expenditure.

Rust-proof radiators, installed near the ceiling or recessed in the walls and well screened, prevent burns and other injuries.

Shower Heads.   Showers installed at average shoulder height and tipped downward prevent wetting the hair. It is essential that the shower head be equipped with a removable face to facilitate cleaning, and that the universal joint be adjustable only with a wrench, never with the hands.

A unit control, which enables an attendant to regulate all showers, is preferred when groups shower at the close of physical education classes. Individual controls are desirable when only a few persons shower at one time. It is recommended that both the individual controls and a unit control be installed. In either case thermostatic control is essential as a safeguard against extremely hot water.

Where individual-control showers are installed, the single valve which automatically mixes hot and cold water is preferred to two valves —one for hot water, the other for cold.

Soap Containers.   Approved plans involve a central nonrust container for liquid soap, with metal pipes attached to the wall near the shower heads. Individual outlets should be controlled with an automatic shutoff device. For reasons of safety, glass containers are unsatisfactory.

VENTILATION

Ventilation is adequate if the system used clears the shower room of excessive heat and humidity. Usually mechanical ventilation is necessary.

LIGHTING

In addition to outside windows (preferably of the overhead type) artificial lighting is essential for dark days and evening use. Fixtures should be placed overhead and protected by moisture-proof reinforced cages. The lighting system is safely controlled by a switch located in the dressing room.

SUPERVISION

Competent supervision of the shower room while students take baths, reduces the possibility of accidents, insures proper use of the facilities, and provides excellent opportunities for education. Since the shower bath constitutes a regular part of the physical education period, supervision of the activity imposes no particular hardship.

The degree of order expected of students during the shower varies with instructors, and depends largely upon the educational methods employed in physical education classes. Accidents may occur in the shower room, usually because of pranks students play on each other. On the other hand, the shower bath should represent a reasonably joyous occasion if the best educational values are to be obtained. For proper organization, carefully established procedures with which students are thoroughly familiar should be used, together with the reasons why these regulations are imposed. Herding students through showers often fails to engender enduring interests in physical education so essential to the ultimate success of the program.

TOWELING ROOM

An area approximately the size of the shower room, called a toweling room, should be provided between the shower and dressing rooms. A curb of suitable height should be installed between the shower and toweling rooms. The floors, walls, and ceiling of the toweling room require the same material used in the shower room. Sufficient passageways are carefully located to insure safe ingress and egress to adjacent facilities.

PROBLEMS FOR DISCUSSION

1. Draw a plan for the location of shower rooms giving attention to: (1) toweling rooms, (2) dressing rooms, (3) lavatories, (4) gymnasiums, and (5) swimming pools. Explain by arrow the passage of students through these facilities.
2. Draw a plan for routing bathers through: (1) gang showers; (2) unit showers—toweling room and dressing room; and (3) individual compartments and gang showers (girls). Explain the advantages and disadvantages of each.

3. You are chairman of an association of women physical education teachers in a school district. The director of physical education, a man, has recommended the gang-type shower arrangement for girls similar to that used by boys. The superintendent of schools has asked for your opinion. How would you reply?
4. Instructors and students may implement the above with problems gained from their own experience and observation.

REFERENCES

Conventional Gymnasium vs. Geodesic Field House (Report). Educational Facilities Laboratories, Inc., 477 Madison Avenue, New York.

High Schools 1962 (Report). Educational Facilities Laboratories, Inc., 477 Madison Avenue, New York.

Planning Space for Physical Activity. Journal of Health–Physical Education–Recreation, American Association for Health, Physical Education, and Recreation, Washington, April, 1962.

Scott, H. A. and Westkamper, R. B.: *From Programs to Facilities in Physical Education.* Harper & Row, Publishers, New York, 1958.

Second National Facilities Conference: *Planning Facilities for Health Education, Physical Education, and Recreation.* The Athletic Institute, Inc., Chicago, 1956.

CHAPTER 19

OUTDOOR FACILITIES

THE IMPORTANCE OF OUTDOOR FACILITIES

Outdoor facilities, commonly called the school playground, deserve thorough consideration in the total pattern of school-community recreational facilities. Years ago the school playground was regarded as a place where children spent their time during recess periods and immediately before and after school. Few teachers utilized this area for organized educational activities, and playgrounds were closed when schools were not in session.

Newer concepts recognize education *through* play as a basic method of teaching and as a means of accomplishing the desired objectives. The modern play area and classroom deserve the same attention with respect to construction, equipment, and use.

School playgrounds should provide for educational experiences of pupils during the day and serve the community outside of school hours. Today this part of the school plant becomes, in reality, a neighborhood play area for youth and adults.

TYPES OF FACILITIES

Local conditions and needs determine the types of facilities. Attention to the functional needs of neighborhoods and communities combines school facilities with educational and recreational needs of youth and adults. The park-school concept of joint school-community use of facilities is most practical and economical. For the urban community there are three types of plots proposed: (1) neighborhood park-school for elementary school; (2) community park-school for junior high school; and (3) community park-school for senior high school. For the rural com-

254

munity, there is the community park-school, consolidated or central, for grades kindergarten through 12.*

NEIGHBORHOOD PARK-SCHOOL (ELEMENTARY SCHOOL)

This school should comprise 15 acres or more, depending upon population. It is an elementary school-recreation building in a park setting. Designed to be close enough to the people for ready use, it has a service radius of $\frac{1}{4}$ to $\frac{1}{2}$ mile.

The function of the neighborhood park-school is to provide for persons of all ages. Its facilities are for indoor and outdoor education and recreation activities for all seasons. Such activities include tennis and other court games, modified field games, gymnasium activities, apparatus play, social and small group gatherings, preschool activities, arts and crafts, gardening, picnicking, outdoor education, day camping, dancing, drama, music and other activities that give enrichment to neighborhood life (Fig. 33).

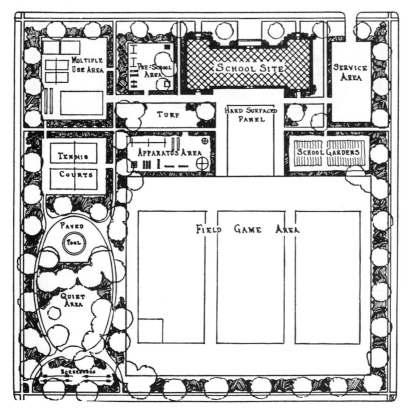

Figure 33. Neighborhood park-school (elementary). (Courtesy of National Facilities Conference. *A Guide for Planning Facilities for Athletics, Recreation, Physical and Health Education.* The Athletic Institute, Inc., Chicago.)

* Second National Facilities Conference: *Planning Facilities for Health Education, Physical Education, and Recreation.* Rev. ed. The Athletic Institute, Inc., Chicago.

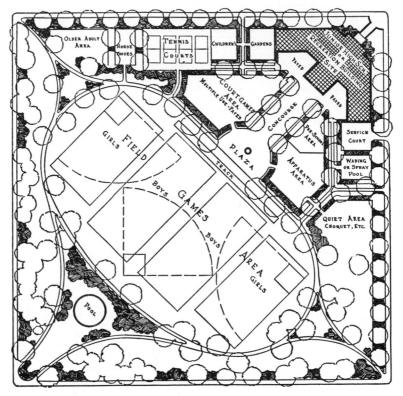

Figure 34. Community park-school (junior high school). (Courtesy of National Facilities Conference. *A Guide for Planning Facilities for Athletics, Recreation, Physical and Health Education.* The Athletic Institute, Inc., Chicago.)

COMMUNITY PARK-SCHOOL (JUNIOR HIGH SCHOOL)

This school should comprise 25 acres or more. It is a centrally located junior high school building in a park-like environment (Fig. 34). The service radius is ½ to 1 mile.

The function of this unit is substantially the same as that of the neighborhood park-school except that the geographic area served is larger. It should be kept in mind that as the age of school children increases, their activity programs include activities which require more space. This unit also may be used for purposes which require participants to travel greater distances and for which there is not sufficient area in the neighborhood unit (tennis, various athletic events, and others). The over-all community facilities plan should include provision for outdoor education and camping.

COMMUNITY PARK-SCHOOL (SENIOR HIGH SCHOOL)

This school should comprise 40 acres or more. It is a centrally lo-

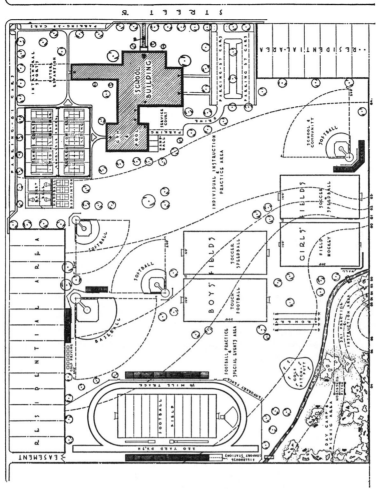

Figure 35. Community park-school (senior high school). (The Second National Facilities Conference. *Planning Facilities for Health, Physical Education, and Recreation.* The Athletic Institute, Inc., Chicago. Courtesy of the office of A. Carl Stelling, Consulting Landscape Architects and Site Planners.)

cated senior high school building in a parklike environment (Fig. 35). Its service radius is 1 to several miles.

The function of this unit is substantially the same as that of the community park-school (junior high school) except for interschool athletics, spectator space, and additional parking area.

COMMUNITY PARK-SCHOOL (CONSOLIDATED OR CENTRAL SCHOOL-GRADES KINDERGARTEN TO TWELVE)

This school should comprise 40 acres or more. It consists of an elementary and secondary school building, or buildings, in a parklike area.

It serves the community, which includes both the village or town and the surrounding open country.

The function of this area is to provide, for persons of all ages, facilities the year round for such educational and recreational activities as swimming, field sports (illuminated for night play), court games, winter sports, drama, music, dancing, food processing, high school and adult homemaking and farm shop, arts and crafts, and picnicking.

In planning facilities for the rural community, both urban and rural needs should be recognized as being of one community. Likewise, the general patterns of rural living, as influenced by seasonal activities, Saturday shopping, problems of pupil transportation, and the like, should be recognized. In communities where there is seasonal influx of migratory laborers or vacation visitors, the need for special facilities should be considered.

TYPES OF PLAY AREAS

Outdoor facilities serving school-community needs require a variety of play areas. There are provisions for pupils of both sexes, of different ages, and of special interests. To insure adequate minimum areas, primary consideration should be given to locating the building at one end of the total site rather than in the center.

Multiple-Use Paved Area. This area is essential for both neighborhood and larger community schools. It insures an all-weather section for various games such as basketball, volleyball, badminton, tennis, paddle tennis, and shuffleboard. It also serves well for a variety of school or community activities such as games of low organization, dancing, roller skating, and hopscotch.

Tot Lot. A fenced-in area, a portion of which should be hard surfaced, serves children of preschool and kindergarten age. It is equipped with climbing structures, swings, slides, and other suitable apparatus. Some authorities condemn a sandbox for sanitary reasons.

Apparatus Area. Apparatus can be made interesting, attractive, and safe for children by play sculpture and new design. Desirable shapes to stimulate play can be constructed in reinforced cast concrete which is good material to insure long-term wear. Careful planning with respect to location of the apparatus area favors one which provides either natural or artificial separation from game areas.

Many items of the traditional iron or aluminum equipment are safe and durable. Too many of the traditional types—such as swings, slides, and see-saws—have a relatively short interest span for the majority of children. The new concept of non-moving equipment stimulates children to engage in active and creative play and maintains their interest for long periods of time.

Field-Games Area. The largest area of outdoor facilities is planned for such games and activities as archery, baseball, softball, field hockey, football, touch football, soccer, and speedball. It may be used for intramural and interschool activities as well as for regular physical education classes and community recreation. Game areas, goals, and backstops should be laid out to permit multiple use of the total area.

Table 8. *Recommended Dimensions (in feet) for Game Areas**

	Elementary	Upper Grades	High School (Adults)	Area Size (sq. ft.)
Basketball	40 x 60	42 x 74	50 x 84	5000
Volleyball	25 x 50	25 x 50	30 x 60	2800
Badminton			20 x 44	1800
Paddle Tennis			20 x 44	1800
Deck Tennis			18 x 40	1800
Tennis		36 x 78	36 x 78	7200
Ice Hockey			85 x 200	17,000
Field Hockey			180 x 300	54,000
Horseshoes		10 x 40	10 x 50	1000
Shuffleboard			6 x 52	648
Lawn Bowling			14 x 110	7800
Tetherball	10' circle	12' circle	12' circle	
Croquet	38 x 60	38 x 60	38 x 60	2275
Handball	18 x 26	18 x 26	20 x 34	1280
Baseball			350 x 350	122,500
Archery		50 x 150	50 x 300	20,000
Softball (12" Ball)†	150 x 150	200 x 200	250 x 250	62,500
Football—with 440-yard track—220-yard straightaway			300 x 600	180,000
Touch Football		120 x 300	160 x 360	68,400
6-Man Football			120 x 300	49,500
Soccer			165 x 300	57,600

* Table refers to a single unit; many of above can be combined.
† Dimensions vary with size of ball used.
(Courtesy of Second National Facilities Conference. *Planning Facilities for Health, Physical Education, and Recreation.* The Athletic Institute, Inc., Chicago.)

Diagrams of various types of playing areas may be found in *Planning Facilities for Health, Physical Education, and Recreation.* The Athletic Institute, Inc., Chicago (revised edition).

Court-Games Area. In addition to the multiple-use paved area, there may be a series of court areas for specific sports. The surface may be earth or paved. The latter reduces maintenance problems. Included in this area may be separate courts for tennis, volleyball, handball, horseshoes, and basketball.

The Athletic Field. A separate area for interschool games and contests is an essential facility for senior high schools. It also is used for neighborhood and community activities.

Of primary importance are: (1) location, (2) drainage, (3) turf, (4) skating facilities, (5) parking facilities, (6) fencing (pedestrian traffic control), (7) lighting, and (8) landscaping.

A quarter-mile oval track, with a 220-yard straightaway and with spectator stands on both sides, forms the basic plan for an average athletic field. The football gridiron is located inside the running track. As a safety precaution, the oval within the track should be large enough to allow a minimum of 25 feet between the sideline of the football field and the inside curbing of the track.

Special care should be given to the location and construction of jumping pits and runways. Too often these are planned with limited regard for safety in order to accommodate spectator interest.

FENCING

All outdoor play areas should be enclosed as a safety precaution and to facilitate adequate control of activity. Many authorities recommend the chain-link or wire-mesh fence, mounted on 3-inch galvanized iron pipes sunk in concrete footings which extend below the frost line. The upper end of the pipe is closed and the concrete base rounded off to shed water. All chain-link fencing should have "knuckled selvage" both top and bottom. An iron picket fence requires proper installation with all pickets curved at the top, for reasons of safety. Openings for safe ingress and egress should be strategically located in boundary fencing. Each opening should be provided with a baffle for safety purposes.

The height of the playground fence depends upon the intended use of the area, the types of activities employed, the size of the playground, and its proximity to the street or other safety hazards.

BEAUTIFICATION

Adapability to purpose and attractiveness go hand in hand in the design of playgrounds and athletic fields. Many of these areas present a bare and unnecessarily ugly appearance. Fences of proper design, set in from the street, provide opportunities for attractive landscaping. A fence may become a thing of beauty with shrubbery and trees banked against it and with climbing roses or vines allowed to cover the homely iron and concrete. Such a structure discourages adventurous boys who otherwise might decide to use the fence as improvised climbing apparatus.

Properly placed trees add to the attractiveness of playgrounds without interfering with the primary purpose of the area. Shaded plots make ideal playgrounds for small children.

Plans for playgrounds and athletic fields call for the assistance of a landscape architect. In the final analysis his services yield tangible results in terms of beauty and economy.

LIGHTING

Intended use of playgrounds during the evening suggests the importance of proper illumination. This problem involves such factors as:

(1) desired intensity of illumination (15 to 20 footcandles on playing field); (2) quality of illumination (placement of fixtures); (3) efficiency of the system; (4) cost and convenience of installation and maintenance; and (5) appearance of the entire installation. Dark play areas restrict the program and prevent adequate supervision. Installation of lights by a competent engineer insures adequate illumination and avoids posts and wires which interfere with program activities.

SURFACING

Varying local conditions and differences in expert opinion indicate the difficulty of recommending definite standards for surfacing and drainage. No one surface contains all of the qualities desired. Each play area, moreover, presents special problems requiring study in the selection of a satisfactory surface.

In general terms a playground surface should be: (1) porous enough to permit rapid drainage; (2) compact enough to withstand hard use; (3) free from mud in wet weather; and (4) free from dust in dry weather. A porous subsoil requires a reasonably shallow foundation. A nonporous subsoil, such as clay composition, demands a much deeper foundation. Experiments are conducted with local materials to determine the ingredients or combination of materials best suited to the particular soil.

In selecting a surface one should consider such items as: (1) intended program; (2) cost of construction and maintenance; (3) safety; (4) resilience; (5) firmness; (6) abrasiveness; (7) smoothness; (8) durability; (9) drainage; (10) appearance; (11) freedom from dust and mud; (12) effect on equipment; and (13) effect on clothing.

Many authorities recommend *turf* as the best surfacing material for general purposes, especially on large game areas of 2 or 3 acres or more. About 9 inches of loam provides a satisfactory top layer for grass. The type of grass mixture selected should be that which thrives best locally and is resistent to intensive usage. In some localities sodding is more effective than seeding. Disadvantages of turf are: (1) the cost of initial application and maintenance; and (2) its moisture retention after rain is for a longer period than some other materials.

A *concrete* surface gives reasonably satisfactory service for playgrounds in constant use. Advantages of concrete are that it: (1) provides a smooth, hard play area irrespective of weather conditions; (2) permits the control of drainage; (3) minimizes maintenance; and (4) retains permanent markings for games. Disadvantages of concrete include the: (1) cost of installation, and (2) numerous skin injuries and bruises that occur unless the surface is covered with an asphalt preparation.

Clay, sand clay, crushed stone, and *cinders* may be used to advantage in a moderate climate with good drainage facilities. Except for the accumulation of dust, *sandy loam* contains many of the virtues of turf. Some authorities prefer loam to turf for reasons of economy of installation and maintenance and its availability for use after rain.

Standard technics for the elimination of dust are: (1) frequent sprinkling with water; (2) use of playground oil; and (3) occasional application of a thin coat of calcium chloride. Drawing moisture from the air and soil, calcium chloride provides an excellent means of keeping exposed dirt surfaces in usable condition. One reasonably heavy application followed by subsequent light coats every three or four months will suffice.

All-weather resilient surfacing for running tracks and field event runways is gaining preference over the traditional cinder surface. This type of track is more expensive to construct but it practically eliminates the problem of mainteance which is essential to the cinder track. Also, it provides a smooth, resilient surface which may be used with a minimum of regard for weather conditions.

Bituminous or *blacktop* is most satisfactory for smaller play areas receiving heavy usage. This type of surface has the same advantages as concrete, it is easier to repair, and it possesses varying degrees of resiliency. To minimize glare, a green covering is preferable to black.

There is evidence that many authorities favor blacktop under playground apparatus.

DRAINAGE

In addition to other surface composition, playgrounds require adequate subsoil drainage. Too much drainage results in dusty playgrounds and the need for artificial moisture application. Usually a surface grade of 6 inches to each 100 feet provides a satisfactory standard. Drain tiles are inserted only where the heavy subsoil beneath the turf prevents natural drainage. Concrete or bituminous surfaces are pitched toward the drains to insure rapid disposal of moisture.

EQUIPMENT

Appropriate playground equipment depends largely upon the program for which it is intended. A beautiful playground with limited equipment suggests the absence of wise program planning. Conversely, a small playground so filled with apparatus that its use endangers the safety of children never justifies official sanction. Efficient playground administration results in the scientific blending of facilities, program, leadership, and equipment.

PROBLEMS FOR DISCUSSION

1. The board of education adopts an "open gate" policy inviting public use of

the playground for recreational purposes outside of school hours. No additional funds are appropriated in the school budget for maintenance. Furthermore, city legal authorities rule that funds allotted to the community recreation program cannot be used for maintenance of facilities. What course of action should the director of physical education take?

2. For no apparent reason the outdoor play area never has been cleared since the school building was constructed. There are gravel piles and large cracks in the ground. The department is told to hold classes where the ground is in best condition. This still presents a hazard, because students in their enthusiasm often overrun the safety boundary. As the administrator you make personal contacts with the maintenance department to have the ground cleared, but nothing is done. What is your next approach?

3. Select and describe a given school situation. For this situation: (1) plan an adequate playground area; (2) prepare a layout to accommodate the various age groups; (3) select appropriate surfacing material; and (4) determine the types and amounts of equipment needed to conduct the program.

4. Instructors and students may implement the above with problems gained from their own experience and observation.

REFERENCES

Butler, G. D.: *Recreation Areas, Their Design and Equipment.* ed. 2. The Ronald Press, New York, 1958.

Butler, G. D.: *Introduction to Community Recreation.* ed. 3. McGraw-Hill Book Company, Inc., New York, 1959.

Planning Space for Physical Activity, *Journal of Health–Physical Education–Recreation.* American Association for Health, Physical Education, and Recreation, Association for Health, Physical Education, and Recreation, Washington, April, 1962.

Scott, H. A. and Westkamper, R. B.: *From Programs to Facilities in Physical Education.* Harper & Row, Publishers, New York, 1958.

Second National Facilities Conference: *Planning Facilities for Health Education, Physical Education, and Recreation.* The Athletic Institute, Inc., Chicago, 1956.

The Pennsylvania State University College of Agriculture Extension Service; *Athletic Fields—Design, Specifications, Construction, and Maintenance.* University Park, Pennsylvania.

PART IV

COMMUNITY AND STATE

The first four chapters deal with significant problems that confront the administrator in making the schools an integral part of community life, and explain the normal relationships that should exist between the community and state. Health education and physical education represent areas of unique value in bridging the unfortunate gaps that arise at times between the schools and other community agencies, and no other area of education contains richer potential opportunities for the development of sound administrative policies that promote mutual understanding and respect between the local district and the affairs of state. The last chapter is concerned with the problem of evaluation.

CHAPTER 20

THE SCHOOLS AND
COMMUNITY RECREATION

SCHOOL AND SOCIETY

Sound administration of public education proceeds in relation to the needs of the community as expressed by the interrelationships of social, economic, and political change. Education began as a means of teaching young people to read, thus enabling them to appreciate more fully the doctrines of piety and sacrifice as exemplified by the scriptures. The history of education in this country reveals the continuous addition of areas or subjects intended to keep pace with an ever-changing culture.

Just as the social inheritance of each generation brings forward the winnings of the race thus far, in like manner that generation adds new and more complex experiences for its descendants. Society calls upon education to assist youth in meeting these problems. Thus, after reading came writing and arithmetic, with spelling, geography, history, and citizenship following in rapid order. During the latter part of the nineteenth century, science, music, art, manual training, physical education, and other subjects or areas of learning found their way into the American public school.

The modern school reflects the impact of social change. Sometimes the school seems to forge ahead and to represent a primary force in altering the conditions of community life. At other times education lags behind, awaiting the stimulation of an outside force to prod the schools into effective action. In rare instances a community may even decide that another official organization can best perform a function closely associated with avowed educational objectives.

Examples of the role education has played appear in numerous

267

affairs of contemporary life. The schools have taken the lead in the improvement of community living by establishing excellent school plants and by providing broad educational opportunities for youth. In vocational education the prodding stimulation of management and labor led to improved state and local vocational schools wherein boys and girls learn the fundamental skills of various occupations. With respect to certain aspects of health, and in recreation, many communities have decided that these areas properly belong, respectively, to the board of health or recreation commission rather than to the school.

RECREATION AND LEISURE EDUCATION

All governmental organizations operate under the general administrative policy of service to society. As civilization develops, each generation establishes new or redirected services aimed to enrich the lives of people. These services may begin as a private enterprise or as activities sponsored by voluntary organizations. When the service has demonstrated its value to the community, it usually joins the ranks of the official agencies financed by public taxation. The more common official agencies include the respective departments of education, health, welfare, police, fire, and several others.

Among the problems facing the present generation, recreation or leisure education assumes a position of prominence. The industrial revolution transferred the production of consumer goods from the home to large manufacturing plants, creating congested areas of population. The invention of automatic machines and the discovery of improved manufacturing processes facilitate the production of more goods in less time. Labor unions demand shorter hours of work with increased pay. The natural resources of America, coupled with the ambition and ingenuity of its people, have produced a standard of living surpassing that of all other great nations.

Throughout the history of the world improved standards of living go hand in hand with increased leisure time. Many economists believe that the present standard of living in America represents but a crude beginning to a great era of better things produced by an age of automation and planned economy. Even the less optimistic look forward to more hours of leisure for the average man, and readily assert that wholesome leisure constitutes one of the most serious problems facing education.

For some years the problem of recreation has challenged the attention of certain groups interested in social welfare. Churches, youth organizations, community centers, recreation commissions, and more recently the schools have accepted the challenge to a greater or lesser degree. No list of educational objectives has appeared in the past half-century without education for leisure stated as a worthy purpose.

Because of these serious though unrelated and individual efforts of various groups, a public consciousness has arisen to the need for improved recreational opportunities. Leisure may become a great social force for good or evil. Many hobbies or recreational interests serve to improve and brighten the lives of individuals by directing them toward wholesome pursuits approved by society. On the other hand young people, especially, may use their leisure hours to acquire habits that violate the legal and moral code. Obviously recreation presents a problem of sufficient magnitude to justify the appropriate utilization of all community resources to insure full realization of the desirable benefits inherent in leisure, and to prevent the dangers of misspent idleness. No civic enterprise deserves more thoughtful and competent administration, and no set of ideals or basic beliefs concerning the importance of recreation can be translated into effective action without the motivating force of administrative organization.

TYPES OF ADMINISTRATIVE CONTROL

Communities vary in the methods employed to establish recreation as a governmental agency. Of first concern is adequate state legislation which permits a community to exercise initiative in this matter consistent with local needs and resources. Probably the best kind of legislation consists of an *enabling act* which authorizes the district to assign the administration of recreation to an existing organization of government, or to create a separate official agency if local conditions appear to justify this procedure. Without such legislation a community may exceed the rights granted to it by the state legislature. A power not delegated by the legislature, either by fact or intent, presumably does no exist; hence the governing body of a community may not delegate to a subordinate institution of government an authority withheld from the parent organization. Public funds used to finance such an activity might be held by the courts as money spent without legal authority.

Since recreation constitutes a relatively new community enterprise, the laws in several states fail to indicate clearly the rights of local governments in this matter. In these states, revised or established legislation is indicated.

Assuming the existence of appropriate state legislation, public recreation may be administered by: (1) the board of education; (2) a recreation commission or council; (3) the park department or board; or (4) some combination of these official agencies.*

No one type of administrative control enjoys universal acceptance as the best plan for all communities. Most experts agree that the best administrative organization in a given district insures optimum results consistent with efficiency and economy. Surely the cooperative effort

* The discussion here refers to official organizations (those financed primarily by tax funds). Many voluntary agencies (supported by gifts, donations, memberships, or drives) render outstanding service to community recreation. Voluntary agencies, industrial organizations (largely confined to industrial and commercial concerns which provide recreation for employees), and private enterprise (conducted for profit) are omitted because their functions extend beyond the limits of this text.

of the above groups is essential, irrespective of adminisrative organization.

THE BOARD OF EDUCATION

Many logical reasons favor board of education control of community recreation. First, the schools already furnish instruction in most of the activities which comprise a well rounded program of leisure education—physical education, music, arts and crafts, literature, clubs, dramatics, forums, group work, and others. Since many schools have adult education programs as well as those intended for youth, proponents of this type of administrative organization contend that education for leisure represents merely an additional emphasis on objectives and activities already established.

Second, the board of education has access to facilities beyond those available to any other group. Playgrounds surround the schools, or buildings are located adjacent to parks. The schools contain gymnasiums, playrooms, locker and shower facilities, swimming pools, physical education equipment, lavatories, music rooms and instruments, art rooms and equipment, auditoriums, assembly halls, conference rooms, and other facilities and equipment too numerous to mention. Besides, an increasing number of boards of education operate school camps with these facilities available to the public.

Third, the board of education employs highly specialized teachers who have devoted years of study to leadership in the precise activities that comprise public recreation. No other administrative organization could assemble a group of leaders with such outstanding professional qualifications. In brief, say the proponents of this plan, the board of education has the program, the facilities and equipment, and the personnel.

Those who oppose board of education control of recreation point out several factors in support of their position. First, the mounting cost of education often threatens the program now established, without incurring the further risk of public criticism by requesting additional funds to support public recreation. Anyway, a separate organization for recreation might obtain more public money for recreation than could the board of education which already receives about one-half of the local tax funds.

Second, few school authorities regard recreation as a worthy educational enterprise. This attitude characterizes many school administrators and teachers. Their preparation and experience deal with the fundamentals and technics of instruction; seldom can they acquire the "play attitude" so important in recreation. Although school authorities have included leisure education as one of the objectives of education for more than 25 years, little has been done in the schools to promote this important objective.

Third, the overcrowded curriculum of the average public school suggests the wisdom of not adding a new enterprise to compete with traditional subjects. Further, typical school organization adds another subject when an area of experience must be included in the curriculum. Recreation is not a *subject* to be taught like mathematics or history, or a program which lends itself to demonstrated standards of achievement for promotion or graduation; *leisure education demands free choice of activities, participation on the basis of interest in the activity itself, standards of excellence set by the individual, and limited superimposed authority so long as the activity meets the approval of the social group.*

Fourth, while the schools have many facilities and an abundance of valuable recreation equipment, the board of education has no *a priori* ownership to these materials which restrict them from being made available to another institution of government by appropriate legislation or regulation. After all, these facilities and this equipment were purchased from public funds, and all public enterprises operate according to the basic policy of contributing the greatest good for the greatest number of citizens. In brief, say the opponents of this plan, the board of education cannot effectively administer public recreation.

THE RECREATION COMMISSION OR COUNCIL

Many communities administer public recreation by a recreation commission or council. Usually such a commission or council consists of members appointed by the mayor or other authority provided by the statutes, with representatives from official departments of the district—education, health, welfare, police, safety, park, libraries, and others—together with several members-at-large selected because of their interest in the program and in civic improvement. The commission or council receives an appropriation by the usual procedures and is authorized to spend money for the program, equipment, and personnel.

The commission or council expects to enjoy the cooperation of existing official agencies by means of membership as described in the preceding paragraph. The commission or council is concerned primarily with *program*. Thus, the local park department may construct and maintain parks, playgrounds, and camping sites, while the commission or council plans and conducts the program of activities.

The recreation commission or council type of organization has several advantages. First, it performs but one clear-cut function—the development of a leisure education program for the community. Its functions are not dissipated by a wide range of activities, many of which may bear only a slight relationship to others.

Second, the commission or council, by the nature of its organization, enjoys the cooperation of other established organizations of government. In most states the law stipulates that a power delegated to one department of government may not be redelegated to another department. Thus, if the law states that school children shall receive an annual health examination by the board of health, this board may not redelegate the responsibility for such examinations to the board of education. Commissions or councils, on the other hand, may operate with considerable freedom among the various governmental departments. Departments of government are somewhat similar to line officers in the administration of education; the duties and responsibilities are relatively fixed. Commissions or councils are similar to staff officers in that they may work anywhere along the line.

Chief objections to the recreation commission or council are: (1) it complicates government by creating a new official agency whose functions overlap or even conflict with those of existing agencies; (2) an existing agency might perform the same functions more economically and efficiently with less duplication of facilities, staff, and equipment; (3) because of its single purpose, the recreation commission or council often tries to impress the community by promoting recreation beyond justifiable limits in terms of values received—even sponsoring activities of questionable character; (4) as a new enterprise, the recreation commission may adopt early policies in accordance with the needs and interests of the community, but soon the commission settles down to the same routine of tradition found in other governmental agencies; and (5) not enjoying the stability of a department of government, the commission or council often becomes a political "football" with pressure exerted to employ staff personnel inferior in preparation and experience to licensed teachers in the schools or physicians and nurses in the board of health, whose qualifications are fixed by state department regulation or by law.

THE PARK DEPARTMENT

In some communities the park department administers the program of community recreation. Even in those districts where another official body controls the *program,* the park department usually provides and maintains the *facilities.*

Those who favor this type of organization contend that maintenance of *facilities* and the *program* should go together for reasons of economy. Opponents of the plan hasten to point out that the park department renders effective service to the community in the construction and maintenance of *facilities,* but that the avowed purposes of the department fail to include *program* functions for which it is poorly equipped, and that communities adopting this type of organization frequently have a wealth of facilities but an impoverished program.

JOINT ADMINISTRATIVE RESPONSIBILITY

This type of organization refers to two or more organizations agreeing to employ an administrative director who assumes the responsibility of conducting public recreation (Fig. 36). While a power specifically

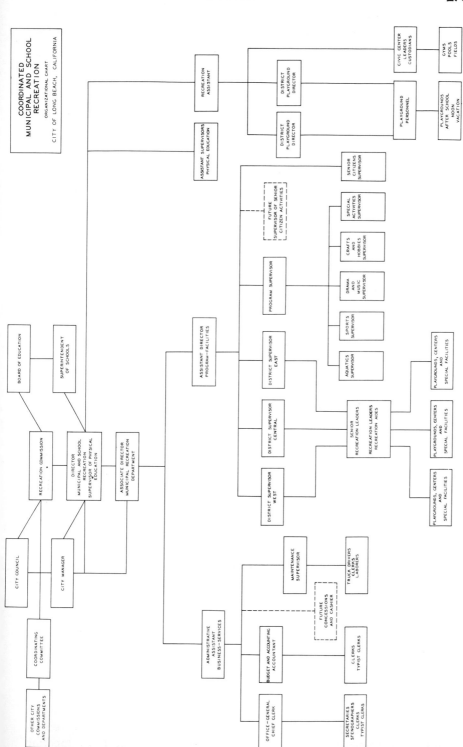

Figure 36. Organization showing joint administrative responsibility. (Courtesy of City Council, Board of Education, and Recreation Commission, Long Beach, California.)

delegated to one organization may not be redelegated to another institution of government, two or more organizations concerned with various aspects of a similar function may join forces to the extent of selecting the same person to administer the function. In this situation the person employed serves as the agent of cooperative organizations.

The two agencies most often concerned with this problem are the board of education and the recreation commission or council. Again, the person most often selected to administer the program is the director of health education and physical education or the director of adult education. He then earns the title of director of health education, physical education, and recreation, or director of adult education and recreation. Since leisure education presents a greater problem for youth than for adults, and since a large part of the recreation for youth involves physical activity, the director of health education and physical education assumes this joint responsibility more often than the director of adult education.

A review of the advantages and disadvantages presented with respect to administrative control by the board of education, a recreation commission or council, or by the park department, indicates at once that joint responsibility circumvents many of the problems encountered by any one of these separate organizations. Both the board of education and the recreation commission must agree on the qualifications and personality of the person chosen as the administrator. A joint committee composed of board of education members and persons from the recreation commission assist the administrator in the formulation of policies and procedures which become official *when approved by the parent organizations.*

The plan has the distinct advantage of assuring greater continuity between the program of physical education conducted in schools and the after-school and vacation recreation activities provided for the same children. Most authorities recognize the additional advantage of having physical education activities in schools taught with the end in view that these activities become recreational pursuits, and of recreational periods representing laboratory experiences in which skills and appreciations previously learned receive further attention. In this situation the experiences of school and recreation supplement each other.

Some authorities emphasize the difficulty encountered by an administrator in serving two masters—the board of education and the recreation commission. In reality both of these organizations must concern themselves with the best interests of the people; hence each organization may well serve as a responsible check on the other in perpetuating mutual programs for school and neighborhood improvement.

SOME BASIC CONSIDERATIONS

From the preceding discussion it becomes apparent that numerous problems confront the municipality desiring to administer public recreation in an efficient and satisfactory manner. Shall the board of education assume the entire responsibility, or shall a recreation commission or the park department provide for the leisure of children and adults after school hours and during vacation periods? If the municipality prefers a dual organization, shall the board of education and the recreation commission jointly employ a director of health education, physical education, and recreation or another person with broad educational and recreational experience?

In the search for satisfactory solutions to these problems, authorities run headlong into conflicts relating to the absence of clearly defined legislation, the tradition of long-established practices, state and national organizations with vested interests, and local interests of commercial, professional, and political character. Yet leisure education represents a public responsibility of such magnitude that it deserves the coordination of all resources in the community. The fact remains evident that examples of communities throughout the country exemplify the successful operation of recreation under each type of administrative organization described above.

THE CHANGING EMPHASIS

Until comparatively recent years community recreation was regarded as an enterprise of temporary nature, used to fill in the gaps between periods of work, study, or worship, or employed to increase the satisfaction derived from these things. The belief that man must have amusement finds justification in the chronicles of history which describe the ancient courts of kings, festivals associated with the church, the husking bees and barn-raisings of early America, school playgrounds constructed more than a century ago, and scores of similar examples leading to the present decade. But such transitory amusement, although serving a useful purpose, fails to recognize fully the importance of enduring recreational values. Acquiring skill and interest in wholesome recreation represents a societal need, comparable to learning the skills of a vocation, mastering the essentials of worthy home membership, securing adequate food and reasonable shelter, and maintaining sound health.

Commercial interests produced the theater, cinema, poolroom, tavern, bowling alley, and great athletic festivals. Voluntary agencies and private clubs afforded amusement or social improvement for specific groups during leisure hours. Finally, persons responsible for community planning came to the realization that organizations of government should accept certain responsibilities for public recreation.

Out of this rather haphazard development at least three conclusions emerge: (1) the continuing influence of commercial, voluntary, private, and official agencies must receive consideration in the future planning of leisure education; (2) most recreation programs aim to provide only for the amusement of persons during leisure hours, without fully recognizing the importance of developing in the individual recreational skills and attitudes which contribute widely to improved home and community living; and (3) there is a great need for utilizing the cooperative resources of the community, supplemented by state and federal governments, to organize recreation as a potential and powerful force in a democracy with many national and international implications.

Thus, it would appear that recreation must be viewed as a great educational enterprise. A few enlightened leaders in this field have pushed back the horizon of recreation beyond the limits of mere amusement, and regard the values of appropriate leisure education as a vital factor in modern life. When the family goes to the seashore for a day's outing many things may happen to increase the satisfaction of family living in addition to the automobile ride, an hour's swim in the refreshing water, and the lunch around a camp fire. When parents as well as children spend a few days at the school camp the closer relationship between the school and community becomes obvious. Planned recreational opportunities where representatives of management and labor join together in games and music festivals might lead to fewer disputes between these two great forces. The social and educational advantages of inter-school and intercollegiate athletics never have received appropriate attention. The Olympic Games and other international events provide occasions without parallel for the interchange of social, economic, and political ideas, and for mutual understanding. Many illustrations will occur to the reader wherein recreation may serve humanity to a degree not apparent in other normal life activities.

Education for leisure deserves a place in the curriculum. Recreation must challenge the attention of leaders in local communities, in the various states, and in the nation as a whole.

SIGNIFICANT ADMINISTRATIVE POLICIES

A brief discussion of certain policies may assist in pointing the way toward the successful administrative organization of public recreation. One policy based on political economy is as follows: *The interests of economy and efficiency favor the administration of a given enterprise by one municipal department of government.*

Duplication of program often produces confusion and waste. Many activities conducted by the school parallel those organized by the recreation commission or park department. In fact, most boards of education have established programs which include nearly all the activities sponsored by such commissions or departments—games and sports, music, dramatic art, arts and crafts, literature, forums, and others. Extension of public education now provides opportunities for: (1) children in nursery schools and kindergartens; (2) students of compulsory school age; (3) continuation schools for young men and young women engaged in industry; (4) junior colleges or institutes in many localities; and (5) adult education programs for older persons. If the community desires to establish two or more official agencies for recreation, the program conducted by each agency must supplement rather than conflict with the others. Frequently these programs, although practically identical in content, present quite different objectives resulting in confusion if not actual waste.

Duplication of staff leads to unnecessary extravagance. Where two or more governmental agencies have responsibilities for public recreation, each organization usually employs a separate staff. All of these staff members receive their salaries from funds raised largely, if not entirely, by local or state taxation. A single department or commission of government in charge of recreation might effect a financial saving to the community by the regulation of employee schedules to render maximum service.

Duplication of facilities and equipment increases the tax burden. Often the equipment and facilities of schools remain idle while the recreation commission or park department conducts its program. Many communities attempt an administrative organization whereby two separate departments of government use the same facilities and equipment. The plan seldom proves satisfactory because of controversies between departments concerning supervision, breakage, loss, and misuse.

Duplication of administrative responsibility restricts program continuity. A direct carry-over from the skills learned in schools to recreational pursuits enjoyed during the vacation period represents sound administrative organization. This carry-over process operates with less friction when the same guiding principles underlie both education and recreation—perhaps one of the principal reasons why many authorities favor the board of education as the most competent single agency to administer public recreation.

Duplication of administrative control leads to inequalities in professional leadership. The qualifications of leaders employed by recreation commissions and park departments frequently differ from those established by the board of education. Usually the board of education is less influenced by direct political manipulation than other public agencies which might administer the program.

A second policy is: *Whenever necessary, appropriate legislation should be enacted to permit an official organization to administer public recreation.* A municipality derives all of its powers from the state, either by direct legislation or by charter. In some states existing legislation fails to delegate specifically the responsibility for community recreation to one or more agencies of government. The absence of such authority probably restricts an agency from legally spending public funds for leisure activities. Where the law does delegate the responsibility to one agency only, other agencies may not infringe upon these rights without danger of liability.

The law should contain broad provisions enabling a community to establish its recreation program according to the best interests of the district as determined by the appropriate officials of local government.

A third policy may be stated as follows: *With respect to public recreation, the resources of the community should be coordinated to serve all residents of the district.* This policy suggests the need for community planning. The problem of leisure education assumes greater importance with fewer hours devoted to earning a living, the increasing complexities occasioned by rapid means of communication, the growing necessity of finding a solution to certain interracial difficulties in this country, and the position of the United States in international affairs.

The local district represents the initial unit in which cooperative planning must take place. Such planning requires the reconciliation of vested interests concerned with recreation—official, voluntary, private, and commercial. All of these agencies have a place; the task of sound administration is to utilize the best resources of the community and to organize them into an appropriate pattern of leisure education for everyone. Once established in the local community, the fusion of these plans constitutes the state program, and effective programs in the various states mean improved recreational opportunities for the country as a whole.

PROBLEMS FOR DISCUSSION

1. A recreation commission is established in a rapidly growing suburban community. The board of education grants the commission permission to use school facilities and fixed equipment for its program. Frequent stealing and considerable damage to school property results. Three possible courses of action are considered by the school board: (1) assess the commission for payment of all stealing and damages; (2) insist that the community recreation program be administered by a person equally responsible to the recreation commission and the board of education; (3) withdraw premission of the recreation commission to use school facilities. Outline the course of action you recommend and discuss on the basis of sound administrative principles.
2. The recreation commission in a city with a population of 50,000 appoints a new director. One of his first moves is to organize a city-wide basketball program for boys and girls from 9 to 12 years of age. Teams are organized to represent the schools by name and mumber. All teams are organized by neighborhood play directors during the after-school recreation periods held at the various elementary schools. The public school director of physical education first learns of the program through the sports pages of the local press. What professional action do you recommnd to develop better administrative relationships between the recreation commission and the public schools?
3. In a large city a citizens committee becomes interested in a broad recreation program, and appeals to the park-recreation board for sufficient funds to procure personnel for 30 unstaffed playgrounds. The board expresses its sympathy but defers action on the committee's request on the basis that all available funds must be applied to building a municipal stadium and sports center for professional sports. Do you agree?
4. In a city where the administrative control of community recreation is the responsibility of a municipal department of recreation, public school physical education facilities are extensively used for the recreation program. The re-

sponsibility for assignments of participating groups rests with the recreation department but the department of education issues the official permits for use of facilities. List those statements of policy which you believe essential to an effective working relationship between the two municipal departments.

5. Instructors and students may implement the above with problems gained from their own experience and observation.

REFERENCES

American Association for Health, Physical Education, and Recreation: *Leisure and the Schools.* Fourth Yearbook. Washington, 1961.

American Association for Health, Physical Education, and Recreation: *School Recreation.* Washington, 1960.

Anderson, J. M.: *Industrial Recreation.* McGraw-Hill Book Company, Inc., New York, 1955.

Butler, G. D.: *Introduction to Community Recreation.* ed. 3. McGraw-Hill Book Company, New York, 1959.

Butler, G. D.: *Playgrounds: Their Administration and Operation.* The Ronald Press. New York, 1960.

Cox, P. W. L. and Mercer, B. L.: *Education in Democracy.* McGraw-Hill Book Company, Inc., New York, 1961.

Hutchinson, J. L.: *Principles of Recreation.* The Ronald Press, New York, 1951.

Meyer, H. D. and Brightbill, C.: *Recreation Administration: A Guide to its Practice.* ed. 2. Prentice-Hall Book Company, Inc., Englewood Cliffs, 1956.

CHAPTER 21

STATE RESPONSIBILITY IN HEALTH EDUCATION AND PHYSICAL EDUCATION

NATURE OF THE STATE

The state is a large governmental unit and, in America, is coincident with the governmental units of the several states. The state is composed of men and women of average ability, with an occasional brilliant individual and an occasional dull one in its membership. A child learns to respect the state as he learns to love his home, his town, and the countryside; and so he respects state authority as he has been taught to honor local authority vested in the mayor, the board of education, or the health department. But in compliance with American tradition, the mayor may incur disfavor with the people and lose his office, and in similar fashion the state succumbs to the will of the people. This is elementary political science which portrays the simple fact that the state represents, in theory at least, the combined mature judgment of the people; that laws created by the representatives of the people may be repealed; that regulations enacted by the servants of the people may be changed; and that the state is constituted to serve the best interests of all its citizens.

EDUCATION, A FUNCTION OF THE STATE

How did the state gain control of education? The answer is to be found in constitutional amendment. The Constitution of the United States made no mention of education. When this important document was signed, education was largely a private or charitable enterprise. Ten amendments, called the Bill of Rights, were passed soon after the signing of the Constitution. The first eight of these amendments dealt with such matters as freedom of religion, of speech, and of the press. The ninth and tenth amendments, especially the latter, made clearer the line of demarcation between the powers of federal and state governments.

Thus the tenth amendment virtually gave to each state the power to organize a system of education. So completely did the national government absolve itself from powers associated with education that later, when federal grants were made to found state universities, the money was given to the commonwealth for disbursement. Again, this principle is represented in the administration of governmental aid for vocational agriculture, home economics, and industrial education apportioned to local public school districts through the state education department.

It is interesting to trace the effects of the tenth amendment. In one broad sweep the national government literally washed its official hands of educational matters. At that time state departments of education either had not been established or were in their infancy. As might be expected, some states took no notice of education. Others made provisions only for weak districts. Still others directed their attention only to public schools. A few set to work at once and built strong state departments of education. This interest has developed gradually until most citizens have become state-minded in matters of public education.

As a result of the tenth amendment the federal government has been prevented from taking an active part in education. In recent years efforts have been made to reestablish in the national government some of the authority delegated to the various states in matters of education. Proponents of the plan believe that improved means of communication now make geographical areas of the north, south, east, and west more easily accessible than migration within state borders a century ago. This intermingling of persons from different parts of the country demands some common bases of thought, of action, and of ideas. The state has accepted this responsibility by establishing minimum standards for education, and by furnishing financial assistance and professional leadership so that weaker districts may approximate the level of education desired for the commonwealth as a whole. It seems apparent that rapid communication and changing economic conditions point toward increased leadership and financial support by the federal government as a means of equalizing and improving educational opportunity among the various states. Thus far, traditional ideals of state's rights, vested interests, and political expediency have prevented the federal government from exercising strong influence on American education.

GROWTH OF STATE CONTROL IN EDUCATION

Prior to the development of state departments of education, much of the control was assumed by local school districts.

The struggle to establish free schools in communities resulted in strong local sentiment for public education. Attempts to transfer to the state education department some of the functions which the town or city had earned by prodigious effort met with local opposition. There is pride in worthwhile achievement. Those who fought for improved educational opportunities in town meetings and at other public gatherings were loath to accept a developing state consciousness which would transfer to the state capital administrative control over certain educational affairs. The controversy continues.

State departments of education operate on the principle that the commonwealth can perform certain functions more efficiently than the individual town, county, or city. Since it is the duty of the state to protect the educational rights of all its children, financial aid is distributed by the state to weaker districts (sometimes to all school districts), standards for teacher preparation and certification are imposed, length of the school year is determined, and assistance is given in supervising the instruction in the local community and in the construction of new buildings. On the instructional side, numerous states provide curriculum materials and qualified personnel to assist local districts in developing specific programs.

General policy has been accepted that the larger the school unit—within limits—the more intelligence there is in it. A corollary assumes that greater intelligence among the people indicates improved educational resources.

Thus, large cities often have better schools than smaller ones, and the educational offerings in consolidated districts usually surpass those obtained in small rural areas. There is more wealth in the larger unit, as a rule, and better leadership can be obtained.

Where a state department is properly organized the schools in every local area are benefited; those in the weaker districts are helped to attain the minimum standards established for the state as a whole, and those in districts with adequate resources are stimulated and encouraged to improve present educational offerings.

While certain powers have been withdrawn from cities and towns, the state education department is careful not to thwart local initiative. State control must exist in some matters, but the state attempts to stimulate and encourage local administration rather than to impose unwanted reforms by arbitrary measures. The state may establish standards for teacher certification, yet local boards of education employ the teachers. State aid may be available, but the county or district board of education distributes the funds. Length of the school year is established by state regulation, still the calendar is planned locally.

Although wise public policy indicates the need for stimulating local iniative and local support, one should not forget that public education is distinctly a state function. This has been demonstrated repeatedly by expressions of the highest courts in judging the validity of numerous educational laws. Decisions referring to health regulations, duties of school officials, construction of school buildings, minimum salaries for teachers, and rights under city charters further establish the precedent that public education is a function of the state and that the commonwealth shall protect the happiness of all its people by insuring an education for everyone. Likewise the state exercises certain regulatory powers over teachers' colleges and other colleges and universities.

THE STATE LEGISLATURE AND THE STATE DEPARTMENT OF EDUCATION

Public education is governed by law which lays down certain general policies. Thus the state legislature provides by law for a general and uniform system of public instruction wherein tuition shall be free and which shall be open to all. Such a pronouncement is usually followed by:

1. Defining the types of school districts.
2. Naming the title of the chief school executive officer.
3. Providing for a state board of education or its equivalent, and for local boards of education with specific powers and duties.
4. Indicating the items in the state school fund.
5. Stipulating the basis for apportionment of the state school tax.
6. Stating the minimum school term or year.
7. Designating the manner by which teachers shall be prepared and certified.

Preferably the general school *law* leaves to the state department of education the right to establish *regulations* in such matters as the preparation and certification of teachers, issuing state curriculum guides, providing school building codes, and others. Even though the law delegates numerous responsibilities to the local district, it remains for the state education department to insure the carrying out of these commissions. In addition to the general school law there are numerous legal enactments governing specific activities.

It must be remembered that all powers of the state education department and of local boards are obtained from *statutes.* Authority is sometimes *assumed,* but such power, if not enumerated in the law, is likely to be held by the courts as nonexisting. For example, it is frequently assumed that state and local boards of education may exercise jurisdiction over interschool athletics on the basis of powers delegated to these bodies by general education law. In many states the law fails to delegate this responsibility clearly to any official organization.

Besides the relatively important aspects of legal control, the state department should be especially active in perfecting policies for the physical, mental, and social welfare of school children. Failure to respect this obligation is to deny the platform upon which a state program of education is founded. Mutual relationships between local units and the state education department constitute the state program of education; neither can be most effective without the assistance of the other. In this sense the state program represents a fusion of the educational offerings in local districts.

STATE DEPARTMENT PERSONNEL

The chief executive officer may have the title: State Superintendent of Public Instruction, Commissioner of Education, or Director of Education. He is elected by popular vote in three-fourths of the states, appointed by the governor in a few, and chosen by the state board of education in others.

Ordinarily, members of the staff are selected by the chief executive officer. Departmental heads usually receive the rank of Assistant Superintendent or Commissioner, Deputy Superintendent, Director, Supervisor, or Consultant.

Judged by the functions which staff members are expected to perform, they are very responsible persons. By preparation and ability they should be superior to their associates throughout the state. Whereas the local worker has the opportunity to remain with his task until it is finished, the state agent must produce results in a single day or visit. Moreover, the local district has a right to expect experienced counsel and guidance from the state representative. On account of their potential influence, staff members should have a salary that is sufficient to command respect. Unfortunately this is not always the case.

THE LEGAL STATUS OF HEALTH EDUCATION AND PHYSICAL EDUCATION

Someone has said that laws represent ideals which people hope to obey some day. If this is true the American people have high ideals about health education and physical education in view of the attention given to these programs by state legislatures. Doubtless a part of this interest was sharpened by draft statistics, because much of the legislation appeared subsequent to 1917, although certain laws relating to health education were passed as early as the middle of the nineteenth century. Doubtless, too, leaders in this field, recalling that legislation aims to equalize educational opportunity, have seized the propitious occasion of world crisis to insure programs of health education and physical education in backward communities as well as in the more favored districts.

RELATIONSHIP BETWEEN THE STATE AND LOCAL PROGRAM

The division of health education and physical education in the state department of education renders two types of service to local communities: one of an indirect nature affecting the state as a whole; the other directly concerned with specific programs within a given community.

Indirectly, the division promotes health education and physical education by fostering an interested and cooperative attitude toward the program. An excellent means of accomplishing this purpose is through an active state association for health education, physical education, and recreation which is affiliated with the state teachers association, with policies and procedures shaped in accordance with modern educational objectives and standards. Sometimes the state association for health education, physical education, and recreation is a separate organization; this is unfortunate because greater unity of purpose and successful accomplishment are assured when the state teachers association is composed of sections or departments representing the various types of public education offered within the state. Besides being a part of the state teachers association, the state association for health education, physical education, and recreation is an important adjunct of the respective district association, and the American Association for Health, Physical Education, and Recreation (a department of the National Education Association) with adequate representation in these organizations.

The division of health education and physical education may be of indirect assistance to local districts through the unique cooperative relationship existing between various departments of state. Thus the department of education, department of health, department of motor vehicles, finance commission, and others work together for the mutual benefit of each service organization and the promotion of public welfare within the commonwealth. The state director of health education and physical education and his staff are in a position to enlist the support of these state official organizations as well as to secure the aid of such state voluntary groups as the public health association, parent-teacher association, medical association, dental association, women's federation, and others, encouraging them to work through their local representatives in furthering a well rounded program of health education and physical education.*

Direct relationship between the state education department and local districts is almost wholly advisory in character. The director in a town or city has the right to expect sympathetic and expert assistance from the state department representative in such matters as giving advice on appropriate curriculum materials, recommending standards for facilities and equipment, speaking at meetings of teachers, parents, or luncheon clubs, assisting with surveys to show desirable accomplishments and needed improvements, and securing improved public support for the program.

There is another form of direct relationship which is not advisory but mandatory. Although it is seldom expedient to exercise the authority of *law* in compelling local districts to comply with approved standards of education, the use of this instrument sometimes is imperative. It may

---

* The difference between official and voluntary organizations is that the former are authorized as departments of government by the state legislature, whereas the latter, although very influential in many instances, do not enjoy this distinction. Voluntary organizations usually have a state charter.

be applied as a last resort when other methods fail to produce results. The state department of education sets the minimum standards for education and establishes machinery for enforcing these edicts. When health education and physical education are required by law or by regulation of the state department of education, local districts must provide suitable programs in these fields or run the risk of losing state financial aid or of being removed from the list of schools approved by the parent body.

State health education and physical education represent a service program. They succeed only insofar as they reflect the achievements obtained in local areas, brought about by the cooperation of various agencies throughout the commonwealth. Thus the local district has a right to expect guidance from the state department, and the state department in turn deserves cooperation and assistance from the local district. Success for one means professional achievement for the other. Their responsibilities are mutual.

PROBLEMS FOR DISCUSSION

1. Discuss the implications of the statement, "The state education program represents a fusion of the educational offerings in local districts."
2. Prepare policies indicating the relationships which should exist between the state education department and local districts, and *vice versa*.
3. Proponents of federal support for public education hold that this can be realized without federal control. Discuss this in light of the local situation with which you are most familiar.
4. A bill is introduced in a state legislature providing for salary increases for teachers statewide. It is passed by the legislature but the governor vetoes the bill. He contends that the responsibility for raising teachers' salaries rests with the local school district. What legal factors are involved?
5. Instructors and students are encouraged to include other problems for discussion based upon their own experiences and observation.

REFERENCES

Educational Policies Commission: *The Central Purpose of American Education.* National Education Association, Washington, 1961.

Edwards, N.: *The Courts and the Public Schools.* The University of Chicago Press, Chicago, 1955.

Grieder, C., Pierce, T. M. and Rosenstangle, W. E.: *Public School Administration.* ed. 2. The Ronald Press, New York, 1961.

Hanna, P. R.: *Education.* McGraw-Hill Book Company, Inc., New York, 1962.

Knezrich, S. J.: *Administration of Public Education.* Harper & Row, Publishers, New York, 1962.

Morphet, E. L., Reller, T. L. and Johns, R. L.: *Educational Administration—Concepts, Practices, and Issues.* Prentice-Hall, Inc., Englewood Cliffs, 1959.

CHAPTER 22

LEGAL FACTORS
IN HEALTH EDUCATION
AND PHYSICAL EDUCATION

BASIC FACTORS OF LEGALITY

Difficulties frequently arise in describing the legal provisions behind administrative functions. First, law itself is complex and bound by an infinite variety of details and technicalities. Second, educational legislation differs in the various states and, when combined with state education department regulations and other pronouncements which may carry as much authority as law, confusion and complications often occur.

Public education is a function of the state, but the actual business of educating children rests largely with local governments in towns, counties, or cities. Powers exercised by local governments are contained in *laws* passed by the state legislature. Within the framework of these laws, state and local boards of education establish *regulations* to facilitate the administration of schools. When difficulties arise between individuals or groups, the matter may be taken to a court which renders a *decision*. The decision of the court establishes a precedent in settling subsequent disputes of similar nature, or until the state legislature passes or revises legislation on the subject. *Interpretations* of the law itself, or of its intent, may be requested of an attorney general. In summary, the state legislature passes *laws*, state and local boards of education establish *regulations*, courts render *decisions* which serve as precedents, and attorneys general provide *opinions* on legal *interpretations* of the statutes.

HEALTH EXAMINATIONS

Provisions for health examinations of school children were among the first health measures to receive legal sanction, although the importance of these measures was barely recognized until the third decade of the present century. These laws vary widely in the different states; some *mandatory* requiring health examinations at periodic intervals, other *permissive* enabling state and local boards of education to require such examinations as may be desired. Either the education department or health department may be charged with the responsibility of administering the examinations, or joint action is sometimes indicated.

Usually the term "examine" is restricted to functions performed by physicians and dentists. Nurses and teachers "inspect" or "observe" children. Frequently the line of demarcation between examination and inspection is difficult to determine.

Where legislation is contemplated in dealing with the health examinations of school children, perhaps the following items will prove helpful:

1. The law should be mandatory in indicating the governmental organization (board of education or board of health) responsible for setting standards and giving the examinations.
2. The minimum number of examinations during the public school life of the child should be stated, together with the minimum list of items to be covered, with no limit restricting the optimum number of items or thoroughness of the examination.
3. The law should stipulate that all teachers be qualified to detect signs of communicable disease and of gross physical defects.
4. Provisions should be made for a coordinated report of health and mental examinations (the latter performed by adequately qualified personnel), and for the use of these coordinated reports in improving the educational guidance of children.

VACCINATION AND IMMUNIZATION

Great variation exists among the several states in the legal provisions dealing with vaccination and immunization. A few state laws prohibit compulsory vaccination. In other states boards of health may adopt such measures as are deemed proper and necessary. In other states health authorities may insist on vaccination if smallpox shows a tendency to become epidemic. The laws or regulations in some states specifically require vaccinations for school attendance; occasionally this provision applies to both teachers and children. In most states matters of vaccination and immunization are left to the discretion of official health departments.

Many judicial decisions of the courts uphold the requirements of compulsory vaccination and immunization when deemed necessary by the board of health, except in the few states where requirements are prohibited by law.

SCHOOL PLANTS

Regulations of the state education department, that have the effect of laws, often establish the requirement of size, location, and suitability of school grounds. In addition to grounds, regulations may provide standards for the construction, remodeling, and sanitation of schools.

Most states have laws requiring the use of fire-resistive materials in the construction of school buildings, although many school plants still are fire traps of the worst kind.

The laws in many states specify ventilation standards based upon old and faulty notions. Despite more than a half-century of accumulated knowledge, these archaic laws remain on the statutes. During the latter part of the nineteenth century it was believed that the carbon dioxide in expired air was a menace to health. In response to this belief laws were passed requiring a stipulated amount of fresh air per minute for each child in occupied classrooms. Although later scientists proved that the factors of movement and temperature are more significant in maintaining health than the chemical composition of air, few new laws were passed. Most of the old ones remain on the books even though they are ignored.

HEALTH INSTRUCTION

Most states have laws which require the teaching of physiology and hygiene. Every state requires instruction on the deleterious effects of alcohol, with narcotics and tobacco mentioned in several of these statutes. In some states the legislators even went so far as to indicate that textbooks shall devote a specified proportion of the book, or a definite number of pages, to the effects of alcohol and narcotics.

Legislation or state education department regulations on health instruction may establish this program as a special subject, combine it with physiology and hygiene, or include it with physical education. Such legislation or regulations often prescribe: (1) the use of textbooks; (2) grades in which instruction shall be given; (3) the number of minutes per week to be devoted to the subject; and (4) suggestions as to method.

PHYSICAL EDUCATION

Nearly all states provide for physical education through special legislation, incorporation of this item in the general education law, or by state education department regulation. Most of these enactments followed closely after World War I. There is need for recodification of legislation in this field, bringing the terminology up to date, deleting obsolete standards, and reorganizing fragmentary and isolated sections into large units in accordance with modern administrative practices.

ESTABLISHING OR REVISING HEALTH EDUCATION AND PHYSICAL EDUCATION LEGISLATION

While methods used to secure the passage or revision of legislation vary widely among the various states—to such an extent that specific suggestions seem unjustifiable—it is possible to indicate the general items which should be considered in formulating an acceptable law dealing with health education and physical education.

1. *Proper Title.* With the growing acceptance of the term "health education and physical education," this title is recommended.
2. *Comprehensive Statement of the Purpose of the Law.* Frequently the statute lists the purpose in such ambiguous terms that boards of education may abuse the intent of the law either through ignorance or by design.
3. *Mandatory Items Enumerated.* Does the law apply to all students attending the public schools, private schools, and teacher-education institutions approved by the state, or are there exceptions? Shall a director or supervisor be appointed? Shall state curriculum materials be provided? Details of program should be left to the state department of education, not enumerated in the law.
4. *Time Requirement.* Most laws now prescribe a definite time allotment for the program. Unfortunately many school administrators accept this standard as *maximum* instead of *minimum* as originally intended. Because of this fact it is recommended that no time requirement be specified but that approval of local programs be designated as a function of the state department of education.
5. *State Director or Supervisor.* Instead of making this a mandatory item, it is recommended that the law permit the chief executive officer of the state education department to appoint such staff members as may be necessary.
6. *Financial Support.* This applies to funds for maintaining the division and state aid for local districts. It is recommended that the law carry no specific appropriations either for a separate division within the state department, or for health education and physical education in cities, counties, and towns. Instead, finances for the division are to come from the general state appropriation, and assistance to local districts from the usual channels of state aid. Statutory appropriations to specific divisions within the department of education are not in accord with modern administrative practice and, in addition, they are easy prey for those who seek to curry favor with an uninformed constituency in times of economic retrenchment or political strife.
7. *Cooperative Relationships.* In furthering the state program it is essential that cooperative relationships be established with certain other official organizations, notably the state board of health.
8. *Qualifications of Teachers and Supervisors.* Since standards for teacher preparation change frequently, whereas a law usually enjoys

a marked degree of permanency, the law should specify that standards for the preparation and certification of teachers and supervisors
shall be established by the state department of education.

9. *Qualifications of Academic Teachers for Health Education and
   Physical Education.* Elementary classroom teachers frequently are responsible for health education and physical education, hence some
   preparation is necessary. As in the above item the responsibility for
   setting standards should be delegated to the state department of
   education. The same policy applies to academic teachers who coach
   athletic teams, or who serve the total program in other respects.

10. *Credit.* So long as credit for promotion, graduation, and college
    entrance is given for other subjects, the same policy should apply to
    health education and physical education. The law in this case will
    affect the public schools, and may apply to state institutions of higher
    learning, although private and denominational schools will not be
    affected unless such schools are maintained in part by public funds.

11. *Coordination of Present and Past Legislation.* Difficulty sometimes is
    encountered because provisions of the new law are at variance with
    older legislation. This is especially true in such matters as military
    training, medical inspection, and instruction relating to the deleteri-
    ous effects of alcohol and narcotics. Legal assistance should be
    secured while the bill is being framed and the statutes searched to
    prevent duplication. Where it seems desirable to include or to modify
    some of the former mandates, the proposed bill should contain a
    clause stating that the present legislation takes precedence over cer-
    tain older sections, naming them.

IS STATE LEGISLATION NEEDED?

It is impossible to answer this question with any degree of assurance
because of the conflicting evidence given by those in positions of administrative responsibility. Probably the majority of opinion would favor
some sort of legislation, either special laws, or by mention of health education and physical education in the more general staute which enumer-
ates the subjects which may or must be taught.

Under the philosophy that pervades modern social theory a state is
consciously aware of its constituents, and accepts as one of its responsibilities the provision of equalized educational opportunities. Hence laws
and regulations are passed requiring all local districts to comply with
certain minimum standards compatible with the best interests of the
state as a whole.

The pace of education is set by the tread of the backward communities. Therefore it is the duty of the state to indicate through laws
and regulations the speed of the educational activities of these communities. On the other hand, the state must be an incentive to better
districts, encouraging them in their efforts to improve the educational

offering. Legislation, regulations, and an enlightened public go hand in hand; occasionally one precedes the other, but in the final analysis all are essential.

CONFLICTS BETWEEN LOCAL AGENCIES

Conflict in the administration of play and recreation in municipalities is real and its by-products harmful to the program. Local municipal authorities with budgets and patronage to dispense compete for the right to serve children. As a result some communities possess two sets of playgrounds, two sets of equipment and facilities, and two staffs. This duplication is wasteful of tax money, produces conflicts between and makes rivals of local officials, and contributes nothing to the object of all their endeavors—the education and welfare of children and adults.

The lack of unformity and orderly planning for play and recreation is due largely to the Topsy-like character of urban growth and legislative development. Municipal functions and responsibilities have increased without master plans that might have brought efficient and more useful service to the community.

Legal aspects of the conflict add to the difficulties. In states with genuine home-rule provisions, cities may determine freely the conditions under which recreation shall be conducted. Some states have laws specifically dealing with recreation. But in most cities the board of education is elected locally and in some is appointed by the local city government. This has serious political relationships. A city government operating under the emblem of a political party often makes its decisions with respect to political advantage, and frequently conducts its administration to strengthen its political future quite regardless of recognized policies of orderly and progressive administration. This procedure aims at patronage and political power rather than service to citizens.

A Cooperative Plan.   There is one way out of the difficulty. This is a cooperative arrangement between the board of education and the city government with respect to the administration of play and recreation in the community.

The same sort of cooperative action sometimes is established in the health services. Where the state law requires the board of health to be responsible for the health of children, it is impossible for the board to delegate its authority to school physicians, for in law a delegated authority cannot be redelegated. The board of health, cooperating with the board of education, however, can appoint jointly with the board of education the same person to conduct the health services in schools.

In similar fashion the city government and board of education may unite in the selection of one executive officer to administer the physical education activities of school children and the recreational and developmental activities of preschool and adult groups on city parks or school properties. Less complete integration can be secured by an agreement

with respect to the use of facilities, but the larger values of unified administration favor one executive officer.*

Legal Provisions Necessary. In cities with home-rule rights the joint
action indicated above is easily possible, although legal difficulties would
be prevented by the passage of an enabling act by the legislature granting
to proper local authorities the right to spend tax money for recreational
purposes. In many states the school law restricts the powers of the
board of education to the legal sessions of the school term, hence the
board of education is unable to provide money for recreational purposes
after the school day is closed or during vacation periods. In numerous
states such power is assumed under the broad provisions of home-rule
charters that give the local government considerable freedom. In some
states governmental authorities assert that no such power of boards
exists. School codes should be drawn to permit boards of education, in
cooperation with city governments or alone, to conduct recreational programs and to spend tax money for them.

Similar difficulties often arise in the administration of safety education with school authorities, the police department, the fire department,
and the local safety council competing with each other for program development. Here again improved municipal planning could effect a kind
of safety program that utilizes the resources of each agency and avoids
conflict.

LIABILITY OF BOARDS OF EDUCATION

American law draws much of its content from England, and some of
its precedents are set by the social institutions out of which they grew.
In the days of limited monarchy the king could not be held responsible
for the acts of his servants. Municipal and state governments have supplanted in the United States the king's government, but the precedent,
"The King Can Do No Wrong," remains in the modern American city,
which is not liable for the acts of employees.

Boards of education are regarded as quasicorporations charged with
governmental functions. As such they are not liable for injuries caused
by the negligence of agents, although boards are liable for their own
negligence. In this case negligence must be proved, and depends largely
on defects of construction of facilities or defects in maintenance which
have been reported by the person in charge to the board which is responsible for keeping the facilities in good repair. If the board of education
employs a certified or licensed teacher of physical education, and the
teacher fails to notify the proper authorities that the equipment or
facilities are unsafe, the teacher rather than the board is remiss in the
performance of duty.

In legal parlance the question of conducting an "attractive nuisance" poses a complex problem. Gymnasium and playground apparatus

* See Chapter 20: The Schools and Community Recreation.

attracts children who may be injured in using these facilities unless proper supervision is provided. Lawful use of such apparatus in regularly scheduled physical education classes, and during recreation periods, does not constitute a nuisance *per se,* provided adequate supervision is available. The doctrine of "attractive nuisance" does apply when such facilities are used by children who trespass in playing on the apparatus at times when school is not legally in session.

When fees are charged for the use of facilities, or for attendance as spectators, a different situation arises with reference to the liability of boards of education. If the activity is provided for the sole benefit of the public, and not for profit to the municipality, the board of education usually is not liable even though a small charge is made to help pay current expenses. If, however, such property is maintained primarily as a source of revenue, and a person is injured either as a participant or spectator, the municipality is liable. Court decisions and opinions by attorneys general fail to indicate clearly the responsibility of boards of education when bleachers have collapsed injuring spectators, or when spectators have been injured in other ways while attending school affairs for which an admission fee is charged.

Since the liability of boards of education so frequently remains in doubt due to varying state legislation and to the exigencies of particular situations, it is recommended that legal counsel advise the board concerning the establishment of appropriate policies and procedures to protect the safety of persons who use school facilities.

LIABILITY OF TEACHERS

Many teachers believe that employment by a government agency exonerates them from personal liability in case of accidental injury to students. This is not true. Administrators and teachers are liable for neglecting to perform properly various duties and responsibilities normally assigned to them.

The statutes in one state often are unlike those in another state, hence the need for school employees to inform themselves regarding the laws of the state in which they are employed.

The treatment here of liability makes no pretense of completeness. The purpose is to suggest types of liability that exist and, by this introduction to the problem, to awaken the desire of administrators and teachers for accurate information in accordance with the prevailing local statutes.

The basis of liability is *negligence.* Such negligence may represent errors of omission or commission. Fortunately, perhaps, a person in this country is considered legally innocent until guilt is proved, which explains why few teachers are convicted of negligent acts. Public opinion is against suing the teacher unless flagrant violation of rights is apparent.

LIABILITY TO THE DISTRICT

A person accepting employment as a teacher in the public schools thereby agrees to perform his duties in conformity with the statutes and according to regulations adopted by the board. If he is negligent in the performance of these duties he is liable to the district for any loss or damage caused thereby.

In some states a teacher is punishable by fine for neglect of statutory duties. In the absence of a statute or regulation specifically covering the matter the board has no power to impose a fine on a teacher for dereliction of duty. The board, however, may properly dismiss the teacher and, if he persists in using the school building in defiance of the board, he is a trespasser and liable for damages incurred.

LIABILITY FOR BREAKING CONTRACT

The school district is liable for damages to the teacher for breach of its contract with the employee. In like manner the teacher is responsible to the district for failure to fulfill his contract to the district. In such cases the court usually decides that the board or teacher is liable to the other for at least nominal damages.

LIABILITY FOR INFLICTING PUNISHMENT

Before punishing a school child it is advisable to examine the laws and regulations where the teacher is employed. In some states it is possible for the teacher who punishes a child to commit the crimes of assault, battery, or false imprisonment—depending on the circumstances. Prosecution rests largely upon whether the teacher exceeded the limits fixed by law or regulation.

Permission granted by the parent to chastise a child does not absolve a teacher from liability if the punishment results in disfigurement or permanent injury. This statement is based on the principle of law that a parent cannot delegate a greater authority than he himself possesses. Athletic coaches who obtain written permission from parents for sons to engage in interschool competition, with such permission expected to absolve the school or coach from blame in case of injury, have reason to consult legal advice in this matter. If an injury causes permanent disfigurement or death, the municipality or coach may be liable for negligence.

LIABILITY FOR SUSPENSION OR EXPULSION

In the suspension or expulsion of a student the teacher or administrator must exercise discretion or judgment. Damages for errors of judgment do not constitute liability if the act is committed without malice, wantonness, or intent to wrong the pupil. If the pupil is suspended or expelled illegally, the person responsible for the act is liable for damages.

LIABILITY OF AUTOMOBILE DRIVERS

This question is of interest to athletic coaches or individuals in charge of athletic teams who transport players by private automobile. It also concerns teachers accustomed to taking children home who become ill in school, and teachers of classes in driver education.

Again the laws vary in the several states, and the driver or owner of the vehicle should be informed of his responsibility. In case of accident the question of liability probably will be settled on the basis of whether the driver exercised reasonable care. In some states the courts make a distinction between occupants riding at the invitation of the driver and those riding at their own request. In other states the fact that the driver is reimbursed for the trip places him under the jurisdiction of laws regulating omnibuses and other public vehicles with attendant problems of omnibus licenses, insurance, and liability.

The board of education would appear to have the moral obligation of obtaining legal sanction for methods used to transport school children for any reason whatsoever. Teachers and coaches should be assured by competent legal authority that they will not be held liable in case of accident while transporting school children, assuming that reasonable precaution is exercised.

SUGGESTIONS FOR ADMINISTRATORS

Many of the liabilities indicated above can be avoided by careful attention to: (1) legislative enactments and board regulations; and (2) the avoidance of negligence. Regarding the first, the facts should be ascertained. Has the state given to the municipality the power to perform the function involved? If the state has given the city a charter in which the right to conduct playgrounds after school hours does not appear, the matter must await charter revision or act of the legislature. The status of the municipal powers in this respect can be learned from the office of the city attorney. Has the board of education established policies and procedures aimed to protect the health and safety of school children, and do these measures enjoy legal sanction? The status of these policies and procedures may be obtained from the school superintendent.

Regarding measures for avoiding negligence, two factors are important:

1. Employment of competent personnel.
2. Construction of sound and safe equipment with appropriate inspection and maintenance.

   Employment of Personnel. Only competent and properly certified personnel should be employed. Policies and procedures should be established for reporting all accidents immediately after they occur. These technics should be approved by the board of education. All activities used in the curriculum should be listed and the curriculum approved by the board of education. Activities must be supervised and reasonable care exercised in dangerous events.

Construction and Maintenance of Equipment.   Activities conducted in the gymnasium or pool or on the playground usually are vigorous in nature. Youth should be encouraged to perform feats requiring courage; the slogan of "safety first" should not unduly restrict the purposes of physical education. On the contrary, permanent gain results in the development of skill which reduces injuries to a minimum.

Purchase of standard apparatus from a responsible firm is a wise investment. Installation of equipment by competent persons is essential. For example, swinging apparatus requires sufficient space to protect children from possible injury.

Regular inspection of all equipment with immediate replacement of worn parts decreases accidents. After years of use, wooden horizontal bars often bend slightly toward the floor. Such bars must be replaced without delay. Torn mats, frayed ropes, loose couplings, and split bats are safety hazards.

The prescribed administrative procedure should be followed that the gymnasium, swimming pool, and playground are to be used by children only when a qualified instructor is present.

Indoor and outdoor bleachers need attention. Inspectors from the municipal department of buildings should authorize the use of these facilities prior to each event to which the public is invited.

Insurance.   In recent years boards of education and teachers have adopted the policy of resorting to insurance as a means of protection. It is a sound policy for everyone. On the one hand, parents are compelled to send children to school where they become wards of the state and are quite beyond the sphere of parental supervision. Again, the expanding curriculum includes numerous activities that challenge the interests of adventurous youth, yet accidents may happen in the performance of these activities. On the other hand, the municipality is liable if negligence is proved, and teachers may be hauled into court to stand trial for failure to exercise reasonable precautions. Proper insurance and adequate supervision protect parents, children, boards of education, and teachers.

At first, insurance policies were purchased by teachers, with premiums paid out of their meager earnings. Later, boards of education bought the insurance. Since public education is recognized as a state function, perhaps the state should provide the insurance with premiums paid jointly by the state and municipality. Such action may require a change of statutes in some states.

In communities with sound insurance plans the number of accidents has decreased, fewer cases claiming negligence have found their way into the courts, and the protection afforded teachers and parents has improved the mutual interrelationships of school and community.

THE MORAL FACTOR

The conduct of any enterprise involving human relations must depend largely upon the mutual confidence and respect that exist between all persons concerned. These qualities of honor and trust—the moral factor—often transcend the practicality of legal pronouncements.

Moral obligations characterize the good citizen who accepts laws and regulations as basic elements, but who also follows the precepts of the Golden Rule. Teachers and administrators imbued with the spirit of optimum growth and development among children, concerned about adequate provisions for individual differences, and interested in the best possible educational welfare of the community perform their assignments in a truly professional manner. Likewise parents and the general public have moral obligations. The parent who is quick to bring legal suit against a teacher or school for an alleged wrong, or the organization in a district that refuses to cooperate with other agencies in an activity of proved worth, may live within the legal code but fail miserably in abiding by the moral code.

Good schools help to produce good citizens, and good citizens have confidence in and respect for sound education.

PROBLEMS FOR DISCUSSION

1. There has been an increasing number of law suits against teachers for negligence in your community. This is particularly true in physical education, and some type of teacher insurance appears necessary. Study the problem of liability insurance in your community and propose a satisfactory plan based upon legal and moral implications.
2. Assume that a child is injured by slipping on loose gravel in the school yard and there is the possibility of a liability charge. A teacher had previously reported this hazard to the administration which did nothing about it. The board of education was not notified. Who would be liable?
3. As a new teacher, you are unfamiliar with liability affecting you as a teacher of physical education. You learn that in at least one case, a teacher of physical education has been held liable when an injury occurred to a student in his class. How can you determine your exact legal status, and what steps must be taken to protect yourself from legal action in case of such accidents?
4. Review the laws and regulations in your state dealing with health examinations, vaccinations, construction and operation of school plants, health instruction, physical education, and recreation. Discuss these documents in regard to more efficient administration.
5. Instructors and students are encouraged to include other problems for discussion based upon their own experience and observation.

REFERENCES

American Association for Health, Physical Education, and Recreation: *Current Administrative Problems.* Washington, 1960.

Edwards, N.: *The Courts and the Public Schools.* The University of Chicago Press, Chicago, 1955.

Grieder, C., Pierce, T. M., and Rosenstangle, W. E.: *Public School Administration,* ed. 2. The Ronald Press, New York, 1961.

Knezrich, S. J.: *Administration of Public Education.* Harper & Row, Publishers, New York, 1962.

McCloskey, G.: *Education and Public Understanding.* Harper & Row, Publishers, New York, 1962.

Morphet, E. L., Reller, T. L. and Johns, R. L.: *Educational Administration—Concepts, Practices and Issues.* Prentice-Hall, Inc., Englewood Cliffs, 1959.

National Conference for City Directors of Health, Physical Education, and Recreation: *Administering City and County School Programs.* American Association for Health, Physical Education, and Recreation, Washington, 1960.

CHAPTER 23

PUBLIC RELATIONS

THE NEED FOR PUBLIC RELATIONS

While the wheels of progress in public education produce a constant change in materials and methods, a widespread popular understanding of the need for these changes—or indeed of what they actually are—is sadly lacking. Improved facilities demand greater expenditures of public money, and these funds can be obtained only by the sanction of officials whom the voting citizens place in positions of administrative or executive responsibility.

Too often members of the department of health education and physical education are so absorbed in the affairs of daily routine that they neglect to acquaint the various publics with information relative to activties for which support is sought. Knowledge of the program is essential to any real understanding of its worth, and intelligent support rests upon reliable public relations.

EDUCATION AND CHANGE

Some parents, businessmen, and employers believe that the youth of today receive an education inferior to that of a generation ago. To be sure, educational methods and philosophy have changed, but in the minds of numerous taxpayers the schools fail to pay dividends on the increased financial investment. An uninformed and hesitant public mutters about fads and thrills.

In an effort to reduce operating costs, taxpayers' leagues or other well intentioned pressure groups frequently attack health education and physical education. This is not hard to explain because the program was nonexistent in many communities when the present citizens attended public schools. Further, health education and physical education enjoy a sort of uniqueness in that they affect the immediate lives of most families, and have close relationships with numerous agencies in the community to a greater degree than most other school programs.

Health education and physical education demand good public relations. Unmistakable evidence demonstrates that retrenchment measures seldom affect adversely the development of sound educational programs if the public understands the value of these programs.

What is the duty of the department of health education and physical education? Obviously it should follow the general plan of public relations outlined for the school system as a whole, if such a plan exists. Boards of education in many large cities employ a person who keeps the public informed about school matters. Cooperation with this individual is imperative. The average taxpayer could not give satisfactory answers to the following vital questions, yet the department expects his cooperation and support. Why are health examinations indispensible? Should the schools examine children and omit the necessary follow-up program? Are textbooks needed for health teaching? Is physical education concerned primarily with giving boys and girls a "workout" or with fitness, or are there other significant values to be obtained? Why is it unwise to employ seasonal athletic coaches? Why should teams not play intersectional games? Why is playing in the school band, doing chores at home, or running errands an inadequate substitute for physical education? Do all high school boys and girls receive instruction in physical education, and in health education?

The qualified health educator or physical educator knows the answers to these questions but the general public, to which he must turn for support, does not. The people must know what those in charge of the department are doing to make the program as effective as possible. Once the public understands the problems involved and the needs of the school, support will follow.

WHAT IS PUBLIC RELATIONS?

For health education and physical education *public relations is the utilization of various and desirable methods to guide public opinion in the direction of intelligent group action and support for worthwhile education.* This calls for development of two-way channels of information and understanding between school personnel and citizens of the community. It involves more than publicity alone.

CONTINUOUS AND RELIABLE PUBLIC RELATIONS

Health education and physical education need continuous and reliable public relations. People have a right to know the degree of success obtained by enterprises they create and support, and to be informed about future community problems. Oftentimes the administrator shuns the public until an emergency occurs and then hastily organizes a campaign to raise funds or to oppose some resistive force. Campaign publicity savors strongly of propaganda. Instead of an orderly presentation of reliable information aimed to give a true picture of the problem, fragmentary information is rushed forward which the promoter believes suitable to obtain his immediate goal. Only through continuous and reliable public relations may the people be guided to an unfailing support of the program. To acquire this is worth striving for; to be satisfied with less is to lose where failure is tragic and destructive of professional morale.

THE PROGRAM ITSELF

Naturally the program itself is the best single means of continuous and reliable public relations. The daily or yearly program provides objective evidence that can be seen at any time. Unfortunately routine affairs often are taken for granted unless called to public attention. Before inviting public inspection, the program should exemplify the highest standards possible under present conditions. It must be constructed according to the most scientific rules of curriculum building, based upon sound educational principles, and conducted as an educational enterprise.

Parents and taxpayers are attracted by activities about which they have some knowledge, hence interscholastic athletics or setting-up exercises to them may represent the entire program, even though the department has developed an excellent plan of health teaching or a system of intramurals far more educational in scope than some activities which enjoy the sanction of tradition. Notwithstanding the fact that a well rounded program is of paramount importance, continuous efforts must be made to keep the public informed, especially concerning those aspects of greatest educational significance, or about which there is likely to be limited public understanding.

IMPORTANCE OF AN EFFICIENT AND LOYAL STAFF

The director, aided by the superintendent and school principals, is responsible for the efficiency and loyalty of his staff. An *esprit de corps* which radiates high professional ethics both within and outside the school markedly affects the public attitude toward health education and physical education.

The Director. The administrator himself should be a likable person. Personality is difficult to change but there are manners of speech, dress, walk, and general attitude that may be altered to advantage. There can be no compromise with selfishness, guile, and moroseness. He must exemplify unselfishness, frankness, and good cheer; he must humanize his department. There are directors who give careful attention to staff meetings, making them interesting and helpful, who encourage the staff to exercise initiative in planning departmental development, who give credit to individuals instead of claiming it for themselves; and there are department heads who compel their teachers to suffer martyrdom in long inconsequential meetings, who dictate minute procedures enforcing strict obedience to countless rules, who expect all favorable comment toward the department to react to their own glory—while laying the blame on someone else when adversity threatens. Life is full of contrasts, but actions are best classified by effects. The men and women characterized in the second illustration above not only violate the principles of effective public relations, they also suppress the professional spirit of staff members. Effective teaching and public relations have reciprocal relationships; each should kindle the spark of interest and promote initiative and action.

The Staff. Like the bus driver who goes for a ride on his day off, teachers frequently discuss school affairs with their families and friends. Many of these relatives or acquaintances are influential persons in the community who guide, either directly or indirectly, public opinion and support for education. If the teacher possesses intelligence and typifies a professional mind, a favorable impression toward the program may be established. Should he lack these qualities the entire program may be characterized by his misrepresentation. The teacher who is dissatisfied, who voices complaints about the inefficiency of superior officers, who grumbles over the hours of work, who deplores the inadequacy of equipment, and who bemoans the meager salary—that teacher is building public opinion detrimental to the program.

Personal Relationships. Efficient staff members promote good public relations as an integral and important part of their professional assignment. Among other things, the competent staff member: (1) discusses tactfully complaints raised by students, parents, and laymen; (2) accepts invitations to meet with groups representing such organizations as the parent-teacher associations, Y.M.C.A., Y.W.C.A., Y.M.H.A., Y.W.H.A., and others; (3) serves on committees like the council of social agencies; (4) affiliates with one or more community service groups—Rotary Club, Kiwanis Club, the church of his choice, American Legion, as examples; and (5) develops cordial relationships with his educational colleagues.

THE DAILY NEWSPAPER

The newspaper is one of the most important agencies through which people learn about school activities. Practically everyone reads the newspaper. Moreover, the printed column carries an authority frequently more potent than the spoken word. In the hands of the skilled reporter an idea, a single instance in a remote gymnasium, or the experience of an individual child is spread throughout the entire community and generally accepted as authoritative. Newspapers are powerful; their influence may be constructive in promoting a worthy community enterprise, or destructive in organizing opposition against it. Since the reporter is interested in stories which have news value and in presenting facts, usually without personal bias, it behooves members of the department to know what aspects of the program can be publicized to best advantage, and to develop a cooperative relationship with newspaper representatives.

WHAT IS NEWS?

Satisfactory and concise definitions are difficult to find. It is generally believed that news is best characterized by freshness, human interest, timeliness, conflict and strife, as distinguished from other information.

A city editor of the *New York Herald Tribune* in writing on "What Is News" once said in part:

> News is that inexact measure which journalists seek . . . to chart the ebb and flow of the tides of human aspiration, the ignominy of mankind, the glory of the race. . . . There is no exact definition of news. . . . (It) comes when the earth shudders and yawns and a great city is ruined; it comes when a young man flies the Atlantic alone. . . . In addition to this 'spot' news which, like a fast-flying game bird, must be shot quickly on the wing, there is a vast field of material which lies in a sort of misty borderland between what is obviously news and what cannot be news. This material consists chiefly of situations of puzzling trends, of subtle changes in the manners and customs and thoughts of a whole people. . . . The great newspaper strives for an acute social consciousness; it takes the long view of current events, . . . and does its best to present a comprehensive picture of contemporary civilization.[*]

Thus, one way of regarding news is to think of it in terms of conflict and strife, and to dramatize certain parts of the program on the basis of these qualities. At a large public meeting attended by several hundred educators, the late President Russell of Teachers College, Columbia University, wanted to emphasize some of the significant features of American education. Instead of reciting past achievements as a series of historical episodes, he prepared a text somewhat as follows: "Education is not the gift of such men as Henry Barnard or Horace Mann, but a fight for the Right by the American people to wrest those democratic ideals inherent in the Constitution from the mill owner, the manufacturer, or the moneyed aristocracy." The strength of this appeal is at once apparent.

Doubtless the factors of conflict and strife are responsible for the general interest shown in athletics. But news stories reside in other features of the health education and physical education program. During the health examinations numerous defects are found; will the child overcome his difficulties? Special attention is given to adapted physical activities for physically underdeveloped students; how will this emphasis

[*] S. Walker: What Is News? *The Forum,* October, 1931.

aid in the adjustment of these students to the total school program? A community recreation program is planned; will it keep children off the streets, reduce juvenile delinquency, or provide opportunities for children and adults to spend their leisure in pleasurable recreation? Each of these illustrations involves the elements of overcoming obstacles, of success despite opposition.

Again, news deals with rules of conduct, the customs of a people, or a quickened social consciousness. Affairs of health education and physical education are rich in such material. The character values of play provide a fertile field for influencing rules of conduct. Free public education is a custom of the American people, and modern education gives a prominent place to wholesome recreation. A program of wholesome recreation designed for *all* youth, as well as for the more highly skilled, fulfills this American custom. A social consciousness can be aroused in favor of educating the whole child, physically as well as mentally.

Another quality of news is freshness. Reporters want the story as soon as it breaks. For example, a board of education votes to enlarge the playground at a given school. If properly handled the morning paper will carry a story which begins something like this: "A new playground is planned for the Roosevelt school, it became known today," followed by details of human interest that describe how boys and girls will benefit by this addition. A rival newspaper might use the same facts in the afternoon by stating, "Two thousand pupils in the Roosevelt district held a mass meeting this afternoon rejoicing over the new playground to be erected immediately." Note that the second story uses essentially the same facts as the first with any additional information which can be obtained to bring the news item up-to-date. Note also that the *lead* is the cream of the news. It answers briefly the questions in which the reader is interested, viz.: who, what, where, when, how, and why? This is based upon the assumption that newspaper readers are busy, and that they appreciate short-cuts to facts.

THE NEWS REPORTER

News reporters and photographers deserve the same cordiality and respect accorded other visitors. This does not mean that administrators or teachers should fawn upon the reporter or attempt to establish a false sense of hospitality. Such a procedure is quickly noticed by the alert journalist whose daily routine brings him in contact with all sorts of people. The reporter represents the public, and if the public is to be convinced, the reporter must *first* be impressed.

Often the city editor represents the person who needs educational enlightenment. On him falls the responsibility of decision in the kinds of community enterprises that deserve special consideration by the paper, and he may accept or reject the stories written by reporters. If the city editor supports the avowed purposes and accomplishments of health education and physical education, the department has the right to expect appropriate coverage by reporters.

Instead of entertaining the reporter in the office, astute administrators or teachers take him to the gymnasium, athletic field, swimming pool, or health suite for actual observation of existing conditions. An efficient news representative is not content to write stories about those things which educators believe the public should know. He demands first-hand information. In the office he obtains ideas relative to administrative policy; in the schools he sees how these policies actually operate.

Fortunately, reporters usually prefer to visit the plant, talk with the executive or teacher in charge, and write the story themselves. Occasionally, however, the administrator needs to prepare a news release for his department. Every director should know how to perform this task in an acceptable manner.

The writer must first learn what is news, and remember that the press operates primarily for the profit of stockholders. If the material contains news of general interest, releases should be furnished to all local papers. Feature articles may be sent to one paper only. The writer should select a few sentences or phrases which attract the interest of the reader. These should appear at the beginning of the article. Style and content are adapted to the intellectual level of those for whom the article is intended; thus a story for parents differs from one written for children. A copy of all releases should be filed.

The following illustration suggests an appropriate form for releases:

Department of Education
3 East 25th Street
Baltimore 18, Maryland

Office of the Superintendent
  of Public Instruction

For further information call: **FOR IMMEDIATE RELEASE**

    Robert C. Lloyd   September 19, 1963
    Special Assistant
    General Administration
    HOPKINS 7-4000, Ext. 812

    Ref. No. 57-10

Emphasizing that school sports should serve the educational welfare and development of students and that any tendency toward over-emphasis or commercialization would be considered contrary to policy, the report of a special school athletics committee of the School Board was submitted at the first meeting of the Board for the current school year.

To make the benefits of participation available to a maximum number of students, the committee recommended expansion of the athletic program as rapidly as funds, facilities, and staff can be obtained.

STUDENT PUBLICATIONS

The school newspaper reflects the educative processes conducted within the institution. As an organ of publicity the student publication:

(1) fosters clear understanding and harmonious cooperation among all departments within the school itself; (2) casually and unobtrusively informs parents about the ideals and functions of the educational system as they read articles written by their own or other children; and (3) encourages the student writer to accept the responsibilities of the school as his own. As he prepares his article he must understand the problems involved; he must present the necessary facts accurately and in an interesting manner. The department that fails to utilize the school newspaper as an excellent means of disseminating information about health education and physical education loses a golden opportunity.

Cooperating with Student Reporters. Student reporters deserve helpful guidance and sympathetic cooperation. In dealing with them the same general procedure is followed as that employed with newspaper reporters except that here the news may be more personal. One should mention the names of individual children who have made some accomplishment in health education and physical education. Marked copies of these papers should reach the home. There is no need to be fearful of using the parents' names as well; persons of all ages like to see their names in print.

PUBLIC SPEAKING

On frequent occasions members of the department are invited to address public and professional groups; thus the staff member must become a passable speaker. At such time the speaker reflects the efficiency and worth of his department, a reflection that may win friends or make enemies for the cause he represents.

Preparing the Speech. Some general principles may be of assistance to the person who finds himself scheduled to make a speech before a certain group, at a certain time, and on a certain topic. Moreover, it is recognized that varying situations demand different approaches:

1. Select material which will interest your listeners. The same general topic, but treated in a slightly different way, may be used with different groups varying in age or in intellectual or social status; in other words, gauge the material to fit the audience.
2. Unless you are accustomed to the public platform, plan the speech so that it may be given in not more than 20 minutes. In these days of rapid communication long declamations are taboo.
3. If the occasion is important—and most of them are—write the speech in full, giving careful consideration to the choice of words, rhetoric, the thoughts involved, an interesting lead, and a clear dynamic summary or conclusion. With sufficient experience the speaker may prepare notes instead of writing the manuscript in full. The use of notes is less time-consuming, although the former method is recommended for the novice and for important occasions, largely because writing helps to clarify one's thinking about the topic. Even though the speech is to be given extemporaneously it is better to write it first.

4. Vary the style to avoid monotony. Change occasionally from exposition to narration or description. Turn from the abstract and use actual cases for illustrative purposes. Attack the problem in another way, but move forward always, not merely in a circle. Intersperse long involved sentences with short zestful ones.

5. Memorize the beginning and ending of the speech. Almost everyone is slightly nervous in addressing a strange group, and it is essential that a friendly atmosphere be established at the beginning. If the summary or concluding remarks have been memorized, the speaker can lay aside his notes or manuscript and talk directly to his audience. This gives emphasis, and has the additional advantage of permitting the speaker to lead up to his final point at any time. It is important to know how and when to stop. Frequently a speaker is seen "fishing" for an ending, and if he catches one, he is more lucky than smart, for the odds are against him. He should have "terminal facilities" and know the proper switch to open to bring him into the home station.

Making the Speech.* Assuming that the speech has been prepared carefully, several suggestions may assist the beginner in making the address more effective and interesting to his audience.

1. When speaking from the stage, know exactly where you are to sit upon reaching the platform. Observe the laws of balance in getting seated to avoid awkwardness. Adjust yourself to the chair and stay adjusted, although it is permissible to move slightly at the end of speeches. After you are seated, and with as calm a mental attitude as you can muster, make a pleasant contact with the entire audience by looking at the people seated on the main floor and balcony.

2. Just before you are about to speak get your voice warm. There are several methods in common use for this purpose.

3. Upon being announced, walk to the speaker's stand and recognize the chairman leisurely. Don't rush forward like a cheer leader. It is essential that your first contact with the audience be pleasant; smile, and if the group is new to you, establish some bond of common interest without patronizing them. Instead of gazing straight ahead, look out over the assembly. Speak to the last person in the room; make your voice carry through.

4. With reference to the body mechanics of public speaking, the following "do's" and "don'ts" may prove helpful:

a. Keep the hands under control; use gestures sparingly; pockets are not made for the speaker's hands; avoid fumbling with papers or other objects on the lectern—don't lean on or grip anything.

b. Use the feet to keep the body well balanced, stand erect but not tense; avoid rocking back and forth upon the heels and toes; don't walk around.

c. Always keep your breath and poise; awkwardness and hurry fre-

---

* Many of the notes for this section were prepared by Dr. E. C. Davis, Professor of Physical Education, University of Southern California. Errors of interpretation should be credited to the authors.

quently distract the audience; when articulation is too slow things become heavy and interest is lost; when pressed for time put ideas in concise statements and use fewer illustrations; never look at the clock; unexpectedly lowering the voice or a brief illustration automatically attract attention; cultivate a smooth pleasing voice and speak in conversational tones; don't shout.

5. In delivering the speech:

a. Choose words to fit the audience, expressing your thoughts in terms they can easily comprehend. Flowery oratory is largely of the past generation.

b. The headline of the daily paper attracts the reader's attention. Get an arresting opening that seizes attention immediately.

c. Formulate clearly at the beginning of your speech the three or four main concepts you wish to present.

d. Repetition may be used to advantage. The successful speaker repeats his most important points, using a different phraseology each time to avoid monotony.

e. Unified concepts are obtained by having sentences hang together, and the elements of each sentence organized in proper sequence. The unmodified statement strikes home more forcibly than the one with modifications and exceptions.

f. The peculiar twist of a phrase may give new significance to an old truth.

g. After an idea has been expressed in ordinary technical terms, repeat it in everyday English or use a homely analogy.

h. Indicate clearly the transition from one point to another.

i. Human interest stories are preferable. If a humorous story is used it should be directly related to the occasion. Seldom is the story itself funny; the humor is in the way it is told.

6. In presenting your address try to lead the audience to your point of view by the selection of facts pertinent to the problem. Avoid telling listeners what their conclusions should be. The average citizen is confident that he can arrive at the decision which is best for the public good, and resents your attempt to make up his mind for him. In reality you are furnishing the material out of which he formulates his judgment.

The Chairman of the Meeting. It frequently happens that a staff member is called upon to act as chairman of a meeting, and in this capacity he reflects the department and the profession either creditably or discreditably. Appearing before the public in this role is quite different from accepting an invitation to speak. In acting as chairman of a meeting there are certain points to keep in mind.

1. Be certain that each speaker has been given a definite topic and that the program is a unified whole. Topics may be assigned by you or selected by the speakers, subject to your approval. Since you are largely responsible for the success of the meeting, you may expect to

have some voice in choosing the speakers, indicating the length of the talks, and reviewing the general ideas to be presented. The invitation to out-of-town speakers should state the time, place, and nature of the meeting, possibly a suggestive title for the address, the amount of time which the guest may have, the type of audience to be addressed, whether the occasion is formal or informal, and the honorarium which he may expect either with or without expenses.

2. Just before the meeting begins be sure you know the names and official positions of the speakers and the exact title of each address. These should be memorized and several interesting facts about the guests may be used in introducing them. The chairman should notify each speaker when he is to appear.

3. Having decided beforehand where each person is to sit, the chairman, leading the way, steps out upon the platform or stage followed by the speakers. When everyone is ready the chairman leisurely takes his seat which is a signal for the others to do likewise.

4. The chairman opens the meeting by mentioning the occasion and paving the way for the first speaker.

5. In introducing a speaker be natural, stick to facts, don't attempt to give a flowery oration, say pleasant things but avoid taking in the entire universe. Introduce him as one person to another. Mention the field in which he is an authority. Give the speaker and his audience something in common. Give the exact title of his address. It is better to name the speaker last. Introduce *him to the audience*; the formal phrase is still good: "I take pleasure in introducing Mr. so-and-so." Make it definite that at this moment he is being introduced, then stand to one side until he recognizes you.

6. At the end of the address and after he is seated always thank the speaker and comment briefly on his speech.

ANNUAL REPORTS AND SPECIAL BULLETINS

As originally conceived, the annual report represented a means whereby the public learned how those in charge of the schools were carrying out their trust. Except in smaller communities the annual report of today frequently is a mass of involved tabulations and statistics. As an organ of public relations this report should aim primarily to describe fairly and accurately affairs that have taken place during a given period, and problems relating to future needs.

Usually the various departmental reports form sections in the larger volume prepared by the superintendent. Here is an opportunity for the administrator of health education and physical education to collect from staff members or division heads a chronicle of outstanding accomplishments during the year, and a statement of needed changes. These can be reorganized, compiled and edited, furnishing a departmental report which serves the purpose originally intended for this type of document.

The annual report is more dignified than the newspaper article and may contain graphic representation in the form of pictures, charts, and diagrams along with descriptive or narrative material. Care must be exercised to avoid long and involved statistical tables. All tabulations should be clearly explained and interpreted.

Success in enlisting public support will depend upon: (1) the excellency of the program itself; (2) the selection of appropriate topics—those possessing human interest value; (3) the honesty and fairness with which these topics are treated—telling the truth and avoiding exaggeration or outlandish claims; and (4) the attractiveness of the composition.

In addition to annual reports, periodic bulletins describing unusual events such as a safety education campaign, a drive against polio in cooperation with the local board of health, or the need for an extended health services program may be used effectively. In such bulletins attention is focused upon a single activity or an individual event of timely importance.

ASSEMBLY PROGRAMS

School assemblies offer an excellent opportunity to educate pupils, parents, and teachers in departmental objectives and accomplishments. Here can be featured programs, such as demonstrations of sports' technics, safety measures, talks by the school physician, or fashion shows with emphasis on posture.

MOTION PICTURES

As an extremely potent force in gaining popular support the motion picture may be used to advantage in public relations. Reduced costs of operation together with increased interest in private ownership, especially of the 16-millimeter type, suggests more extensive use of the motion picture to disseminate accurate and vital information among parents and taxpayers.

RADIO AND TELEVISION

Results obtained by numerous state departments with an organized broadcasting service indicate the value of radio in keeping the public informed regarding the needs and accomplishments of schools. Except in rare instances the radio has been used but little to popularize health education and physical education. To be sure, commercial concerns advertise their health commodities daily or weekly, but this is to be regarded as indirect public relations for the school. While the radio is impersonal, it is a mighty instrument for shaping public opinion.

Television represents a more personal and realistic technic for acquainting the public with school needs and accomplishments. There is increasing use of this service throughout the country for both teaching and public relations purposes.

SPECIAL COMMUNICATIONS TO PARENTS

Unlike radio and television with their generalized appeal, the special communication to parents is direct and specific, calling the recipient to immediate and—it is hoped—constructive action. Letters to parents describing the proposed vaccination or nutrition program and notices showing the health status of individuals are common examples of this type of public relations.

EXHIBITIONS AND DEMONSTRATIONS

Sometimes the words "exhibition" and "demonstration" are used to designate very different presentations. Here they are used synonymously and refer to any display of school children or their work viewed by the public for popular interest or community support.

Many of the activities of health education and physical education lend themselves to this type of public relations because they deal with action, and action attracts attention. Exhibitions marked by originality in organization and conduct provide occasions where teachers and parents meet on common ground.

Demonstrations should present an accurate picture of the schools' accomplishments. In some communities a large part of the school year is spent in preparing for public demonstrations, to the detriment of the regular program. At other times the wrong impression is given; activities are demonstrated which "show" well but which have little or nothing to do with the daily work. Examples of this type are: intricate marching with flags, gaudy costumes, or exploitation of individual children in events not learned in school. Educationally, these are unsound practices; in business they would be termed "sharp" practices. The exhibition should be used to demonstrate to the public the types of activity used in the regular program, to point out the need for improved facilities, or for similar purposes.

Generally speaking, there are three variations of the exhibition in common use:

1. The exhibit of pupils' work displayed in some public place, such as in store windows, or on school bulletin boards. In smaller or neighborhood communities the window display of health projects, posters, and slogans serves as a desirable means of keeping the public informed about school health affairs. Although restricted somewhat by the type of material which may be shown to advantage, the plan has possibilities which need to be explored.
2. The exhibition held as a special session of the school to which parents are invited and at which regular activities of the program are pre-

sented. In this type of program the entire school may cooperate in giving parents and friends an opportunity to witness the various school functions in their natural setting.

3. The special demonstration characterized by May Day programs, field days, health demonstrations, or annual sports contests. Interschool athletics and play days might be included in this list. The organization and content of these activities present such a variety of factors, depending upon the community, that only the most general suggestions can be given. A demonstration that focuses attention upon one general theme or series of events is better than one that contains too great a variety of activities. Care must be exercised in planning the time and place of the exhibition to insure the largest attendance possible. Interest in the coming event can be developed by using the various means of advertising—newspapers, posters, school bulletin board, notes to parents, school publications, and others. The use of tickets, even though there is no admission charge, adds interest. Cooperation of various local organizations may be secured for special purposes—for example, the board of health and the public health association for May Day programs, the parent-teacher association for health demonstrations, and the American Legion for annual sports contests.

The success of properly organized and conducted demonstrations bears evidence of their effectiveness as agencies for desirable public relations.

STATE AND LOCAL ORGANIZATIONS

There are a number of state and local organizations with avowed platforms favoring improved physical welfare of children. Their services should be enlisted. Two important veterans' organizations, the American Legion and the Veterans of Foreign Wars, are interested in the youth of the nation. The Legion presents annually a national platform in behalf of the child. The Legion has been prominent in enacting and saving physical education legislation. Its power in countless local communities has been demonstrated. The wise director will use it.

The National Congress of Parents and Teachers stands for improved health among school children. From the national office and the state association to the local organization is a chain which binds together a great and powerful body interested in matters of health education and physical education. Their interest often has been expressed in the Summer Round-Up, school feeding, health teaching, and wholesome recreation.

Units of the Junior Association of Commerce have demonstrated intelligent interest in the welfare of children and youth. This organization deserves recognition in furthering programs of health education and physical education.

Numerous other organizations of state and local character can be brought to the support of health education and physical education. These are the local boards of health, public health associations, federations of women's clubs, the grange, the league of women voters, the international association of home and school, Y.M.C.A., Y.W.C.A., the state motor vehicle department, the state highway department, the state police department, and others. Perhaps no other school activity enjoys such a prominent "supporting cast" as health education and physical education.

The influence of the state department of education in rendering assistance to local districts is discussed in a preceding chapter. The chief reason for establishing a division of health education and physical education in the state department is to aid in the promotion of local programs. It is customary to speak of a state program; this is largely a myth. A state program does not exist as such. It functions only as cities, towns, and districts in the state are helped to obtain increased facilities, improved instruction or services, and more vigorous public support. The state director welcomes the opportunity to cooperate with local efforts. His aid should be enlisted.

THE SURVEY

Every department might well maintain a continuous survey, and from time to time make public its findings in the annual report or in special publications. The survey provides facts and other data for public relations unobtainable from any other source. This technic insures the accumulation of all pertinent information from which comparisons are possible for any desired period or subject.

The survey may be used to present facts showing how the department has made use of resources previously requested; and to present other facts aimed to enlist public support for a new venture. Thus survey reports should emphasize items in which the community excels, as well as those for which additional resources are sought.

PROBLEMS FOR DISCUSSION

1. In an urban community a "Citizens' Recreation Committee" is organized to promote a better recreation program. The director of health education and physical education is invited to serve as a consultant. He declines, giving the following reason: "The recreation program is the responsibility of the Recreation Commission. In these days of budget cutting I have all I can do to defend the school physical education program." Do you agree with the director's reply?
2. A city director of health education and physical education spends considerable time in his office meeting the public, handling correspondence, and preparing bulletins. The superintendent suggests he might improve his public relations program if he joins one of the leading service clubs and

visits the schools more frequently. Discuss this in the light of good public relations.

3. A leading director of health education and physical education writes, "One of the greatest problems confronting physical education today is to motivate administrators as to the vital necessity of inaugurating a realistic program in the elementary schools and providing funds and expert leadership to do the job. It's in the beginning school years that we need periodic health examinations, correction of remediable defects, health instruction, and a program of teaching games, sports, and recreational skills. A good job done on this level will solve most of the problems on higher age levels." What relation does this problem have to good public relations?

4. Instructors and students may implement the above with problems gained from their own experience and observation.

REFERENCES

Cook, L. and Cook, E.: *School Problems in Human Relations.* McGraw-Hill Book Company, Inc., New York, 1957.

Educational Policies Commission: *Mass Communication and Education.* National Education Association, Washington, 1958.

Griffiths, D. E.: *Human Relations in School Administration.* Appleton-Century-Crofts, New York, 1956.

Moehlman, A. B. and Van Zwoll, J. A.: *School Public Relations.* Appleton-Century-Crofts, New York, 1957.

National Conference on Interpretation of Physical Education: *Conference Report.* The Athletic Institute, Inc., Chicago, 1961.

CHAPTER 24

EVALUATION IN
HEALTH EDUCATION
AND PHYSICAL EDUCATION

THE ROLE OF EVALUATION

Every worthwhile educational activity requires evaluation of one kind or another to determine its success in relation to certain established standards. These standards conform to clearly defined objectives. Programs of health education and physical education should have: (1) a series of specific objectives defining the aim in terms of tangible and obtainable results; (2) a group of carefully selected activities for realizing the objectives; (3) approved methods and technics of instruction and supervision; (4) efficient policies and procedures of administration; (5) appropriate standards for the activities; and (6) satisfactory evaluative instruments for each of these items. The plain truth of the matter forces the conclusion that determination of standards, as well as appraising them, rests on effective evaluation.

Technics of evaluation usually reflect the concepts of the prevailing educational philosophy. An accepted view that education is a *science* leads naturally to the search for precise measuring instruments to appraise the child's progress in school. When teaching is regarded as an *art*, scientific accuracy in measurement gives way to a more general evaluation of *quality* rather than *quantity*, with learning designed to reconcile the complexities of biological nature with the variable responses essential to success in an ever-changing social world. Current educational philosophy holds that education is both a science and an art, hence the use of accurate testing instruments for certain forms of instruction, and methods of observational evaluation for the many associate or concomitant learnings resulting from experiences in the school, home, and community.

Oftentimes these associate learnings, although vitally affecting the development of desirable attitudes and appreciations, do not lend themselves to scientific measurement. They may, however, represent values of greater ultimate significance than knowledge or skills for which precise measuring instruments are available. For example, it is a reasonably simple matter to measure the time required for an 18-year-old boy to run 100 yards, but it is extremely difficult to evaluate accurately, with technics now at hand, his attitude toward other members of the team or his appreciation of physical activity as a desirable recreational pursuit. Standardized health knowledge tests measure with surprising accuracy what the student knows about nutrition and social hygiene, but the kinds of food he selects at the cafeteria and associations with his family and fellow students more clearly indicate the effectiveness of school instruction. Strength tests predict abilities to lift weights and to perform other feats requiring muscular energy, but the administrator who assumes that these tests represent satisfactory instruments for measuring all sorts of human strengths and weaknesses perpetuates a kind of chicanery for which the laws provide no recourse in court.

Views of Evaluation.   The composite attitudes of persons in health education and physical education toward evaluation approximates the normal curve of distribution in other qualities. The majority can "take it or leave it alone," depending upon the exigencies of the particular situation. At one extreme appears the group that holds fast to the tenets of standardized tests for the salvation of an education fraught with dire evils. At the other extreme stands the group which views such tests with suspicion, voicing the opinion that a properly educated teacher or administrator with the usual common sense will evaluate with surprising accuracy the objectives sought.

Probably a middle ground best serves the purposes of health education and physical education. Surely standardized tests which measure a great number of the desired results remain undiscovered. Likewise estimates based on observation must face the verdict of unreliability. Obviously a *combination of objective measurement and expert observation represents the best course to follow*—one supplementing the other. When objective tests are available, their use provides reliable scores; in the absence of such tests, the subjective judgment of discerning teachers and administrators gives evidence of eminent practicability and value even though such evidence does not lend itself to translation into Arabic numbers.

SOME BASIC THESES OF EVALUATION

Several basic theses express the convictions of those who regard with approval efforts to appraise educational outcomes. Some of the more important ones are:

Evaluation Refers to Everything Associated with the Learning Process. The older and narrower term of measurement normally applied to pupil classification and achievement. Evaluation as a broader term includes measurement and encompasses as well the myriad of details associated with administration, guidance, and supervision—the entire range of instructional and service activities. Thus pupil achievement in a given subject depends in large part upon the availability of equipment and various other conditions that surround the learning process. True evaluation takes into account all of these things in their appropriate perspective.

Evaluation Applies to All the Objectives Sought. Instruction, administration, supervision, and guidance are inextricably bound together in the pattern of education. Although the areas of teaching and learning on the one hand, and services on the other hand, may have unique objectives of their own, these objectives complement and supplement each other in the effective school. Evaluation helps to determine the degree of accomplishment in each of these objectives, and indeed to appraise the worth of the objectives themselves as a means of producing the desired results.

Evaluation Represents a Continuous Process. Older forms of measurement dealt with pupil achievement at a given time or with capacity to achieve centain standards. Used in this way, measurement was applied at the beginning and end of a stipulated period to indicate potential or actual growth or progress. True evaluation represents a continuous process wherein all factors that affect learning receive constant and unified appraisal.

Evaluation Involves Many Persons. Everyone connected with the program has a function to perform in purposeful evaluation. Teachers accept the primary responsibility for instruction in health education and physical education, although the nature of the home and the care of school facilities by the custodian often affect the quality of instruction. Administrators and supervisors provide the equipment and recommend procedures designed to improve instruction, but teachers should have a voice in appraising the equipment furnished and the procedures suggested. Further, democratic administration and contemporary educational philosophy assign to students an increasingly prominent role in the selection of objectives and in the determination of procedures. From the illustrations just cited it is evident that teachers often can assist administrators in evaluating the numerous facets of administration, that parents and custodians could have a part in appraising instruction, and that giving students the opportunity to help in judging many educational results improves the technic of evaluation and doubtless increases student insight with respect to the objectives sought. Of course not all persons connected with the home and school are equally capable in evaluating all things; the physician is a better judge of tonsil conditions than the guidance counselor, and the athletic coach is more competent to select a team than the principal—that is one of the functions of specialization. A comprehensive program of evaluation in a school makes use of various human resources, molding them into a unified pattern.

Whatever Exists at All, Exists in Some Amount.   This principle is demonstrated adequately in numerous affairs of daily life. With respect to the individual, standards are available for measuring accurately such qualities as height, weight, length of arms, size of feet, heart rate, and blood pressure. Other qualities cannot be measured so precisely, although they do exist in certain amounts. Examples of this type are ability to play tennis, appreciation of modern dance as an art form, loyalty to the team, desire to engage in physical activity as a recreational pursuit, and belief in public health as a worthy institution of government. Until more exact measuring instruments are provided for these last qualities, a person's achievement is appraised by such descriptive words as excellent, good, fair, poor, or intolerable.

Anything that Exists in Amount Can Be Evaluated.   This does not imply that valid instruments are now available for evaluating all traits. It does mean that measuring instruments may be constructed at some future time. It means further that teachers now have the responsibility of evaluating as objectively as possible pupil competence in those traits which education attempts to develop.

All Evaluation Is Not Perfect.   The complexity of human traits poses a difficult problem for the researcher who attempts to construct a standard test. Even the quality of physical fitness contains so many diversified elements that few experts define the term with satisfaction to everyone.

Unfortunately, the novice who inadvertently uses a faulty technic may condemn all evaluation as a result of his limited experience. Numerous appraisal technics have passed the stage of experimentation and enjoy a prominent place in the field. Doubtless the intelligent use of those now available will create a demand for better ones.

Evaluation Is Indispensable.   Occasionally an administrator or teacher contends that the practical affairs of his work leave no time for attention to *evaluation*. In a sense evaluation is like bookkeeping in business; it indicates direction, and shows degrees of accomplishment. The worth of administrative procedures and teaching methods remains obscure or unknown unless their effects are evaluated.

ERRORS COMMON TO EVALUATION

At least four errors common to evaluation confront the administrator. They are: (1) selection of faulty or inaccurate instruments; (2) incorrect use of valid instruments; (3) unsound interpretations of results; and (4) failure to use the results. These errors relate to both standardized tests and to subjective evaluations.

The Selection of Faulty or Inaccurate Instruments.   The selection of precise instruments depends upon the trait or factor in question and intended use of results. Some evaluative procedures fail to meet the requirements of *objectivity, validity,* and *reliability.*

Although these terms properly belong to statistical measurement, where their application for years has guided the efforts of research workers, these same requirements relate to successful clinical evaluation. *Validity* refers to the efficiency with which the technic employed measures what it *attempts* to measure. *Reliability* depends upon the consistency with which the technic measures what it *actually does* measure. *Objectivity* rules out the personal bias of the investigator.

Incorrect Use of Valid Instruments.   Most standardized tests contain specific directions for use. The examiner may employ methods in using an instrument contrary to its intended purpose. Thus the stethoscope is a reasonably valid instrument, although accurate observation requires the removal of clothing. Likewise a test designed to measure native capacity seldom proves adequate as a measure of achievement, and a knowledge test may not properly evaluate attitudes.

Unsound Interpretation of Results.   The chief difficulty in interpreting results lies in securing data which mean one thing and assuming that they indicate something else. A high score on a health knowledge test does not guarantee the practice of correct health habits or the establishment of proper health attitudes. Success on a strength test does not suggest excusing the student from physical education on the assumption that he has fulfilled the requirements of the program. The criterion of administrative efficiency may not alone justify the adoption of policies and procedures that ignore the differing personalities of staff members.

Failure to Use the Results.   Besides selecting the appraisal technic with care, and applying it correctly, proper use of the results bestows a responsibility. Proper use should: (1) improve instruction; (2) increase student interest; (3) assist in the diagnosis of specific strengths or weaknesses; or (4) effect more desirable administrative practices. Frequently teachers and administrators fail to make use of evaluation results. Throughout the country hundreds of files contain millions of test scores, health examination records, survey data, and studies made by groups of staff members that await analysis and use in improving the effectiveness of education.

THE STATISTICAL VERSUS THE CLINICAL APPROACH

In academic education the period of most pronounced growth in statistical measurement occurred during the early part of the present century. Although attempts to evaluate health and physique appear in the records of Quetelet, Seaver, Hitchcock, Sargent, and others, a redirected emphasis in the preparation of standard tests developed after 1920. Perhaps the increased attention to health education and physical education, and the acceptance of new technics in statistical procedure, prompted this emphasis. Professional literature contains a wealth of material on standardized measurement, while educators debate the virtues and vices of the movement. The sound administrator or teacher studies the problem carefully before selecting his course. Viewing the problem in perspective by comparing two basic differences in the approach to evaluation may help. These approaches are: (1) the *statistical approach;* and (2) the *clinical approach.*

The *statistical approach,* based on the law of averages, finds immediate use in science where various factors or elements react consistently when treated under controlled conditions. Standards for the broad jump among 12-year-old boys might easily be prepared by selecting a suitable number of pupils of this age, measuring their broad jumping ability under controlled conditions, and treating the data obtained by approved statistical procedures.

There are, however, a number of commonly expressed objectives in health education and physical education so complex that the statistical approach fails to take into account a sufficient number of variable factors. Take the development of robust health as an example. Health includes a number of variable elements, and strength in one element may readily compensate for weakness in another. This fact suggests that it is inappropriate to regard health as a unit quality, to establish norms for a single element using statistical measures, and thus classify an individual as normal, subnormal, or supernormal on the basis of these data. Approved methods for evaluating health use the *clinical approach* which does not rely entirely upon the law of averages but takes into account numerous strengths and weaknesses of the individual, translating them into their probable effect upon the many and varied functions of the whole organism.

In the *clinical approach* the clinician views the term "normal" with skepticism when used to express average or typical, or when it relates to a standard. He recognizes that individuals vary one with another with respect to certain qualities. According to him these variations do not necessarily imply inadequacy or incompetency in terms of the ordinary demands of life. The clinical person believes that such variations do not necessarily constitute abnormality merely because they differ from a statistical average. Again, instead of a numerical average the clinician would include a permissible range of variation, probably avoiding the terms "type" or "normal." The clinician would describe the person by adjectives expressing individual characteristics. Thus the clinical approach pays tribute to individual differences among persons, and gives due regard to extenuating factors in administrative details.

In actual practice the football coach employs the clinical approach. He has, or it would be reasonably easy to develop, standardized tests for numerous football skills—running, charging, tackling, throwing, kicking, and blocking. But the contest requires a peculiar blending of these qualities, plus certain others (such as courage, emotional stability, and competitive spirit) for which tests are not available. Consequently the coach cannot assume that ability in any one or more skills sufficiently guarantees success in playing the game. The prospective team member receives instruction in the various fundamentals of the game, and demonstrates his ability as a contestant. The shrewd coach notes specific strengths and weaknesses in the player, and selects or rejects him upon the basis of his probable contribution to the success of the squad. The peculiar blending of traits among the various players indicates the optimum strength of the team.

The successful teacher or administrator must realize that both the *statistical* and *clinical approaches* have their place in evaluation. Having clearly defined the traits or procedures he desires to appraise, the administrator or teacher utilizes the growing resources of standardized measurement currently available, and evaluates certain items by the clinical method.

TRENDS OF EVALUATION IN HEALTH EDUCATION AND PHYSICAL EDUCATION

In early years, the concept prevailed that *structure* determines *function*. This belief pertained to health as well as to abilities and potentialities in physical activity. Prior to 1880 such men as Sargent and Hitchcock employed a series of anthropometric measurements to determine norms for physical achievement among age groups. Based upon the structure of the individual, these norms purported to evaluate the student's physical attributes. Sargent finally concluded that strength and power represent factors of greater potential value than structure as a means of predicting success in physical activity.

This change in point of view resulted in a redirected emphasis away from structure and toward the measurement of function. It became more important to answer the question, "What can he do?" rather than "How does he look?" Many improved measures in physical education combine certain static measures of structure with others which test function.

Since 1920 the trend of measurement in physical education favors the determination of function. Obviously the definition of "function" lends itself to many interpretations. Test makers appear to vie with each other in seeking new or different meanings for the word, and in developing test materials in accordance with their own hypotheses. Physical fitness tests prepared by various branches of the armed forces during World War II present an example. The Army, Navy, and Air Force developed different tests, although all of these branches had in mind a measuring instrument for such qualities as agility, strength, and endurance.

Likewise the trend in measurement in health education moves in the direction of function. The examining physician or dentist, even though he employs a greater number of standardized instruments and technics than in years past, finally evaluates the health of the individual according to his functional capacities. A good teacher evaluates the worth of health instruction in terms of applied knowledge and skills as the student uses them for the improvement of daily living in the school, home, and community.

In similar fashion the administrator evaluates the success of his policies and procedures according to their effectiveness in producing a better functioning environment in which education takes place.

In the following discussion of evaluation relating to health education and physical education, explanation of individual tests and appraisal technics must give way to the presentation of *types* which may prove helpful to the teacher or administrator. This plan appears justifiable since most graduates of approved institutions majoring in the field have pursued courses in tests and measurements or evaluation.

EVALUATION IN HEALTH EDUCATION

One important aspect of the increased attention given to health education in schools refers to the evaluation of potential health capacity and health status. Perhaps the most significant technic yet devised is the examination by a qualified physician.

The Physician's Examination as a Measure of Health. The physician's examination attempts to: (1) determine present health status; (2) indicate certain abnormalities in need of correction; (3) evaluate the success of health education in school, home, and community; and (4) suggest necessary modifications in curricular or extracurricular activities.

The physician uses several objective measures and numerous others of a subjective nature. The reliability of the examination depends upon the ability of the physician to apply these measures accurately. Thus the physician employs various technics for testing the heart, lungs, blood, nutrition, vision, and hearing. He may use such instruments as the clinical thermometer, stethoscope, sphygmomanometer, Snellen chart, audiometer, weighing scales, and stadiometer; technics also are available for measuring such factors as posture, the condition of the blood and urine, and many others.

The routine examination lacks standardization. Appropriate standards would enable two or more physicians to examine the same child at approximately the same time and obtain equivalent results. Owing in part to the subjectiveness of the examination itself, but more especially to perfunctory technics, comparable data seldom are available. Often the physician's primary interest lies in the number and severity of defects found, rather than in the degree to which the student approximates satisfactory growth and development.

Perhaps school administrators need to adopt a new emphasis with respect to the health examination. Instead of the present record card containing items similar to those used by the physician in private practice, the schools might adopt a record form designed to provide only those data of practical value in public education. Such data would assist in answering three vital questions: (1) what progress has been made by the child to obtain or maintain satisfactory growth and development; (2) what abnormalities interfere with achieving the optimum development of which he is capable; and (3) what modifications in the school program, if any, are needed to facilitate his development as a useful member of society? In possession of this information the school would provide experiences aimed to meet the child's individual needs.

Vision Tests. In numerous school systems teachers or nurses give vision tests to school children early in the year. Tests of this type screen those with defective vision, and they are then referred to the proper medical authority for further examination and correction.

The Snellen charts often are employed for this purpose. Specific directions for giving the test are prepared by the physician in charge of the health services. Other technics for determining visual acuity include the Betts Visual Sensation and Perception Tests and tests recommended by the Massachusetts State Department of Health.

Hearing Tests. Since hearing the human voice represents the most valuable social asset of the ear, approved tests favor the phonograph audiometer or pitch-range audiometer. Such instruments as the whisper test, watchtick test, and Politzer acoumeter must give way to the advance of science in creating technics of greater accuracy and practicability.

Evaluating Certain Aspects of Posture. Attempts to improve posture represent one of the oldest and most commonly expressed objectives of physical education. Numerous methods have been proposed for evaluating its quality, most of which depend upon rating scales, or the angulation of certain anthropometric measurements.

Evaluating Health Knowledge, Habits, and Attitudes. Several excellent health knowledge tests furnish standards for the various grades. These tests utilize a variety of technics including true-false, matching, multiple-choice, and completion. Health awareness tests and scales to appraise habits and attitudes enable the competent teacher to evaluate his instruction with reasonable but subjective accuracy.

The Role of Teacher Observation. Although lacking the objectivity desired by the statistician, observation by the efficient teacher contributes a most practical and useful means of evaluating health. The basic program of observation includes: (1) appraising the practice of health habits in life activities which surround the child in school; (2) evaluating the exemplified attitudes toward personal and community problems of hygiene; and (3) noting the deviations in health status, then referring students with conditions requiring correction to the proper medical or dental authority. Observation possesses the additional advantage of arousing in teachers a greater consciousness of the need for maintaining a well organized health education program.

EVALUATING PHYSICAL EDUCATION IN THE ELEMENTARY SCHOOL

Acceptable evaluative procedures in this area fall into two groups: (1) classification technics; and (2) achievement technics. Most of them are designed for local use, and apply to the type of program found in that community.

Classification of Pupils. Classification serves the double purpose of providing for individual differences and for homogeneous grouping. The health examination by a physician represents the best single means of indicating the type of physical education program needed.

Should the teacher desire further classification (beyond grade placement) the factors of age, height, and weight provide an appropriate means of accomplishing the purpose. Several technics now devised utilize a combination of these factors; these are known as the *exponent system* or *coefficent* system. A teacher or administrator may construct his own classification system using age, height, and weight expressed as T scores or percentile scores.

Evaluating Achievement. Numerous attempts are being made to evaluate the physical fitness of children in these grades. Doubtless such attempts stem from current national interest in the movement. Insofar as physical fitness contributes to the fulfillment of total objectives in physical education, tests of this nature appear justifiable. Achievement scales in the fundamental skills and game skills, based upon some method of classification, mark the advance toward a progressive and standardized program of physical education. A word of caution in using these scales would limit their application only to their intended use. A numerical score intrigues some teachers by its preciseness, leading them to neglect the evaluation of objectives unsuited to statistical treatment. Many of these objectives contain implications of significance at least on a parity with those that lend themselves to numerical evaluation.

Teachers of physical education in elementary schools may increase the effectiveness of instruction by evaluating pupil interest and development on report cards that reach the parent. Notations similar to the following are suggestive: (1) plays games skillfully; (2) displays leadership in play activities; (3) demonstrates better coordination in games than in rhythms; and (4) shows marked improvement in playing with others.

EVALUATING PHYSICAL EDUCATION IN THE SECONDARY SCHOOL

The wealth of evaluative technics in physical education for the secondary school reveals the need for careful selection and wise application. The great surge toward objective testing materials in this area provides a maze of devices with attendant followers eager to proclaim the virtues of a given test, or opposing forces just as eager to expose its limitations. The sound administrator or teacher is neither swept away by exorbitant claims, nor cast into despair by condemnation. He selects the methods of evaluation apparently best suited to his purpose, experiments with them, and arrives at his decision concerning their value.

Classification of Pupils. Makers of classification tests start with a certain hypothesis and formulate the test according to this hypothesis, using the best statistical procedures obtainable. The following types of available classification tests denote wide variation in hypotheses accepted by experts, all of whom enjoy national recognition: (1) innate motor ability; (2) strength of the skeletal muscles; (3) skeletal muscular strength translated into power; (4) series of neuromuscular skills; and (5) certain combinations of age, height, and weight.

Methods of classification devised thus far attempt to provide for homogeneous grouping or individual instruction in games and sports and in self-testing activities. The areas of rhythmic activities and aquatics remain practically untouched in the construction of classification tests designed to predict accurately individual potential capacity. Teachers of dance and aquatics appear to prefer classification of students upon the basis of actual performance which, after all, has unusual practical value.

Evaluating Achievement. Repeated attempts to construct tests of achievement in physical education have met with varied success. Several plans contribute norms in game skills, track and field events, gymnastics, and other activities in accordance with specified technics of classification. Sound administrative procedure would suggest the preparation of local standards of physical education achievement based upon the classification system and objectives used. If personnel in physical education lacks the technical knowledge to plan the program of evaluation, the research division of the school system may furnish the needed assistance.

Within recent years the profession has embarked upon the preparation of a series of physical fitness tests designed to measure the strength and endurance of secondary school students. The American Association for Health, Physical Education, and Recreation sponsors such a test, and several state associations have developed a similar instrument. Wide use of these tests follows national and political emphasis on the need for fitness or stamina among American youth. At present such measurement pertains to physical fitness alone, although recognition and growing acceptance of the term "total" fitness or "youth" fitness may well lead to a broader concept of such evaluation in the years ahead.

Objective written tests designed to measure knowledge about physical education activities constitute another development in the field. Used alone or in conjunction with skill tests, these devices are recommended by authors in current literature. Continued experimentation leading to the development of appropriate norms may result in the wide use of these instruments as valuable adjuncts to the evaluation program in secondary schools.

CRITERIA FOR THE ADOPTION OF AN EVALUATION PROGRAM

Confronted with the problem of adopting a program of evaluation, the administrator, supervisor, or teacher needs to establish a set of rules to guide him in the selection or rejection of various instruments. The following criteria may prove helpful: (1) *adaptability to purpose;* (2) *accuracy;* (3) *available norms;* (4) *economy of use;* (5) *duplicate forms;* and (6) *standardized and clear directions.*

Adaptability to purpose implies that the person understands precisely what he wants to evaluate. Occasionally the conviction that something should be done about measurement prompts the teacher or administrator to select blindly a test recommended by a friend, reported in current literature, or emphasized by a national movement, with little notion of its application to the local situation. The responsibility to appraise the success of the program as accurately as possible is no less real than the duty to establish worthy objectives, to select appropriate activities, to use effective teaching methods, and to determine sound administrative procedures.

Thus the program of evaluation seeks to determine the degree to which the avowed purposes of health education and physical education actually function in the lives of students. Objective tests solve some of the difficulties, but intelligent subjective judgment supplants standardized tests in many of the objectives sought, and always in the interpretation of results.

The *accuracy* of an evaluative procedure refers to its objectivity, validity, and reliability which have been presented earlier in this chapter. In the selection of a standardized test, the reputation of the author frequently guarantees the worth of the product. Reasonably accurate local technics of observation result when competent observers clearly define the item to be evaluated, analyze and specify the supplementary elements, and agree on the standards established.

Available norms facilitate measurement, since reference to these standards insures an objective means of comparison. Standardized tests contain norms; similar norms are desirable for observational technics.

Economy of use refers to actual purchase cost (including equipment) and the time consumed in applying the instrument. If the test accomplishes the desired purpose, the expense involved justifies the financial outlay. The time required to give the test and to score the results presents a different problem. All things considered, few tests warrant the expenditure of more than 20 or 30 minutes with a group of students. Individual tests which require the presence of an instructor with each student (except the medical examination) seldom justify the time consumed. Observational methods and group studies by staff members deserve careful scrutiny to insure justification of the time devoted to them.

Duplicate forms of the measuring instrument follow naturally in the construction of standardized tests. Most students quickly become test conscious, and memorize or practice the items. Continued use of the same form suggests to the child the value of practicing the test itself, thus destroying its value with respect to its intended purpose. Observational technics easily lend themselves to different ways of sampling the desired responses.

Standardized and clear directions accompany all objective tests worthy of the name. Deviations in giving such tests by taking liberties with the printed directions distort the results, thus rendering them practically worthless for comparison with established norms. Clearly stated directions, followed with meticulous care, increase accuracy and efficiency in all forms of evaluation.

PROBLEMS FOR DISCUSSION

1. A high school principal, meeting with his faculty, stresses the importance of evaluation and reporting grades to parents. However, he emphasizes that the physical education program is extremely difficult to evaluate and allows that the terms *satisfactory* and *unsatisfactory* will suffice. Would you agree?
2. The greatest need at the moment is for reevaluation of the objectives of physical education, with an interpretation and understanding of these objectives by the physical educator. Coupled with this there would be, in all probability, the restructuring of physical education throughout the country to meet these practical goals and objectives. What are your recommendations?
3. A junior high school principal tells you that, in the reorganization of his school, all activities must carry their own "drive." Grades, promotions, and other incentives must be incidental. He finds that he can do this in science, dramatics, and industrial arts, but the activities of the health program seem to lack pupil interest because they represent things pupils do not want to do. He asks you, as the director of health education and physical education, to suggest a remedy for this situation. How would you approach the problem?
4. Nationwide publicity concerning youth fitness declares that American boys and girls are not as physically fit as those in Europe because the former scored much lower in a certain test of muscular flexibility. Explain your reaction to this charge.
5. Instructors and students may implement the above with problems gained from their own experience and observation.

REFERENCES

American Association for Health, Physical Education, and Recreation: *Evaluation Standards and Guide.* National Education Association, Washington, 1959.
Clarke, H. H.: *The Application of Measurement to Health and Physical Education.* ed. 3. Prentice-Hall, Inc., Englewood Cliffs, 1959.
Latchaw, M. and Brown, C.: *The Evaluation Process in Health Education, Physical Education, and Recreation.* Prentice-Hall, Inc., Englewood Cliffs, 1962.
Massachusetts Department of Public Health: *Massachusetts Vision Test.* Boston.
Mathews, D. R.: *Measurement in Physical Education.* ed. 2. W. B. Saunders Company, Philadelphia, 1963.
Meyers, C. R. and Blesh, T. E.: *Measurement in Physical Education.* The Ronald Press, New York, 1962.
Scott, M. G. and French, E.: *Measurement and Evaluation in Physical Education.* W. C. Brown Company, Dubuque, 1959.
Willgoose, C. E.: *Evaluation in Health Education and Physical Education.* McGraw-Hill Book Company, New York, 1961.
Wrightstone, J. W., Justman, J. and Robbins, I.: *Evaluation in Modern Education.* American Book Company, New York, 1956.

APPENDIX

Summary of Recommendations, in *School Athletics: Problems and Policies*. Educational Policies Commission, National Education Association, Washington, 1954.*

Athletics can, and do, serve valuable purposes in school programs. Too much of the educational potential in school athletics, however, is unused or misused. Evils are, rightly, much criticized; but these are abuses in practice and are not in the essential nature of athletics.

Neither the teaching profession nor the general public should remain silent when sports programs serve purposes contrary to desirable educational objectives. The community should not permit any pressures to divert school athletics from the objectives of good education. Schools must make every effort to conduct their athletic programs in ways that will do the most good for children and youth.

Each school or school system should identify clearly the goals it seeks for its athletic program. School personnel should invite the cooperation of students and other citizens in identifying these goals.

All children and youth should share in the benefits of athletic participation. School programs should be so planned that every pupil may have athletic experience.

At all grade levels, elementary and secondary, the curriculum should include broad programs of physical activities in the form of organized games and sports. These programs should be conducted by teachers on the regular school staff and should be under the control of school authorities. In these respects school athletics should be no different from other parts of the instructional and activity program of a school.

Athletic activities should fit harmoniously into the rest of the school program with respect to purposes, schedules, budgets, and demands on the time and attention of students and staff. Athletic activities should be conducted as part of physical education under the direction of teachers with special preparation in the field of physical education.

Programs of athletic education will succeed in proportion to the extent to which they are infused with variety and appeal, matched to the varying needs and interests of different children, scheduled to permit maximum participation, and supported with adequate funds, facilities, and leadership.

The core of the program at all levels should be the athletic instruction and play for all pupils in regular classes in physical education.† This required

* Courtesy of Educational Policies Commission, National Education Association, Washington, D.C.

† The total program in physical education, of course, includes many other things than athletics, both in physical education classes and in out-of-class activities. The reader is reminded that the scope of this volume is confined to school *athletics*, defined by the Educational Policies Commission as "all school-sponsored physical activities in the form of competitive games or sports in which students participate."

program should be supplemented by games and sports that enlist participants on a voluntary basis. The out-of-class, voluntary program should be informal and casual in the lower grades, but increasingly organized at upper levels. For the most part, pupils at all levels should compete only with schoolmates, but occasionally there might well be provided opportunities—available to all pupils— to play with and against pupils of other schools in such informal extramural activities as play days and sports days. Interscholastic competition should be permitted only in senior high school. In elementary school and in junior high school there should be no "school team" (in the varsity sense), no leagues, no tournaments, no interschool championships. In senior high school there should be no postseason championship tournaments or games.

Athletic games, in all cases, should be played with emphasis on fun, physical development, skill and strategy, social experience, and good sportsmanship. High-pressure competition, with overemphasis on the importance of winning, should not be sanctioned in any part of the school program. When such competition is promoted for children and youth ouside the school's jurisdiction, school personnel should not only refuse to sanction it but should also exert leadership in the community to bring about better understanding of what constitutes desirable athletic experience for young people.

Danger of overindulgence in competitive sports is perhaps greatest at junior high school level, where wise leadership and careful guidance are critically needed to prevent physical and emotional injury to young adolescent boys. Strong pressure from divers sources sometimes must be resisted, such as from out-of-school promoters, recruiters of "material" for senior high school varsity teams, parents who desire athletic stardom for their sons. Pressures from the boys themselves, who are driven by altogether natural desires to grow up, to emulate older boys and to achieve recognition, must also be curbed.

Boxing should be taboo at all school levels. Ice hockey and tackle football should not be played below senior high school. Girls should not engage in body-contact sports at all.

Boys and girls, in all grades, should have opportunities to play together in a variety of sports. Beginning with junior high school, the distinctive needs of the sexes call for recognition. In senior high school, boys and girls should be separate for much of the larger part of the athletic program, but there should be considerably more co-recreation at that level than is to be found in prevailing practice.

Girls should share equally with boys in facilities, equipment, and funds allocated to athletic activities in junior and senior high school. But girls' athletic activities should not be imitations of those for boys; girls should play according to girls' rules.

Boys' interscholastic athletics should be governed by the same authorities that control other parts of the school program, at both local and state levels. A state high school athletic association should function under the authority of, and within a framework of policies established by, the legally constituted educational agency of the state government.

Local school authorities should give consistent support, in letter and in spirit, to the rules and standards developed by the several state high school athletic associations and by similar bodies. They should acquaint members of boards of education, sports writers, and other citizens with these rules and standards; develop community understanding of the reasons for them; and resist pressures for practices that would violate them.

State departments of education should become increasingly active in efforts to focus attention of educators and laymen on the needs for desirable educational objectives and effective controlling policies for interscholastic athletics.

Boards of education should establish policies for financial support of interscholastic athletics that will free the interscholastic program from dependence on gate receipts. School and community leaders should make every effort to finance athletics completely out of general school funds at the earliest possible date.

A school's athletic activities should be in harmony with the rest of the total school program with respect to aims and outcomes. Athletic activities should synchronize with the rest of the educational enterprise in matters of schedules, responsibilities of the school staff, demands on the time and energy of students, and allocation of space and facilities. Funds provided for athletics should be generous, but not at the expense of other educational essentials. In short, a school's program in athletics should in all respects be kept in sound proportion to the total school program.

Statement of Policies for Competition in Girls and Women's Sports by the Division for Girls and Women's Sports of AAHPER*

The Division for Girls and Women's Sports of the American Association for Health, Physical Education, and Recreation believes the competitive element in sports activities can be used constructively for achievement of desirable educational and recreational objectives. When favorable conditions are present, competitive experiences may be wholesome and beneficial and result in acceptable conduct and attitudes. Competition in and of itself does not automatically result in desirable or undesirable outcomes.

The adoption of practices best suited for the attainment of desirable outcomes is the responsibility of all associated with competitive events. Sponsoring agencies, players, teachers, coaches, officials, and spectators must share responsibility for valid practices in competitive sports.

DGWS believes participation in sports competition is the privilege of all girls and women. A sound instructional and well-organized intramural program will answer the needs and desires of the majority of young women. For the college woman and high school girl who seek and need additional challenges in competition and skills, a sound, carefully planned, and well-directed program of extramural sports is recommended. The provisions for extramural sports opportunities should be broad, including such events as sports days, leagues, meets, and tournaments. Development of all participants toward higher competencies and advanced skills should be a major objective in all sport programs.

DGWS advocates the following policies through which desirable outcomes in competition may be achieved.

Definition of Competition

Competition is defined as the participation in a sport activity by two or more persons, in which a winner can result. The educational values of competition are determined by the quality of leadership and of the participation. For the best results, there should be comprehensive physical education, intramural, and extramural programs. The organized competitive programs should offer opportunities in terms of individual ability and should be adapted to the needs and interests of the participants.

* Courtesy of American Association for Health, Physical Education, and Recreation, National Education Association, Washington, 1963.

Forms of Competition

Intramural Competition is sports competition in which all participants are identified with the same school, community center, club, organization, institution, or industry, or are residents of a designated small neighborhood or community. This form of competition stresses the participation of "the many." A good intramural program which offers a variety of activities, at various skill levels, including co-recreational activities, frequently is sufficient to meet the needs and desires of the majority of girls and women.

It is the responsibility of the school or agency sponsoring the intramural program to provide the time, facilities, and competent leadership, with preference given to professional, qualified women. Intramural programs should be an outgrowth of and a complement to the school physical education program or the organized community recreation program.

Extramural Competition is a plan of sports competition in which participants from two or more schools, community centers, clubs, organizations, institutions, industries, or neighborhoods compete.

The forms of extramural competition include:

1. Sport days—school or sport group participates as a unit.
2. Telegraphic meets—results are compared by wire or mail.
3. Invitational events—symposia, games, or matches, for which a school or sport group invites one or more teams to participate.
4. Interscholastic, intercollegiate, or interagency programs—groups which are trained and coached play a series of scheduled games and/or tournaments with teams from other schools, cities, or organization.

The extramural program is planned and carried out to complement the intramural and instructional programs. For the best welfare of the participants, it is essential that the program be conducted by qualified leaders, be supported by budgeted funds, and be representative of approved objectives and standards for girls and women's sports, including acceptable conditions of travel, protective insurance, appropriate facilities, proper equipment, and desirable practices in the conduct of the events. When the program affords group participation as a team in a series of games on appropriate tournament or schedule basis, additional coaching by qualified staff members must be provided.

It is assumed that the sponsoring organization recognizes its obligation to delegate responsibility for this program to the supervisor or specialist in charge of the girls and women's sports programs. When admission charges are made, the proceeds should be used for furthering the sports programs for girls (instructional, intramural and extramural).

Adaptation of Competitive Sports for Age-Level Groupings in School Programs

A. In junior high school, it is desirable that intramural programs of competitive activities be closely integrated with the basic physical education program. Appropriate competition at this level should be comprised of intramural and informal extramural events consistent with social needs and recreational interests. A well-organized and conducted sports program should take into account the various skill levels and thus meet the needs of the more highly skilled.

B. In senior high school, a program of intramural and extramural participation should be arranged to augment a sound and inclusive instructional program in physical education. It should be recognized that an interscholastic program will require professional leadership, time, and funds in addition to those provided for the intramural programs. Facilities should be such that the intramural and instructional programs need not be eliminated or seriously curtailed if an interscholastic program is offered.

Specifically, the following standards should prevail:

1. The medical status of the player is ascertained by a physician and the health of the players is carefully supervised.
2. Activities for girls and women are planned to meet their needs, not for the personal glorification of coaches and/or sponsoring organizations.
3. The salary, retention, or promotion of an instructor are not dependent upon the outcome of the games.
4. Qualified women teach, coach, and officiate wherever and whenever possible, and in all cases the professional background and experience of the leader meet established standards.
5. Rules approved by DGWS are used.
6. Schedules do not exceed the ability and endurance relative to the maturity and physiological conditioning of the participants. Standards for specific sports are defined by DGWS and appear in sports guides, published by the American Association for Health, Physical Education, and Recreation. (1201 Sixteenth Street, N.W., Washington 6, D.C.)
7. Sports activities for girls and women are scheduled independently from boys and men's sports. Exceptions will occur when the activities and/or time and facilities are appropriate for both.
8. Girls and women may participate in appropriate co-recreational activities or teams. Girls and women may not participate as members of boys and men's teams.
9. The program, including health insurance for players, is financed by budgeted school or organization funds rather than entirely by admission charges.
10. Provision is made by the school or organization for safe transportation by bonded carriers, with chaperones who are responsible to the sponsoring group.

C. In colleges and universities, it is desirable that opportunities be provided for the highly skilled beyond the intramural program. Regulations for the conduct of collegiate competition have been developed by the National Joint Committee on Extramural Sports for College Women* and are available from the committee for any specific sport activity. While the statements of NJCESCW apply to approval for state-wide or wider geographical tournaments, the principles may also be applicable to or guide the conduct of local and district tournaments.

In addition to the standard previously listed, other standards pertinent to the colleges are:

1. The amount and kind of intercollegiate competition should be determined by the women's physical education department.
2. The financial arrangements relative to all intercollegiate sport events should be administered with the approval of the women's physical education department.
3. The time involved in relation to intercollegiate competition should not interfere with the academic program of the institution sponsoring the event and should not make excessive demands upon the participants' academic schedules.
4. All housing arrangements relative to visiting participants should be approved by the women's physical education department.

* Composed of representatives of Division for Girls and Women's Sports, Athletic and Recreation Federation of College Women, and National Association for Physical Education of College Women. Write c/o American Association for Health, Physical Education, and Recreation, 1201 Sixteenth Street, N.W., Washington 6, D.C.

Adaptations of Competitive Sports for Age-Level Groupings in Public and Private Recreation Agency Programs

The Division recognizes that the sports programs of public and private recreation agencies make a valuable contribution to girls and women. The aims and objectives of community recreation agencies in their conduct of sports programs are similar to those of the schools. By using common rules and applying basic standards in organizing competition, many girls and women can be given the opportunity to develop skills and to enjoy a desirable type of competition.

Students should be informed of the opportunities for participation in the sports activities of these agencies. If a student contemplates entering events which appear to jeopardize her welfare, she should be given guidance which will help her to make wise decisions.

If individuals are grouped according to age and skill ability, the statements of policy outlined above can be applied by these agencies in organizing desirable forms of competition. The formation of leagues is often the organizational structure through which many recreation programs are conducted. The definitions of intramural and extramural competition, as previously stated, may be interpreted to apply to programs provided by public and private agencies.

Modifications will be required in planning policies for competition depending upon the age level involved:

A. For girls under senior high school age, competition may be provided in intramural games, that is, games with teams of the same age and ability from the same neighborhood, playground, recreation center, or league. Extramural events consistent with social needs and recreational interests of junior high school age groups may be arranged with similar teams from other playgrounds, centers or leagues.
B. For girls of senior high school age, it is recommended that all standards listed for senior high school be used for intramural and extramural competition. A player should affiliate with only one team in one sport.
C. For girls over senior high school age, it is recommended that the intercollegiate standards be followed for competition at this age level.

Sponsorship by recreational agencies of the participation of women in tournaments and meets organized at successively higher levels (local, sectional, national) should be governed by the best practices for safe-guarding the welfare of the participants. The organization, administration, and leadership of such competitive events should be conducted so that the basic policies of DGWS are upheld.

Revised May, 1963

Basic Principles—Junior High School Interschool Athletics*

In those junior high schools *in which adequate programs of required*

* Basic principles for conducting a program of interscholastic athletics in the junior high school as outlined in the Report of the Junior High School Athletics Subcommittee of the Joint Committee on Standards for Interscholastic Athletics, sponsored by the American Association for Health, Physical Education, and Recreation; the National Association of Secondary School Principals; and the National Federation of State High School Athletic Associations: *Standards for Junior High School Athletics.* American Association for Health, Physical Education, and Recreation, Washington, 1963.

physical education, intramurals, and physical recreation are provided for all students, a limited program of interscholastic athletics provides for boys with superior athletic ability additional opportunities fully to develop and utilize this talent. Such programs of interscholastic athletics should be organized and conducted in accordance with the principles outlined below.

1. *The interscholastic athletics program for boys in the junior high school should make definite contributions toward the accomplishment of the educational objectives of the school.*

Primary emphasis should be placed on providing *educational* experiences for the participants rather than on producing winning teams or providing entertainment for the student body and the patrons of the school.

Practices that tend to distort the importance of interscholastic athletics in the school program should be prohibited. Such practices include the giving of undue publicity via the press, radio, or television to the accomplishments of individual players or of teams; the organization of pep squads, marching bands, and similar organizations to promote artificial enthusiasm and partisan behavior among spectators; and the holding of pre-game pep meetings, victory celebrations, or letter-award ceremonies to provide special recognition for individual players or teams.

The practice sessions and the athletic contests should be so scheduled that the academic program of the school is not directly or indirectly disrupted. To conserve the time available to the participants for homework, the practice sessions for interscholastic athletics should be relatively short. Under no circumstances should any practice session be longer than 90 minutes. Athletic contests should be held in the afternoons immediately after school hours, rather than at night; and except on rare occasions should be held on the last day of the school week.

The interscholastic athletics program should be so conducted that desirable school citizenship and good sportsmanship are fostered among both participants and spectators.

2. *The interscholastic athletics program for boys in the junior high school should supplement—rather than serve as a substitute for—an adequate program of required physical education, intramurals, and physical recreation for all students.*

If in a school a shortage of facilities, equipment, or personnel with professional training in physical education restricts the quality or the extent of the required physical education program, the intramural program, the physical recreation program, or the interscholastic athletics program that can be offered, the physical education program, the intramural program, and the physical recreation program should hold precedence over the interscholastic program. Under no circumstances should the interscholastic athletics program be provided a disproportionate allotment of time, facilities, or personnel services at the expense of the program for all boys and girls.

The members of the interscholastic teams should be excused from the required physical education classes *only* for the class periods in which the activity being presented in the class is the sport in which the members of the interscholastic teams are participating.

3. *The interscholastic athletics program for boys in the junior high school should, under the administration and the supervision of the appropriate*

*school officials, be conducted by men with adequate professional prepara-
tion in physical education.*

The interscholastic teams should be coached by certified teachers—preferably
teachers of physical education—who are members of the regular staff of the
school in which the coaching is done. For these teachers, the coaching assignments should be considered as part of their regular teaching duties and should
be taken into account in the assessing of their total teaching loads.

The administrative policies for the school should require that the teachers who
coach interscholastic teams give basic priority to their teaching duties.

The teachers who coach interscholastic teams should possess, in addition to
a knowledge of the sports for which they are responsible, a knowledge of (a)
child growth and development, (b) the effects of exercise on the human organism, (c) first aid, and (d) the place and purpose of interscholastic athletics
in the educational program. They should have at least a minor in physical education.

4. *The interscholastic athletics program for boys in the junior high school
   should be so conducted that the physical welfare of the participants is protected and fostered.*

Boxing, as a competitive sport, should be prohibited.

Tackle football—because of its contact aspects, the intensity with which it is
played when emotions run rampant, and its relatively high injury rate—presents certain special problems. These problems are intensified in communities
where there are pressures to use junior high school athletics as a farm system
for the intensive development of high school prospects. Unless these factors can
be controlled—and the kind of equipment, facilities, health supervision, coaching, and officiating that are necessary for the optimum safety of the participants
can be provided—tackle football should not be included in the junior high
school athletics program.

Before being allowed to report for practice or to participate in any phase of
interscholastic athletics, each boy should have a thorough medical examination which includes a careful review of his health history. Subsequent medical
examinations should be given as needed.

Participants should be furnished with complete, well-fitted protective equipment of the highest quality—not hand-me-downs or equipment of inferior grade.

Participants should be so matched in terms of height, weight, physiological maturity, *and* ability that they may to a reasonable degree participate with safety
and satisfaction. Practically, the determination of the relative maturity of participants is not a simple task. However, the Crampton Index (degree of kink-
ing of pubic hair) provides a helpful clue. An estimate by the physician during
the medical examination and continued observation by the coach may also be
of assistance in judging maturity. Sensitivity to the need to appraise maturity
as an important aspect of matching participants is a valuable attribute in the
examining physician, the coach, and others involved.

A written policy should be formulated in which the financial responsibilities for
injuries incurred in interscholastic athletics are clearly defined. The players,
the parents of the players, and the general public should be informed concerning
these policies.

Individual participants should be allowed to take part in interscholastic contests only after three weeks of physical conditioning and training.

The rules, the equipment, and the playing area for each interscholastic activity should be modified in accordance with the interests and the capacities of junior high school boys, as should the length of the playing season and the number of games played during each season. Under no circumstances should the number of contests played by junior high school teams be greater than half the number played by the senior high school teams. No boy should participate in more than one interscholastic contest a week. Interscholastic tournaments should be prohibited.

A physician should be present during all interscholastic contests in which injuries are likely to occur. Definite procedures for obtaining, without undue delay, the services of a physician to care for injuries that occur during practice sessions should be established.

Participants who have been ill or injured should be readmitted to practice sessions or contests only upon the advice of a physician.

Certified officials should be engaged to officiate at all interscholastic contests.

The welfare of the individual boy should be the basic criterion upon which is determined whether or not the boy should participate in interscholastic athletics.

The controls outlined in the above recommendations are essential to a desirable program of interscholastic athletics in the junior high school. Careful observance of these controls assures optimum protection of the health and safety of the participants. A program of interscholastic athletics for junior high school boys should not be contemplated or continued when conditions or pressures prevent strict adherence to the recommended controls.

INDEX

Abnormality, physical. See *Physical disabilities.*
Accidents. See also *Safety; Safety education; and Liability.*
  causes of, 149
  types of, safety instruction and, 152
Activity(ies), athletic. See *Athletics.*
  corecreational, 192
  health instruction, 120
  intramural. See *Athletics, intramural.*
  physical education. See *Physical education activity(ies).*
  recreational. See *Recreation, community.*
Activity calendar, 60
Adjustment record, 102
Administration. See also *Administrator.*
  autocratic and democratic, 28
  definition of, 19
  of health services, 92. See also *Health services.*
  of recreation, local conflicts in, 292. See also *Recreation, community.*
  policies and procedures of, 24
  school nursing and, 112
Administrative program, one-three-five-year, 26
Administrative unit, health education and physical education as, 13
Administrator. See also *Administration.*
  aim of, 21
  facilities and, 22
  health services and, 114
  individual and, 22
  liability and, 296. See also *Liability.*
  objectives of, 22
  philosophy of, 20
  principles of, 20
  school nursing and, 112
  standards and, 23
Advisory council, of director, 34
Agencies. See *Board of education; State departments of education; State departments of health.*

Air conditioning, 133
American Association for Health, Physical Education, and Recreation, Division for Girls and Women's Sports, policies on competition, 331
  organization of, 16
  publications of, official, 16
American Legion, public relations and, 313
Assembly programs, public relations and, 311
Association of Commerce, Junior, public relations and, 313
Athlete's foot, 233
Athletic associations, 198
Athletic coach, 202, 335
Athletic field, 259. See also *Facilities, outdoor.*
Athletics. See also *Competition.*
  as physical education substitute, 83
  interschool, 194–214
    associations in, local, 198
     state, 199
    awards in, 211
    budget for, 52
    coach of, 202
    contracts in, 209
    control of, 198
    elementary and junior high, 201
    eligibility for, 206
    equipment in, purchase and care of, 212
    excuses in, 207
    financing of, 210
    girls', 195
    health examination and, 205
    injuries in, insurance and, 206
     parental permissions and, 205
    junior high school, coach of, 335
    principles of, basic, 334
    legal permission for, 200
    officials for, 209
    outside participation and, 207
    overemphasis in, 197